Sharon Gosling is the author of multiple middle-grade historical adventure books for children, including *The Diamond Thief*, *The Golden Butterfly*, *The House of Hidden Wonders* and *The Extraordinary Voyage of Katy Willacott*. She is also the author of YA Scandi horror *FIR* as well as adult fiction including *The House Beneath the Cliffs* and *The Lighthouse Bookshop*. Having started her career as an entertainment journalist, she still also occasionally writes non-fiction making-of books about television and film. Titles include *Tomb Raider: The Art and Making of the Film*, *The Art and Making of Penny Dreadful* and *Wonder Woman: The Art and Making of the Film*.

Sharon lives with her husband in a very small village on the side of a fell in the far north of Cumbria.

The Forgotten Garden

Sharon Gosling

SIMON &
SCHUSTER

London · New York · Sydney · Toronto · New Delhi

First published in Great Britain by Simon & Schuster UK Ltd, 2023

Copyright © Sharon Gosling, 2023

The right of Sharon Gosling to be identified as author of this work has been asserted in accordance with the Copyright, Designs and Patents Act, 1988.

1 3 5 7 9 10 8 6 4 2

Simon & Schuster UK Ltd
1st Floor
222 Gray's Inn Road
London WC1X 8HB

Simon & Schuster Australia, Sydney
Simon & Schuster India, New Delhi

www.simonandschuster.co.uk
www.simonandschuster.com.au
www.simonandschuster.co.in

A CIP catalogue record for this book is available from the British Library

Paperback ISBN: 978-1-3985-1917-6
eBook ISBN: 978-1-3985-1918-3
Audio ISBN: 978-1-3985-1919-0

This book is a work of fiction. Names, characters, places and incidents are either a product of the author's imagination or are used fictitiously. Any resemblance to actual people living or dead, events or locales is entirely coincidental.

Typeset in the UK by M Rules
Printed and Bound in the UK using 100% Renewable
Electricity at CPI Group (UK) Ltd

MIX
Paper | Supporting responsible forestry
FSC® C171272

For all the teachers, but especially
in memory of Penny Sampson.

Chapter One

The imposing stately home loomed beneath the grey February sky, the pristine yellow sheen of its carved sandstone gleaming against heavy winter clouds. *It's like standing inside an Austen novel*, Luisa thought, of Feldspar Hall. With no sign of modern life visible in the direction in which she looked, it was easy to imagine that she had slipped both back in time and into a parallel universe. At any moment she might turn a corner and stumble upon Elizabeth Bennet sneaking a look at the life she could have had.

Luisa had been quietly keeping notes as Marianne and Lady Caroline toured the site. Now, though, Luisa's boss was simply waxing lyrical about her own merits in an attempt to seal the deal. Luisa had taken the opportunity to walk back to the south overlook to contemplate the grounds again, instead.

It was rare that Luisa got out of the office. This was certainly the most grandiose place that she had ever visited as part of her job. It was hard to believe that there were still estates like this in private ownership, but by some wonder the Percivants' fortune had been passed down through the generations intact. The newest lady of the manor – Caroline, an ebullient woman in her early thirties with shining dark hair tied back in a sleek ponytail – had decided that 'something needed to be done' about the estate gardens. They were beautiful, but could do with modernizing, she said. As Luisa had listened during the tour she'd got the sense that what Lady Caroline was really looking for was a way to leave her own stamp on an otherwise impervious landscape. Luisa understood. It would be easy for a person to sink out of sight entirely beneath the weight of this much history.

The opportunity to completely overhaul the grounds of a stately home like Feldspar Hall was literally once-in-a-lifetime. It had never happened in all the years Luisa had been employed as Marianne Boswell's assistant and she doubted it would ever happen again. Naturally, as soon as she'd heard about it, Marianne had gone into overdrive, desperate to get the contract ahead of what was sure to be many other competitors. This had translated into months of preparation and research, most of which had been done by Luisa herself, condensing weeks of reading into bullet-point cheat sheets. Though after what she'd heard today, Luisa wasn't sure Marianne had bothered to read them. She hadn't asked any of the questions Luisa herself would have asked the client. But then, Marianne rarely imagined that anyone knew better than her about anything, especially not garden design. Just as with Luisa's presence on this visit today, the research had merely been for show.

Luisa, meanwhile, had come to know the grounds of Feldspar Hall in the run-up to this visit so well that the idea of redesigning them had sparked in her something almost forgotten. It had been years since she had contemplated designing a garden herself, but there was something about this huge canvas that had been inspiring. How would one create a modern garden that wouldn't look entirely out of place against the backdrop of such a historically specific building? It was an intriguing challenge.

Luisa leaned against the stone balcony that looked out over the grounds and took out her iPad, flicking to the design app she'd used for her ideas. Holding one of them up, Luisa was pleased to see that the real view melded well with her imagined one. Since their arrival more ideas had occurred to her. Luisa took out her stylus and began to adjust the design. Lady Caroline had commented on how much she loved reading – wouldn't it be wonderful to incorporate a sheltered outdoor reading space? There was also her interest in nature conservation. It would be interesting to find ways of encouraging wildlife in a formal setting. There were the children too, three of them, varying in ages and each with their own interests.

Luisa was so engrossed in her digital sketching that she didn't hear the other two women coming back towards her until Marianne appeared at her side. Luisa turned to find her boss glowering at her while Lady Caroline smiled in interest.

'Oh – were you drawing?' she asked. 'I'm so sorry, I didn't realize you would be the one designing the garden. Can I see?'

Before she could reply Luisa found herself divested of the tablet, Marianne reaching out to pull it from her hand.

'Luisa's my secretary,' Marianne said, with a brief and dismissive smile. 'These designs are extrapolated from my early ideas and research – I did tell you that Boswell Garden Architecture takes preparation as seriously as the project itself, didn't I, Lady Caroline? These are just a basic starting point, but please, do look.'

Caroline's gaze moved from the tablet to Luisa as Marianne passed it to her. Luisa smiled. She was used to standing in Marianne's shadow and Luisa *was* her secretary.

'But – these are already beautiful,' said their potential client, as she looked at Luisa's sketches. 'I love the colour scheme – how did you know my favourite colours? And that concealed bower is wonderful . . .'

Marianne subtly turned Lady Caroline away from Luisa, blathering nonsense about 'intuition' and her inherent ability to 'achieve collaborative harmony between client and project' as they all walked back towards the entrance. Luisa stopped listening – there was nothing here that she needed to record, although part of her whispered that having her boss lying on tape might be useful . . . But no, that wasn't Luisa's way.

Lady Caroline returned the iPad to Marianne as they reached the huge flight of steps that led up to Feldspar Hall's grand entrance.

'Well,' she said, 'thank you both so much for coming. I know it's a long drive and I appreciate it.'

'It's my pleasure,' Marianne told her. 'And really, I do hope that I get to work with you on this spectacular project, Lady Caroline. I believe the plans I have in mind would suit this great estate perfectly. Do let me know what you decide sooner rather than later, won't you? We wouldn't want to miss planting season and the year is drawing on. Spring will be upon us before we know it.'

'Of course,' Lady Caroline smiled. 'I have several other companies I'd like to speak to before making a decision but I have to say that those early sketches,' she indicated the iPad in Marianne's hand, 'really tell me all I need to know.'

'Wonderful,' Marianne said. 'Well, I look forward to speaking to you again soon.'

'It was nice to meet you. And you too, Luisa,' Lady Caroline said, with a pointedness that made Luisa smile again, more genuinely this time.

'What are you playing at?' Marianne hissed, as she and Luisa headed for their cars.

'I was just doodling,' Luisa said.

'Well, I'll remind you that the iPad your *doodles* are on is company property. Therefore the designs belong to Boswell Garden Architecture. I hope that's clear.' Marianne made a disgusted sound as she looked at what Luisa had driven to Feldspar Hall in. 'And to turn up in *that*,' she said. 'I obviously pay you far too much. You're just a secretary, for God's sake, how can you afford a new BMW?'

Luisa contemplated the sleek black vehicle. 'I can't,' she said. 'It's my sister's company car. I'm still driving Dad's old Defender, but it had to go in for work, so—'

'I've got to go,' Marianne said, cutting her off. 'I'll see you Monday.'

'Oh, but I thought I'd have a day off in lieu because I worked today?' Luisa asked.

Marianne was already sliding into her own car. 'Fine,' she said, 'although you really should have asked for that sooner.'

'Thank you,' Luisa said, although her boss had already slammed shut the door of her little convertible. 'I appreciate it, Marianne, really.'

Marianne waved a dismissive hand and started the engine. Luisa only realized that she hadn't returned the iPad once her boss was already driving away. With a sigh, she got into the BMW. She'd just have to ask for it back next week. By then, she imagined her ideas for Feldspar Hall would have vanished. Oh well. It was what it was.

Chapter Two

It was barely four o'clock, but the sun was already dipping lower in the sky as Luisa began the long drive back north to Carlisle. She detested the short days of February: by now winter was dragging. She drummed her cold fingers on the steering wheel, peering out at a heavy grey sky that was threatening another cloudburst at any moment. It was going to take her hours to get home. Luisa wouldn't have minded the journey so much if there had been any real point to her being at that meeting, instead of just as a backlight to Marianne Boswell's ego. Her boss could have taped her own notes and handed them to Luisa for typing up afterwards. Although, Luisa conceded, that would have meant she'd have missed out on the visit to Feldspar Hall, which would have been a pity.

Her phone rang. Luisa glanced at the screen. The name she saw there made her pause for a moment, perplexed. She tapped her Bluetooth earpiece.

'Owen,' she greeted, cautiously. 'How lovely to hear from you. It's been a while. How are you?'

'Better for hearing your voice, my dear.' Owen Lawrence's cut-glass baritone filled her ear. 'How are you, Luisa?'

'Oh, you know,' she said, lightly, wondering why her late husband's godfather was calling her. 'Keeping on, as always.'

'Good, good,' he said, with the air of a man perpetually in a rush. 'Well, look, I'll come straight to the point. Something came up yesterday that I wanted to run past you. An opportunity that made me think of you.'

'Really?' Luisa checked her mirrors, surprised. Owen was one of the north's biggest property developers. He already had a well-established team, including a devoted secretary who had been with him for years. Luisa couldn't imagine where she would fit into that equation.

'I've acquired some land as part of a new deal,' he went on. 'Long story short, I bought out a company who owned it as part of their portfolio and, to be frank, it's of no use to me. It'll never sell for the same reasons I don't want it – it's no use for commercial development. Then one of my wily accountants pointed out that if I donate it to charity, it becomes a tax write-off.'

'Right,' Luisa said, still mystified.

'To be completely honest, I couldn't imagine what charity would want it or what possible use it would be,' Owen added. 'But then I remembered that community garden scheme that you and Reuben wanted to get off the ground, back in the day.'

Reuben. Luisa drew in a breath, her fingers tightening on the steering wheel. A beat passed, then another. It was ridiculous, she chided herself, that just the blunt mention of his name could still derail her so completely.

'Luisa? Have I lost you?'

She swallowed. 'No, Owen. I'm still here.'

'I feel bad that I didn't do more to help you with it at the time,' Owen said. 'The dear boy would have wanted me to.'

'It was a long time ago. You were grieving, too,' Luisa said, faintly, still trying to ride out the pain, which was shockingly physical. *It's only that it came out of nowhere*, she told herself. *That's all. You're fine. Everything's fine.* 'We all were.'

'Yes,' Owen agreed, gentler now. 'Luisa, look – if this is dragging up things best left far behind, I'm sorry. You can tell me to get lost and we'll say no more about it. But on the other hand – if you were ready to give it another go, why not try it with this site? Call it an opportunity to create a proof of concept, if you will. It might help you get further backing from other sources that'll enable us to really get the charity going. I'd offer whatever support I could to help.'

'That's very kind of you, Owen,' Luisa said, her head spinning. 'But I can't. I wouldn't even know where to begin anymore.'

'Well, that's another reason I think this would be good for you,' Owen said. 'You were such a talent, Luisa. Even an old philistine like me could recognize how stunning your garden designs always were. It seems such a pity that you gave that up. I know everything changed for you after the accident and I can understand you wanting to leave the past behind, but I can't help but think it an additional tragedy that you never pursued that path. I thought you might want to think about getting back to it. I'd love to help with that if I can. And . . . it would be such a wonderful commemoration of Reuben himself. Wouldn't it?'

Luisa's eyes blurred a little, a fierce burn encompassing her heart. She couldn't think of anything to say. A memory of Reuben came to her, him on the day that they'd both received their undergrad degrees, the joy on his face, how he'd scooped her off the floor and spun her around, so full of life, so *happy*, neither of them aware of what was soon to befall them both. The grief clenched around her heart again, as potent as if she'd lost him yesterday and not so long in the past.

'I'm sorry,' Owen said, into her silence. 'I've overstepped. You know yourself best, of course. It was just an idea.'

'Thank you,' Luisa said, her voice rasping from a throat grown horribly dry. 'Thank you, Owen, really – it's such a generous offer, but it – I *can't*. It's just impossible.'

'I completely understand,' he said. 'But look. I'll send you the site details anyway, just so you have them. No pressure. And remember – you have an open invitation to join us for dinner sometime. Emilia and I would love to see you. Just give us a bell.'

'Thank you,' Luisa said again, automatically, too stunned by the whole conversation to say more.

They said their goodbyes and hung up. Luisa drove on, trying to sweep the memories of her past back into the shadows that were lengthening in the winter's early evening. Luisa and Reuben had met as students on the same course, where they had both studied horticulture but with career paths that diverged as they approached graduation. Luisa had always been drawn to landscaping and garden design, whereas Reuben's interest had transformed during his studies into a fascination with fungi that was destined for academia. They'd both been convinced that plants could change the world and although their approaches had been different, when they joined forces something magical had happened, both personally and professionally. They had married young (too young, some might have said, though neither took any notice) and been blissfully happy, their future together so bright, so promising, right up until—

No, she couldn't think about that, especially not while driving and when the heavens had finally opened to send a flurry of wet sleet down upon the slippery snake of darkening motorway ahead.

Luisa sucked in a deep breath and tried to ground herself, to regain her equilibrium. By the time she reached Carlisle she was almost back on an even keel. The weather had eased a little. As she pulled onto their street Luisa could see that the kitchen window of the townhouse she shared with her sister was illuminated, spilling warm yellow light out into the wet night. Luisa wondered whether Joanna's fiancé Neil would be there too, briefly hoped not and then immediately felt uncharitable for the thought. She liked Neil – loved him, in fact, couldn't imagine a better match for her fiery younger sister and thought of him as a friend as well as a future brother-in-law. It was just that this evening, after the stresses of the day and that strange, unsettling conversation with Owen, Luisa wasn't sure she could deal with watching the two love-birds at close quarters. But it was Jo's house too – in fact, in just a few months, it would be Jo and Neil's house and no longer Luisa's. Neil was in the process of buying Luisa out and she needed to find somewhere else to live before the wedding at the end of August.

It was high time for a change, Luisa knew that. She was thirty-six, sharing a house with her sister, trudging through every day tied to a job that had absolutely no hold over her heart. Still, the thought of having to find a new place to live, of having to start over yet again, alone . . .

Maybe I should get a dog, Luisa thought, as she drew Jo's BMW to a halt on the driveway. Somehow, though, even the thought of being responsible for the needs of a pet was too much to contemplate. Most of the time she wouldn't even eat dinner if Jo weren't there to remind her. Climbing out of the car, Luisa noted ruefully that her trusty old Land Rover still wasn't back from the garage.

Inside the front door, music danced towards her from the kitchen at the end of the hallway: an upbeat, poppy anthem. As Luisa slipped off her coat she caught sight of herself in the large mirror that was part of the old oak sideboard they'd inherited from their dad. The piece was too big for the space and too traditional either for Jo's modern taste or Luisa's minimalist one, but neither of them could bear to let it go, so there it stood, a constant hazard to passing ankles and a harbour for clutter. Luisa brushed her hair out of her face. It needed a cut, her chestnut fringe was getting wispy and the once shoulder-length bob was now heading for her middle back. She added her boots to the semi-tidy pile around the overflowing shoe rack. The sound of enthusiastic chopping joined the cacophony from the kitchen, but there was no accompanying chatter of voices.

'Hello?' Luisa called.

'Hey!' Jo called back, still chopping. 'I was beginning to think you'd run away with the circus.'

In the kitchen Jo was dispatching an onion. It looked as if the entire contents of the fridge and the spice rack were strewn across the countertop, a cookbook propped open amid the mess, a bottle of red wine and a half-full wine glass also thrown into the fray. It never failed to amaze Luisa that her whip-smart lawyer sister, at thirty already renowned in her profession for her wit and efficiency, could be quite so untidy at home.

'Thanks for the car.' Luisa put the BMW keys back on their hook beside the kettle. 'Had a little fender-bender but don't worry. I Sharpied over the scratches, you'll never be able to tell.'

Jo acted out a silent ho-ho-ho belly laugh to indicate that Luisa was nowhere near as funny as she thought she was. 'How was the trip?'

Luisa made a face and nodded at the wine bottle. 'Got another one of those and a straw?'

'That good, eh?'

'Well, I guess I got a day out.'

Jo sighed. 'I wish you'd ditch that job. I hate the way that woman treats you.'

Instead of the straw Luisa took another wine glass from the cupboard behind her and poured herself a generous measure. 'It's fine. It's just work. Could be worse.'

Jo shook her head and went on chopping. Luisa was grateful that tonight it seemed as if her sister wasn't going to follow this with her usual argument that Luisa really should be doing something better with her life. As if they didn't both already know this as well as knowing that ship had sailed long ago.

Luisa peered at the open cookbook. Mowgli, it looked like. No bad thing. 'Where's Neil?'

'Out with friends.' Jo flashed Luisa a grin and for a moment she was back to being the rambunctious five-year-old who had tormented Luisa with her mere presence. 'Just you and me tonight, sis. Thought I'd treat you to dinner.'

Luisa took a mouthful of wine to disguise her guilty relief. 'Oh yes? Why does the cynic in me think there's an ulterior motive to this act of altruism?'

Jo gave an elaborate groan. 'I've got to pick tablecloths, napkins and swags before lunch with the in-laws tomorrow and if you don't help me do it I will either die of boredom or end up calling off the wedding entirely.'

'Swags?'

Her sister half turned, made a semi-circular motion in

the air with her finger, the knife precariously a-dangle. 'You know, for the back of the chairs in the marquee. *Swags.*'

'Ahh. Fair enough.'

Jo's attitude to her 'big day' could so far be described as lackadaisical. Sometimes Luisa wondered if it was a show for her benefit. Perhaps her sister didn't want Luisa to see her enjoying the process, knowing how tragically Luisa's own early marriage had ended and that afterwards her life had stalled so spectacularly that it had never managed to get going again. Luisa didn't know how to ask without immediately making everything about her in a way she definitely did not want and that neither Jo nor Neil deserved.

This line of thinking took Luisa back to Owen's unexpected phone call.

'What's up?' Jo asked, as she tossed the onions into a sizzling-hot pan that was already emitting the aroma of toasted spices: cumin and fennel, mustard, kalonji. 'There's something sitting on your shoulders, I can tell.'

Luisa leaned back against the counter. 'I had a bit of a weird call from Owen on the way home.'

Jo looked up. '*Reuben*'s Owen? Owen Lawrence?'

'Yes.' Luisa recounted the conversation as briefly as she could, pleased when she managed to say Reuben's name without hesitation.

Jo listened in silent concentration, a slight frown on her face. 'That's an interesting offer, isn't it?' she said, once Luisa had finished. 'How are you feeling about it?'

Luisa swallowed more wine. 'Well, I said no. Obviously.'

15

'Really? Just like that?' Jo asked.

'Of course,' Luisa said. 'That's all in the past.'

Jo paused in her stirring to reach for her wine glass, giving Luisa a speculative look.

'What?'

Her sister opened her mouth to say something as Luisa's phone rang. They both looked at the screen as Luisa took it out of her pocket, Marianne's name flashing as the ring tone cycled.

'Don't answer it,' Jo ordered her. 'It's Saturday evening! She's already wasted half of your weekend.'

Luisa answered it. 'Marianne?'

'Luisa. I'll need the notes from today's meeting typed up and emailed to me before start of play on Monday,' her boss said, with no greeting or apology.

'But—'

'Don't make me wait for them,' Marianne went on, sharply. 'I'm meeting with Duke first thing.'

She hung up without saying goodbye. Luisa checked the time. It was after 8pm.

'Don't do it,' Jo advised. 'If she fires you I'll help you take her to the cleaners for unfair dismissal. Horrible witch.'

Luisa put the phone back in her pocket and checked the recipe. 'Sure,' she said, beginning to dice the potatoes. 'And meanwhile I'll just let you handle the mortgage on this place all on your own in the run-up to the wedding, shall I?'

They worked side-by-side in silence for a few minutes, Spotify still belting out banging tunes. Elsewhere, Luisa mused, young women were dancing around their rooms with their friends as they chose outfits for going out-out. Sometimes she felt very old. Part of her thought she should probably care about that.

Chapter Three

Later, they sat in the living room, Jo's laptop open on the coffee table as they looked at wedding flummery with a second bottle of red and a film on in the background. It should have been a wedding-themed rom-com, but instead they'd gone for something with Liam Neeson, who had a particular set of skills and nothing to lose.

'Where is it, then?' Jo asked, her attention for both linen and Liam spent.

Luisa frowned. 'Where's what?'

'This piece of land Owen wants to give you.'

'I don't know.'

'He didn't tell you?'

'I didn't ask. He said he'd email me the details, but I haven't looked.'

Jo shifted on the sofa, turning towards her. 'Why not?'

Luisa shrugged. 'What's the point? I've already said no.'

Her sister made a frustrated noise. 'What's that got to

do with anything? I'm curious even if you're not, so come on – let's look!'

Luisa waved a hand at the laptop and the TV but Jo would not be dissuaded. 'Fine.' She pulled her phone out of her pocket and brought up the email. She scrolled for a second. 'It's an old factory site. Oh, for some reason I thought it'd be over where he is in Durham, but it's not. It's in Collaton. He says the building's long gone and what's left is scrub.'

'Collaton?' Jo repeated. 'You mean down in West Cumbria? Where we used to go to the beach?'

'Guess so.'

Jo pulled the laptop towards her and typed in a few words. 'Collaton,' she read out, a moment later. 'A small seaside town established during the area's industrial heyday, when it was primarily known for the refining of iron ore and the shipping of coal.' She paused, her voice careful when she spoke again. 'Luisa – are you sure you don't want to think about it? It's not that far away really, is it? It could be the perfect opportunity for you.'

'What?' Luisa asked. 'What are you talking about?'

Jo shrugged, pushing the laptop away and reaching for her glass instead as she settled back into the sofa. 'Couldn't it be the perfect chance to get back to what you love doing – what you *should* be doing, instead of working all hours for that awful woman?'

Luisa shook her head. 'This isn't a job, Jo. It's a scrap of land in the middle of nowhere.'

Jo looked down at her hands, one neatly painted thumb-nail scratching against the glass.

'Come on,' Luisa said, 'spit it out.'

Her sister glanced up at the warbling TV and reached for the remote, flicking it into silence. 'Well,' she said. 'There is still the life insurance money, just sitting there.'

Luisa drew in a breath, shifting sharply in her seat. 'Jo. *Don't.*'

'I know you don't like to talk about it,' Jo said, quickly. 'I know you've never felt that accepting it was right—'

'Jo—'

'Listen, Luisa. Please? Just for a minute. You wouldn't be spending it on yourself. You'd be setting up the charity that Reuben would have established himself if he'd been here. Since you refuse to use it for anything else, wouldn't that be the best possible use for that money?'

'Marianne's about to take on this Feldspar Hall contract and planting season's just around the corner. How much spare time do you think I'm going to have?' Luisa demanded. 'It's only February and I've already worked a day out of almost every weekend of the year so far. Even if I wanted to do it, I wouldn't have *time.*'

'Then quit,' Jo said, bluntly. 'Dump Marianne bloody Boswell on her arse. She deserves it.' Jo caught Luisa's hand before she could protest. 'That money's been sitting there for *years.*'

Luisa shook off Jo's hand and put down her glass. 'You've had too much wine,' she said, her tone sharper than she intended. 'You're talking nonsense. I'm going to bed.'

'Luisa—'

'Enough, Jo.'

'It was your dream, Lu. Building gardens. Wasn't it? It was always your *dream*. This could be a chance for you to finally do that if you just—'

'Reuben was my dream,' Luisa said, shortly, because all this was threatening to overwhelm her and she couldn't let it, she couldn't. '*Reuben* was.'

That shut her sister up, as Luisa had known it would. Jo looked up at her from the sofa, face sympathetic but serious. 'He wasn't all of it. He was *part* of it.'

'I'm going to bed,' Luisa told her, tired of this, which cut far too close to the bone. 'Thanks for cooking.'

'Luisa!' Jo called her back at the door. When she half turned, her sister sighed. 'I'm sorry. I worry about you, that's all.'

Despite her ire, Luisa smiled. 'I know. But you don't need to.' She nodded at the laptop. 'Worry about your swags, instead. Night.'

Jo's voice floated to her as she reached the bottom of the stairs, plaintive in a way calculated to draw a smile, even if it remained unseen. 'But what if I don't even *want* swags?'

It was late, but Luisa knew she wouldn't sleep. She sat at the desk under her window instead, pulling out the recording device she used for all of Marianne's notes. She may as well get the transcription out of the way, leave her Sunday free for better things.

Luisa started work, but couldn't concentrate. She kept

drifting into thoughts of Reuben, little flashes coming to her: his face, his laugh. Luisa sighed as she stopped typing for the third time, pressing the tips of her fingers into her eyes. After a moment she opened the top drawer of her desk, moving papers around until she found what she was looking for – an old, faded photograph in a small silver frame. It was dog-eared because for years she had carried it everywhere with her, but had eventually taken it from her wallet and then, just the year before in what she liked to think was a sign of really moving on, had retired it from display.

The image was of Luisa and Reuben, taken by a friend on one of those golden, carefree afternoons they had all spent on the river at Durham as students. Luisa was rowing – or at least, she was trying to, though the photograph had caught her in a moment of raucous laughter, probably because Reuben had put his arms around her waist from behind and was blowing a raspberry against her neck. The sun glinted off the water, off their sunglasses and their smiles, casting everything in the light of an everlasting halo that persisted in her memory as pure joy. Luisa's world had lost its pigment when Reuben left it. Nothing since had ever seemed as bright.

Luisa blinked, realized there were tears in her eyes and wiped them away. There was no point dwelling on a past that was gone forever.

Still, Jo's argument echoed in her mind, as did her resurfaced memories of Reuben. It had been a complete shock when she'd found out about the life insurance policy. Luisa hadn't known it existed, but in retrospect she shouldn't have been surprised. Unlike Luisa and Jo, Reuben came from family money, a circle containing the sort of titles and affluence within which she had never managed to feel comfortable. When his parents broke the news, Luisa had still been in hospital. The money was hers, whether she wanted it or not.

It was Jo – then still at school – who had persuaded Luisa not to immediately give it away to charity, Jo who had worked out the legalities and set up the account into which it was paid. Luisa hadn't wanted to think about it and indeed even now went for long periods forgetting it existed. She never looked at the statements and had no idea how much had accrued over the years. On the occasions that Luisa *had* thought about it she'd had a vague inkling of gifting it all to Reuben's nieces – who had never known their uncle – when they came of age. Luisa did not want it herself and never would. It wasn't her money. It never would be. She couldn't comprehend the idea of any sort of 'benefit' to her husband's death.

Luisa looked at that photograph again, of Reuben and her together, happy, glowing in golden light. Instead of putting it back in the drawer, she stood the frame on her desk. Luisa wondered what Reuben would have said to Owen's offer, and as the thought occurred to her she knew that he'd have said yes immediately, no matter how impractical the notion. Reuben had been like that – an engine, a powerhouse, a force of nature. His energy was infectious: he lit up every room he walked into and he'd inspired everyone he met to do better, to *be* better, without ever making them feel as if they needed to be anything other than exactly what they were.

A free patch of land! Luisa could imagine him saying, with the grin that had never failed to make her heart stutter. *What better start could we possibly ask for?*

When Luisa finally went to bed, she dreamed of Reuben. He knelt amid the soil of a burgeoning garden, his hands busy in good earth as he looked up at her: happy, free. Whole.

Chapter Four

Jo was making coffee when Luisa came into the kitchen the next morning. Jo was in her running kit and Luisa glanced at the clock. It was well after ten. Luisa had slept in, the symptom of a broken night.

'I'm sorry,' Luisa said, as her sister passed her a steaming mug, made just how she liked it. 'For last night, I mean. I shouldn't have snapped at you. Owen's call was so unexpected – it was all a bit much, I think.'

Jo pulled her into a hug. 'I get it. I'm sorry, too, for pushing.'

'Don't be,' Luisa told her, seriously, as they parted. 'And . . . look, I've done a bit of thinking since.'

'Oh?' Jo turned her attention to the plate of toast on the counter.

'Can I borrow the car again today?' Luisa asked. 'I . . . thought I might take a drive down the coast.'

Jo's eyes widened and she spoke around a mouthful of toast. 'You're thinking about what Owen said? Really?'

Luisa shook her head. 'Let's not get ahead of ourselves. But ... it's a generous offer he's made. It would at least be polite to visit the site, wouldn't it?'

Her sister smiled. 'Want me to come with you?'

'Aren't you supposed to be having lunch with the almost in-laws?'

'Yes,' Jo admitted. 'But I'm sure they'll understand if I cancel.'

'There's no need,' Luisa said. 'Really. I'm just going to take a look.'

The weather worsened as Luisa left the sprawl of the border city behind, the weak winter sun vanishing completely behind low dark clouds that gathered to send shivers of icy sleet in hard spatters across the windshield. She followed the turbulent wash of the wide Solway Firth south, the green of Dumfries and Galloway just visible as a shore in the distance. Wind turbines shone white in the gloom, their turning blades flickering shadows against the low, flat swathes of moorland sweeping between the fells and the water. The infrastructure Luisa passed as she drove spoke of the area's industrial roots transformed for the modern era, vast metal hangars big enough to store whole houses, production facil-ities for everything from paper to running kit. Between were scattered towns and villages: Silloth with its wide, windswept promenade, Maryport with its pretty harbour.

Beyond Whitehaven the Firth became the Irish Sea and the roads stumbled into a winding tangle darkened by the inclement weather and the shortened day. Somewhere up ahead was Sellafield, with the undisturbed sweep of Drigg beach curving a wild, lonely swathe of sand away from its shadow. Luisa remembered childhood trips there with her parents and a toddling Jo, building sandcastles that unconsciously mirrored the unseen towers of the nuclear plant. That was before their mother died, Luisa's first searing experience of loss, but by no means the last. She was still thinking about this when Collaton appeared, presenting itself without preamble through a sheet of cold drizzle.

Luisa slowed. A spread of industrial buildings stretched beside the railway line that ran right along the shore, where other towns would have put a promenade. Despite how close it was to the Lake District – with more light in the sky Luisa would be able to see the great green peaks of Wasdale in the middle distance – Collaton was not and never had been a tourist destination. The vivacity of its busy Victorian heyday was all but forgotten, now more a place to pass through than to visit.

She turned inland, passing long, tightly packed laces of small houses painted in pastel colours that had faded in the sea air. Most had no gardens, only yards, constructed for the workers of years past as cheaply and solidly as possible, close to the refineries and dockyards. Many seemed empty, their windows dark, tenacious weeds forcing their way through the brick and concrete of their surroundings.

Luisa followed the blue dot through the short maze, passing the gates of a deserted breakers' yard piled high with the metal carcasses of vehicles. She turned at a junction and something crunched under her left back wheel. She cursed, searching the rear-view mirror, but the road seemed empty – hopefully it was just a crisp packet or something equally harmless. It wouldn't do to damage the BMW, not when her sister had been so generous about letting her drive it. Ahead, the streets of houses gave way to another factory – or at least, that's what it would have been in years past. Now it was the abandoned parcel of land she had come to see. Over the decades whatever large red sandstone building had once stood there had crumbled, the only remaining evidence that it had ever been there part of a gable-end wall that still loomed over one end of the plot. The rest of the site was a jumble of rubble interspersed with thickets of brambles and split tarmac.

Luisa parked up and looked around. The streets around the site – it formed a kind of square at the centre – were a mixture of residential houses and industrial units, most of which seemed empty. There was a small strip of three shops, all boarded up. On one corner a sign, scoured rough by years of salt air, swung gently outside a pub that probably hadn't opened its doors in this century. The only building obviously occupied was on the far side of the square to where she had parked, two anonymous double doors standing open, yellow light from within pouring out into the day's cloying gloom.

The weather was now so grim that Luisa retrieved the flashlight Jo kept in the glove box before getting out. The door closed a little too hard, the sound echoing like a gunshot. It was cold, an icy winter wind cutting in from the shore to whistle through the silent streets. She crouched to look at the tyre, but it seemed fine. As she straightened up another gust of wind brought with it more icy drizzle and Luisa wished she had thought to change – she'd come out wearing a pair of light blue jeans and only her trusty padded gilet over an old blue wool sweater instead of a proper coat, which was ridiculous – why hadn't she checked the forecast? If Luisa had been in the Defender there'd have been the old Barbour she kept in the back, but Jo's leased Beemer was empty of anything that didn't expressly need to be there.

It's fine, Luisa told herself. *You're not staying long.*

She walked the perimeter of the site first. It was far bigger than she'd been expecting – about the size of a football field, edged by a pavement on all sides that separated it from the road. The empty property had also been ringed by a mesh fence that was about as secure as a kid's piggy bank. Gaps had appeared where the age-slackened panels had been pushed or blown inwards.

Inside, the pocked tarmac took up about half the area and was easy enough to navigate, but beyond it the ground was broken and uneven. It looked as if most of the rubble from the collapsed factory was still exactly where it had fallen. She wondered how long this piece of land had been this way – neglected and decaying with no one to care about it. She tried to look at it the way Reuben would have had he been standing beside her. He'd always had the ability to see the best in everything. This place, though – Luisa thought that even her ever-optimistic husband would have struggled to see a hopeful future here.

She had been right in what she'd told Owen the day before, Luisa realized. She wouldn't know where to begin. For a start it seemed vast – far too big for her to easily get to grips with, especially not if she was starting out alone. It was an impossible challenge.

A blast of wind cut through her gilet and Luisa hopped from foot to foot to stave off the chill. *You came, you saw*, she told herself. *Time to get back in the car and head home. You still need to finish Marianne's notes.*

Luisa made her way back across the blank space and squeezed her way out through the broken fence again. Her mood had dipped, leaving her feeling strangely depressed, although hadn't this been exactly what she'd told herself to expect? What difference did it make? She'd already known she couldn't take on this crazy project anyway.

Another gust of wind brought with it a sudden flurry of sleet that sliced against her cheeks, sharp enough to make her catch her breath. As she hurried back to the car the street seemed darker than before. Luisa caught sight of the back tyre and for a moment she thought she was seeing things – an optical illusion created by the deepening shadows. She dug the little torch out of her pocket and flicked it on, its bright white light illuminating the left rear wheel. She stopped in dismay. The tyre was as flat as a pancake.

Luisa swore under her breath while, as if to mock her

predicament, another miserable blast of sleet swept at her down the abandoned street. As far as she could make out, she had only two choices: either she got on with it and patched the tyre straight away, or she sat in the car for who knew how long waiting for breakdown recovery. As if the situation wasn't bad enough already, unless she left the BMW's doors open to the elements (she could just imagine Jo's face if she told her she'd done *that*) she was going to have to fix the tyre in torchlight because daylight seemed to have exited the situation completely. Luisa went to the car boot and opened it, the sound of sleet pelting the roof as she stood beneath its bare shelter for a moment, gathering herself.

A noise echoed to her from not far away, manic laughter, raised voices. Luisa turned to look across the wasteland and saw a gaggle of figures emerging from the open doors she'd noticed, silhouetted against the brightness of the light behind them. It sounded like a group of teenagers. They hustled along the street, loudly bemoaning the weather, jackets held above their heads, phone screens bobbing like beacons on a high tide. There came another sound, another echo – a larger figure closing the doors, cutting out that warm light. The whole square was in perpetual gloom now, apart from the spaceship glare emanating from Jo's car.

The group of teens continued along the street, heading for an alley that took them out of the square and away. Soon she'd be entirely alone. Luisa hadn't realized until that moment how significant that single sign of life, those lit and open doors, had been. Luisa pushed away from where she'd perched beneath the open boot. The sooner she got on with the task at hand, the better. Her jumper was already damp at the sleeves, her hands, feet and face were freezing, but her core was still warm. She just needed to keep moving. Luisa stuck the torch between her teeth and used both hands to lift the base of the boot out to reveal the jack and recovery kit hidden away beneath.

'Are you all right?'

The voice startled her so much she spat out the torch. It fell to the wet ground and rolled away from her, its light slicing crazy chiaroscuro patterns through the still-falling sleet. Whirling around, she saw a huge man standing a few feet away. He crouched to pick up the torch as it rolled towards him.

'Sorry,' he said, holding it out to her. 'Didn't mean to scare you.'

Luisa wished she could say he hadn't, but that would be a lie. The street was too dark, too abandoned and here she was, alone, with a guy who could have been Jack Reacher's older brother. He loomed at her, broad shoulders, thick dark hair cut short, nose that had obviously been broken at least once. She leaned back into the boot, surreptitiously gripping the handle of the jack.

The man's attention was all for the car's tyre.

'Damn,' he said. 'Hell of a time to get a flat.'

'It's fine,' she said, through teeth that were already beginning to chatter with the cold. 'I'm going to patch it.'

He cast a glance her way as if unconvinced. Luisa flushed, annoyed. Right now she knew she looked like a damsel in distress but she had absolutely no intention of ever being one of those again.

'I'd do it quickly, if I were you,' said another, much younger voice that was so unexpected that Luisa jumped, 'or you'll die of hypothermia before you can drive that thing home. Who goes out in February without a coat?'

There was a girl lurking beside him, hidden by the shadows. Luisa could barely make her out – she was dressed all in black, with short dark hair. She might have been sixteen or thereabouts, Luisa couldn't be sure, but her face was hard, her eyes sharp even in the gloom. She had her arms crossed, one hip jutting out in a defiant pose. She didn't make Luisa feel any more comfortable than her companion – her father? – did.

'Thanks for stopping,' Luisa said, trying to keep her tone light, 'but I'm fine. You two should go, get out of this awful weather. I'm just going to sort this out and head off myself.'

The girl took Luisa at her word and strode past the car in an easy, loping gait.

'We can't just leave you out here. Harper, wait,' said the man. When the girl stopped, he pulled a set of keys from his pocket and held them out to her. 'Take the lady inside. Make her a coffee and put the heater on while I sort out the tyre.'

The girl looked aghast. 'What?'

'Oh no,' Luisa said, 'really, that's not necessary.'

The man gave her a patient look that annoyed Luisa. He shook the keys, looking at Harper again. 'Come on.'

'I've got to get home,' Harper said. 'Max will need his tea.'

'Half an hour, that's all it'll take.'

The girl folded her arms. 'Yeah, right. Tell you what, Mr P, *I'll* sort the tyre, *you* do the hosting thing, all right? Or we'll *all* be here until midnight.'

'Wait,' Luisa said, cutting in, suspecting that they might have forgotten she was there. 'You're both very kind but really, I can manage.'

'Yeah?' Harper stepped off the kerb and into the light from the car's interior. 'Ever patched a tyre on a BMW X5 before?'

Luisa opened her mouth to say yes, of course she had, but that would have been another lie. She wanted to explain to this smart-ass kid that, as it happened, she'd changed and patched plenty of tyres in her life but this wasn't her car. She'd never in a million years choose to own anything this *fragile*. But explaining that would probably make her seem even more pathetic than she did already, so in the end Luisa just shut her mouth again.

The girl smirked. 'Thought not.'

'Look,' Luisa tried again, feeling her grip on the situation slipping away, 'I'm really not—'

Harper leaned past her and lifted out the jack with one strong, smooth movement. 'Don't worry,' she said. 'I won't nick it. Won't take it for a joy ride. Promise.'

'Come on,' said the cryptically named Mr P, palming his

clutch of keys. 'Harper's a genius with cars and she's right. She'll do the job far quicker than me. Let her do her thing. You and me — let's get out of this cold.'

Chapter Five

Cas glanced back at the woman behind him as he headed back to the gym. He'd half expected her to tell them both to get lost — she'd clearly been annoyed at him for butting in. It reminded him of the times he'd managed to wind Annika up, thinking he was being helpful when actually he was, quote, 'treating me like one of your hopeless kids'.

He unlocked the peeling double doors for the second time that evening. An echo rang down the empty corridor beyond as Cas reached in to switch on the light, revealing stark white walls and a scuffed concrete floor in utilitarian grey. He headed along the hallway and turned right into the main room, which was similarly decorated except that this had an old parquet floor. Cas crossed to his small office at the far end and opened the door — this one he never locked — to barrel inside, flicking on the promised oil heater and pulling a brown plastic chair in front of it for her to sit on. Then he continued to the kettle-and-mug assembly on the small table in the corner. After a moment he realized her footsteps had stopped. He turned to look through the large picture window in the dividing wall to see that she was standing in the doorway of the gym, pausing to survey her surroundings.

There wasn't much for her to look at. The main room of the space Cas rented for the club was large, oblong and mostly empty. The focal point was the old boxing ring in the centre, raised a little so that it was possible to see the fraying edges of the foam, the way the top layer of rubber was coming away despite Cas's best efforts at running repairs on the worst of it. He had called in an ancient favour to get it in the first place and it was the most expensive thing they had: there was no way he'd ever be able to replace it. There were various other bits of equipment dotted around too, items he had managed to scavenge. A few punchbags, a line of wire shelving that housed gloves, helmets and other protective gear, a few lockers for the kids. There were mats rolled up along one wall, giving off a decaying, rubbery scent that Cas barely noticed anymore.

He saw the woman's gaze stray to the large banner that had been the first thing he'd put up once he'd finished painting the walls: RESPECT OTHERS AND YOU RESPECT YOURSELVES. It was a mantra he tried to live by and tried even harder to instil into the difficult almost-adults that washed up on this doorstep. By the time they reached him, though, it was often too late. They'd usually already been thrown out of everywhere else, sometimes including their own homes. The notion that there was anyone or anything in this world that deserved their respect, least of all themselves, was met with incomprehension, so his efforts had varying degrees of success.

Cas rubbed a hand over his eyes, the feeling of defeat that had been slowly growing in recent weeks arriving with a renewed wave of tiredness. He'd wanted this place to be a haven, a hope, a lifeboat, but his failures outweighed the victories and in two months' time he wouldn't even have the money to pay the meagre rent this place demanded.

The kettle was boiling as she joined him in the office.

'It's just instant, I'm afraid,' he said.

She gave a wide, bright smile and for a split-second Cas thought another light had been switched on. He blinked, blindsided, as she said, 'Anything, as long as it's hot. Black, no sugar would be great.'

He passed her the mug, inexplicably awkward.

'Thank you, you're very kind,' she said, as she took a seat and then after a pause added, 'Mr ... *P*?'

Cas took the other mug of coffee he'd made and stepped behind his desk to slide into his own chair. 'That's what the kids call me. It's short for Pattanyús, which none of them can ever be bothered with. You can call me Cas, though.'

'Cas,' she repeated. 'Is that short for something too?'

'Casimir,' Cas said, and then, before she could ask, 'It's Hungarian. And you are ...?'

She smiled again, but he was prepared for it this time and it had almost no effect. 'I'm Luisa. Luisa MacGregor.' She looked back out into the gym. 'What is this place?'

'A club for budding boxers,' Cas said. 'At least, that's what it aspires to be. Sometimes I think all I'm providing is crowd control.'

'You're a boxer.' She said this as if it made perfect sense and was the answer to a question she'd already asked.

'No. Well, a little, when I was younger. This place is only open for a couple of hours a few evenings in the week and for afternoon sessions at the weekend. It's specifically an after-school club for teens. My actual job is as a Phys Ed teacher at the high school.'

This time the look she gave him was a surprised one tinged with something a little warmer. 'This is a non-profit, then?'

He laughed at that. 'You could say that. Money doesn't really feature inside these walls, to be honest.' He gestured to the chipped mug that held her cheap coffee. 'In case that wasn't already painfully obvious.'

Luisa McGregor smiled a little, sipping her coffee, but said nothing. Cas tried to figure her out but couldn't.

'Do you mind if I ask what you were doing out there?' he asked.

She shifted a little in her seat. 'I was looking at that empty plot of land. Someone's given me the chance to take it on.'

Cas frowned. 'Really? You're – a developer?' He couldn't imagine why anyone would think it was worth building anything on that lot. It must have been dirt cheap, but still. There were plenty of other houses already unoccupied without anyone building new ones. Unless they were thinking of a tower block, but there was no market for luxury flats here.

'No, I'm a secretary,' she said.

'Right,' Cas said, none the wiser.

The woman sighed, biting her lip for a second. 'I'm a secretary now, but I trained in landscape design,' she explained. 'Quite a few years ago, when I was a post-grad student, I had an idea for a charity. Well, it wasn't just me, but ...' She trailed off and then shrugged. 'We wanted to take parcels of unwanted land in struggling towns and turn them into places that people want to go.'

Cas looked at her. 'You're talking about gentrification.'

'No,' she said. 'No, definitely not. It was about ... urban renewal, I guess you'd call it. We wanted to make something for the people who already live in the area. It was about using a garden to establish a space that would involve and be for the existing community. We thought,' she smiled wryly, as if at herself, 'that growing plants could change lives.'

He was still trying to figure it out. 'You want to build a *garden*? Out there?'

'Not everyone has their own, do they?'

'We've got a pretty good one right on our doorstep,' he pointed out. 'It's called the Lake District.'

'There's a difference between cultivating a garden and taking advantage of the natural world,' she said, mildly. 'Both can be therapeutic in different ways.'

'Well,' he said. 'Anything that tries to put energy into this town is a good thing. I'm just not sure I understand what it is you think you'll achieve.'

She turned away from him, looking out at the shabby excuse for a gym beyond his office window. 'I could ask you the same question,' she said, without rancour. 'This club of yours – what are you trying to achieve here?'

Cas followed her gaze and saw, not for the first time, how this place must look to outsiders. It was a question he'd been asked a million times, often in tones far more combative than the one she'd used. He'd asked it of himself more than once, too, especially on days when he'd looked at his bank account and had to calculate whether he could afford to take Annika for a meal out before payday. It wasn't a position he'd expected to be in at the age of forty.

'It gives the kids a different perspective,' he told her. 'It's a place they can learn to channel their anger, to control themselves and how they feel. I try to teach them respect, not just for others but for themselves, too. They make friends here – they become a community that helps each other, not just inside these walls but outside them as well. That has benefits beyond the time they spend here. And besides any of that it gives them a safe place to be.'

Luisa MacGregor nodded. 'Everything you've just told me is what we wanted the community garden scheme to do, too. That was our plan.'

'Was?'

She shrugged one shoulder, looking out at the gym again.

'Like I said, the charity idea was a long time ago, but it never went anywhere. Yesterday someone gave me a chance if I wanted to try again, but it's too late now. I'm different, my life is different, the world is different.'

'You drove all the way here, though,' he observed. 'Despite that.'

Cas watched as she sipped the last of her coffee. She looked faraway for a moment, a wave of sadness carrying her somewhere she could not be reached. Then she blinked and gave a slight smile, a little shrug.

'I just thought I should take a look before dismissing his generosity completely. That's the only reason I'm here.'

A sound echoed behind them – the gym doors opening and shutting, followed by swift footsteps. Harper appeared in the doorway, her dark hair dripping wet and plastered against her head.

'You're done,' she called to Luisa. 'I've got to go.'

'Oh – wait!' Luisa jumped up, following quickly as the girl disappeared into the corridor again. 'Hang on a second – please!'

Cas followed and saw that Harper had paused on the threshold as Luisa rummaged in her bag. Pulling out her wallet, she opened it and took out a thin sheaf of notes.

'To say thank you,' Luisa said, holding out the money.

The girl held up a hand, warding her off. 'You don't have to pay me.'

'Please take it,' Luisa said. 'Or if you really don't want it, you can give it to Mr Pattanyús for the club.'

Harper looked past Luisa to where Cas stood. He nodded slightly. The girl took the money, still hesitant, and stuffed the fold into the back pocket of her wet jeans.

'Thanks,' she said. 'I've really got to go.'

'Don't forget,' Cas called, before she could disappear, 'what we talked about earlier.'

Harper rolled her eyes at him. 'I know, Mr P.'

'I pulled a lot of strings, Harper. Don't mess it up.'

'I said, *I know*!' A moment later Cas and Luisa were alone again, the sound of Harper's boots echoing away with the wind.

'She's a tough cookie,' Cas said. 'Doesn't have the easiest life. She's smart as a tack, though. She could have such a bright future.'

Luisa smiled slightly. 'I believe you.'

'I wish *she* would,' Cas sighed. 'Look, for the record – I think your idea is great. This place and the people in it could do with a hundred more just like it, to be honest. And hey – I've always hoped that this sorry excuse for a gym could change the world for these kids. Who am I to say that growing plants can't do the same for everyone else?'

He walked her out and watched as she pulled away in a car that could pay his salary for two years or more. *Urban renewal*, he thought. It was a nice idea, but he wasn't surprised she'd taken one look at this place and run a mile. Most people did. Checking his watch Cas uttered a faint curse. He was late again, when he had faithfully promised that this time, *this* time he would be on time. He should have asked for a lift, he thought, as he shifted into a run, sleet batting him in the face as he headed for home.

Cas could feel the storm gathering as soon as he pushed open the front door. It was lurking somewhere in the elegantly white rooms of the place he still thought of as solely Annika's flat even though he had paid half the rent on it for the past three years. They had talked about buying somewhere together, but she flatly refused to put down more roots in 'a place like this' and he flatly refused to put them down anywhere else, which surely should have told them all they needed to know and yet, somehow, here they still were.

'Annika?' Music filtered from the bedroom. Cas rubbed a hand over his face and toed off his trainers. 'I'm sorry,' he called. 'Five minutes. I'll be ready.'

She appeared in the doorway, barefoot and in the silver dress, the one that on any other woman would look like a prom-night mistake but that managed to make her look like a supermodel who'd simply taken a wrong turn on her walk to the runway. Her make-up and hair were perfect. All she needed were her shoes, whereas here was Cas, sweaty gym-bunny and drowned rat in a single unappealing bundle.

'You're late.'

'I know, I'm sorry.'

'You *promised* me—'

'I know,' he said again. 'Something came up.'

She disappeared again, returned with her shoes. 'Something always comes up, Cas. What was it this time? Did one of them mug an old lady? Rob the corner shop? I'm not waiting. Not anymore. You can waste your own time on as many lost causes as you like, but you're not wasting mine as well.'

'It's not a waste. How can you even say that?' Cas wouldn't tell her about Harper's latest misdemeanour. He'd learned his lesson about that early on.

Annika spread her arms. She really was stunningly beautiful. 'Oh, I don't know, Cas. Maybe the fact that I'm about to go out alone *again* because you'd rather spend hours on a dead-end project than on building yourself a life with people who won't just drain it dry?'

'What do you want me to say?' he demanded. 'I've told you I'm sorry. I would have been here if something hadn't happened that I couldn't just abandon.'

'If you gave me half of what you devote to those kids it'd be something,' Annika said. 'I just wanted one night where I don't have to make excuses for my partner being absent because he doesn't care enough about me to bother turning up.'

'Five minutes,' he said. 'I'll be ready.'

By the time he got out of the shower, though, she had gone.

Chapter Six

Harper jogged the two streets back home, the soaked denim of her jeans chaffing against her legs. If it had been her choice she'd have left the woman to sort out her own tyre. Harper had no time for people who had the money to own a top-of-the-range motor but couldn't be bothered to take the time to know the basics of how to look after it. Would have served her ladyship right to break a nail or two.

Of course, that would never have happened, because there was no way Mr P would have walked past and left the woman there on her own. He would have fixed the tyre for her, though Harper knew for a fact he was rubbish with cars. He just couldn't help trying to be a White Knight, that was his problem.

Moron, Harper thought, with an affection she would never acknowledge, even to herself.

Anyway, as a result of Mr P being far too nice a person for anyone's good, least of all hers, here she was, cold, wet and late. Still, there was money in her pocket that hadn't been there before. She hadn't looked to see how much the woman had given her but whatever it was would be more than Harper had left the house with that morning. She'd left the last twenty she'd had on the kitchen table with a clear note that it was to be used to top up the electricity meter, which had been running on empty.

The Sunday evening streets were as abandoned as they had been while she'd worked on the BMW, but noise filtered to her through closed doors and windows: music, laughter, arguments, the usual assorted detritus of lives lived sandwiched against each other and yet barely seen.

Home was a brick-built two-storey house much the same as any other in the street where she lived, although unlike any other street nearby, Harper's home backed onto the old scrapyard instead of another row of houses. This didn't mean much aside from one less row of neighbours, a flagged yard that opened onto the abandoned path between the scrapyard and the back of the houses, and a bit more light. Her little brother Max got that, since his bedroom was the one at the back. The only view he had was of the field of junk that had been piled high beneath his bedroom window since before he was born, but Max didn't seem to mind that. He didn't seem to mind anything, really. Max, like Harper, just got on with whatever came his way and stayed away from everything else. Part of her worried that a nine-year-old boy really should have more friends, but he wasn't being bullied (the kids his age all knew who his sister was and just how well she could look after both herself *and* him if the situation called for it) but another, larger part of her thought that it would be fine if he stayed away from everyone around here forever. Not that they were going to be here forever. Harper was getting out of this place as soon as she could and when she went she'd be taking Max with her. She hadn't figured out how yet, but she'd make it happen. She would.

Harper reached their front gate and pushed it open, crossing the small concrete yard to the front door. She could hear music from inside before she even fitted her key into the lock and what it meant put a scowl on her face. She pushed open the door. A narrow flight of stairs led up from the tiny patch of floor inside. Beside it a short hallway, currently dark, led to the kitchen at the back of the house. To her right was another door and the living room, from which the music was pounding.

'Max?'

Her shout was directed up the stairs, but received no answer. Peering down the hall revealed that the kitchen was also in darkness, empty.

Harper peeled off her jacket and toed off her soaked trainers before shoving her way into the living room. Despite how small the house was she rarely went in there. The stench of fags and other smokable substances rolled out to clog her nostrils as she opened the door. Her dad was sprawled on one of the two sagging grey sofas. He might have been asleep but, judging by the number of beer cans scattered on the floor, it was more likely he'd passed out. The congealed remains of a Chinese takeaway still stood on the stained coffee table, two empty tin-foil boxes and the lingering smell of sweet and sour. Who knew how long it had been there.

Harper kicked her way across the mess on the floor and smacked off the offending music. The resulting silence was a blessing but her head was beginning to pound. All she wanted was a hot shower and beans on toast.

'Hey,' she yelled. 'Did you give Max his dinner?'

The only answer was an unintelligible grunt and Harper knew from experience that she'd get nothing else useful. She briefly considered giving him a good, hard punch in the ribs but in the split-second that the thought occurred to her so did Mr P's disapproving face. Like a really annoying angel on her shoulder, that man was.

'Max?'

Harper went up the stairs, calling again from the landing, but there was still no answer. She assumed he'd be engrossed in something in his bedroom and oblivious to the time and the racket from downstairs thanks to the high-end headphones she'd got him last year. At nine Max was old enough to make himself food if he needed to – she had shown him how to use the hob, just in case – but never did. Her little brother didn't seem to get hungry for anything apart from whatever obsession he'd picked up that month, which was what kept getting her in trouble. Last week she'd tried to suggest that he probably didn't need yet another box of Sharpies to add to the four unopened ones he'd already got stashed under his bed. He'd insisted, though, and Max had little enough in his life, so it was the least she could do to get them for him. Unfortunately, this time she'd underestimated the motivation of the staff in WH Smith, not to mention the speed of the security guard they'd sent after her.

Hence her having yet another reason to owe Mr P. He'd gone to bat for her yet again, managed to persuade them that instead of prosecution what she needed to do was a type of community service that didn't require a court order, just her willingness to show contrition. She wasn't sure how he'd swung it but Harper suspected the shop's manager fancied him so maybe that was it. Mr P hadn't worked out what her punishment (*'It's not a punishment, Harper, it's about building your understanding of the importance of community' yawn eyeroll yawn*) was going to be yet but Harper already knew it would be pointless and boring besides. But whatever.

Anyway, Harper kept hoping that Max's ever-changing interests would one day align with hers and he'd want to come to the gym with her, but he hated the place. Something about the way the sound echoed had made him freak out the first time she'd taken him there. He'd never wanted to go again and she wasn't going to force him, even if it would have made him a lot easier to keep tabs on.

Her brother was not in his room, which meant he wasn't in the house.

Harper ran back down the stairs, back into the living room where their one existing parent was still blacked out amid cushions that should have been landfill years ago. She lurched around the coffee table and was about to punch the prone figure hard on the shoulder when the lights went out.

Harper swore loudly and landed the punch anyway.

'You didn't top up the meter, did you?' she yelled. 'Where's Max? How can you be this useless?'

There was no response, but anyway Harper was already on her way back out of the door. She took the top-up key from the meter case in the hallway, grabbed the only other dry jacket on the hook and went back out, shivering now. As she walked she pulled out her mobile but who could she call? Max didn't have his own phone, though she was saving to get him one. She couldn't think of anywhere he might have gone that wasn't either school or home anyway. Her clueless little brother was out here somewhere in this mess of weather, on his own and with an empty stomach. Harper's own churned fretfully, twining with the anger she felt at her dad, their life, this place, the world. That stupid bitch who couldn't look after her own car. If it hadn't been for her—

Harper reached the corner shop, the meter key already in her cold fingers even as she barged through the door into a commotion as loud as the one that had greeted her at home.

'You can't just take them! That's stealing!'

'It says they're free! It says so, *right there!*'

'Yeah, on the magazine, you little shit! You have to *buy* the magazine, *then* you get the free thing that comes with it!'

Harper recognized the second voice the instant she heard it.

'Max?'

Her little brother peered around the legs of the man looming over him. They were standing beside the magazine rack and Max had his arms crossed over something held tightly across his chest as the guy tried to tug whatever it was free. Three magazines lay on the vinyl floor at their feet, their covers crumpled.

'Harper!'

The guy turned.

'Max, come here.'

He dodged past the guy and ran to reach her.

'It says they're free,' he told her. 'It *says* so.'

'Okay,' she said, pushing him behind her. 'It's okay. We'll sort this out.'

'Damn right we will,' said the shop owner, heading for the counter. 'I'm calling the police, right now.'

'No, don't,' Harper said, going after him. 'I'm sorry. I'll pay for whatever damage he's done.'

'Not good enough. I've had it up to here with the kids around here and their crap.'

Harper bent down to pick up the crumpled magazines. At least it wasn't porn, she noted, although what on earth had attracted Max to *Homes & Gardens* she couldn't imagine.

'He didn't understand,' she said. 'He wasn't trying to steal anything. He's never stolen anything in his life.' *That's what his sister does*, Harper thought to herself, the guilt weighing on her heavily. She'd thought she'd hidden that side of herself from her brother, but Max was smart. Had he figured out where the things she got him came from? Was this her fault? It had to be, didn't it? 'Look, I'll pay for these. All right? He's just a kid. I'll make sure it never happens again. Please.'

She pulled the notes that the woman had given her out of her pocket. Looking at them for the first time Harper realized she held four twenties in her hand.

The guy behind the counter stopped with the phone at his ear. He looked her up and down for a second, then looked past her at Max. The sudden flash of pity Harper saw pass across his face made her want to destroy the place, just smash every last stupid thing in this stupid little shop and then burn the rest of it to the ground. But she couldn't do that. It wouldn't help Max. Harper swallowed her rage instead, tried to school her face into contrition.

The guy put down the phone.

'All right,' he said. 'But he never comes in here again. Got it?'

Harper nodded. 'I promise. Thanks.'

The guy nodded and she passed him the magazines and then the electricity key, too.

'Thirty on that as well, please.'

When they were done the guy held out the magazines. 'You want these?'

Harper, with a weariness that no seventeen-year-old should ever feel, said, 'Sure, why not?'

Outside, the sleet had given way to rain.

'I didn't mean to,' Max said. 'I didn't mean to, Harper.'

Harper rubbed a hand over her face. 'It doesn't matter,' she said. 'But you can't go in there again. Okay?'

'I don't know why people write things that aren't true,' Max said, in a voice so small it made her want to rip someone's arms off. He was still clutching whatever it was he'd taken. Harper knew better than to ask what they were. Max's world was shaped differently to hers and she thought she'd probably spend the rest of her life just trying to find a door that would let her into it.

'Come on,' Harper said, frozen and hungry and still with money in her pocket. 'Let's get sausage and chips.'

'Mushy peas,' Max said.

'Right,' Harper said. 'Mushy peas.'

Chapter Seven

Luisa kept going over her conversation with Casimir Pattanyús as she drove home, thinking about his explanation of why the gym was so important. It had been such a basic place, but she remembered that gaggle of teens she'd seen leave — their laughter, their evident camaraderie. Without his club, where would they have been that night? The 'gym', though, had been shabby and ill-equipped. Luisa wondered whether it got any funding and then, even as she considered it, knew that it did not, or at least not enough to pay for even the running costs. Mr Pattanyús was not only donating his own time but also his own funds. Surely there weren't many people willing to put so much of themselves into so tenuous a project, especially when there was so little to gain in return.

Another face came to her then, one out of a far older memory: Reuben, standing at the front of yet another meeting where they had been trying to convince donors that their kernel of an idea had merit. His energy and dedication had always lit up the room. How Luisa had loved him for it, his determination to persist long after most others would have given up.

She shifted in the driver's seat. The feeling of depression that had immediately suffused Luisa in the wake of seeing that abandoned patch of land had been tempered by something else. A spark of possibility, an impossible thought.

You can do it. It's what Reuben would have told her right then, had he been sitting in the car with her. *You* should *do it. It's the perfect place and it's just sitting there, being offered to you on a plate!*

When she got home, Luisa revealed the BMW's injury to Jo with trepidation and was relieved when her sister seemed sanguine about it.

'It's just a tyre. I'll get it changed before anyone even notices. I'm glad that there was someone around to help – he sounds like a good guy,' Jo observed, after Luisa's brief description of Cas.

'Yeah,' Luisa said. 'I think he is. Anyway, I'd better get these notes done for Marianne or there'll be hell to pay. I'll call the garage about replacement tyres in the morning, okay?'

As she sat at her desk, though, Luisa's gaze kept straying back to the photograph of Reuben that she'd set out the night before.

He would have said yes, she thought again. *He would have been determined to make it work, no matter what.*

Somewhere north of midnight, notes finally completed

and navigating another sleepless night, Luisa checked the balance on the account she had pretended for so long didn't exist. It wasn't a bottomless pit, but it wasn't an insignificant amount, either. She could imagine what a difference it would make to someone like 'Mr P', the good he would be able to do with it. The thought shamed her, in some ways. Here was a small fortune just sitting there, when there were so many ways to put it to good use.

Next morning, bleary-eyed and with the strongest coffee she could stand in her hand, Luisa called Owen. She'd been abrupt in turning him down and even if he understood why Luisa still felt uncomfortable about it. He'd only ever been good to her.

'Ahh, Luisa,' Owen said, when she finally managed to get him on the phone between meetings. 'I'm so glad you called. I wanted to apologize. When I told Emilia about our chat she nearly took my head off for being such an insensitive idiot.'

Luisa smiled to herself. 'You have nothing to apologize for, Owen. It was extremely kind of you to think of me and, really, I'm the one who should say sorry for turning it down so bluntly. It was just a bit of a shock. And look, if you have a few moments, I wanted to talk something through with you. I did actually go over and look at the site yesterday.'

Luisa described her visit, her encounter with Casimir Pattanyús and his valiant efforts to create a gym for the kids.

'I know it's not quite what you had in mind,' Luisa said, 'but perhaps you could look into giving the land to the boxing club? With my gift of Reuben's money as well, I think it would really make a difference to those kids and the teacher who's trying to do some good there.'

There was a moment of silence when Luisa had finished speaking.

'Well,' Owen said at last. 'There might be something there, you're right. But Luisa—' He stopped himself, and sighed. 'Forgive me for pushing this and I really don't mean to sound insensitive. But is there a reason why you don't want to be involved yourself? If you don't mind me saying, you sound far more fired up than when I spoke to you about it on Saturday. You sound, in fact, a lot like that young woman who so enchanted my wonderful godson all those years ago. What's holding you back from giving this a try yourself? Especially if you're willing to use the insurance money as start-up?'

Luisa found herself looking at the photograph of her and Reuben again. He wasn't wrong, she realized. There was a spark there, a little frisson of excitement at the thought.

'It would still be a full-time job and I already have one of those. It's likely that Boswell Garden Architecture will be taking on a pretty big project this year, which will mean I'm even busier than usual through the summer.'

'Ah yes,' Owen interjected. 'Feldspar Hall, isn't it?'

'How did you know that?'

'The Percivants are old family friends.'

Of course they are, Luisa thought. 'Then you know how huge a job that'll be.'

Owen sighed again. 'I hate to see you wasted on that awful Boswell woman,' he said. 'She's a terrible old trout.'

Luisa laughed at that. 'Maybe, but she's a trout that pays my wages.'

He was quiet for a moment. 'Give it six months,' he said, at last. 'Please. If it hasn't worked by then, I give you my word that I'll personally help find you another permanent position. How's that?'

'You're really adamant about this, aren't you?' she said, bemused. 'I'm not sure I really understand why, Owen.'

There were a few moments of quiet. 'I'm getting old,' he said, finally. 'All the things I should have done but didn't are beginning to occur to me with increasing clarity. Reuben believed in you and he believed in that project. I told you, I should have done more to help at the time. This might be my last chance to do that, and also . . .'

'Also?' she prompted.

'I would like to leave something more behind me than money,' Owen said, dryly. 'Give it a try, Luisa. If it doesn't work for whatever reason, then we'll both move on. All right? But at least we'll both have given it a proper shot.'

Luisa took a breath. She couldn't believe she was thinking about this. Two days ago, it would have been inconceivable. And yet . . .

'I'll have to think about it some more,' she said, still hesitating.

'Of course,' Owen said. 'I totally understand.'

'Say yes,' Jo told her, immediately. 'Just do it, Lu. Owen's right. And you know he's good for his word – either way, in six months you'll have a new job, a new start. Who knows where it'll take you? As long as it's away from Marianne bloody Boswell it'll be a good direction to move in.'

Luisa shut her eyes. 'I can't believe I'm actually thinking about this. You haven't seen the site, Jo. It's huge. And it's a total wasteland.'

Jo grabbed her hand, squeezing tight. 'Don't talk yourself out of it. You want to do it. Don't you? And don't lie, I can always tell when you're lying.'

Time slowed for a moment. Luisa thought about how it had felt to stand in the grounds of Feldspar Hall and let her imagination design a garden.

'I do,' she admitted, fear giving way to a spark of excitement. 'When else am I going to have a chance like this?'

Jo punched the air in triumph before dragging Luisa into a bear hug. '*Yes!*'

Making the decision meant Luisa had to tell Marianne. She was dreading the confrontation, but at least the woman's predictable ire provided a surprise silver lining.

'I've already written an official resignation and I'm about to email that,' Luisa said, when she called later that day. 'This was just a courtesy call.'

'Well, it's your loss,' the woman snapped. 'This morning I agreed terms with Caroline Percivant. I'm going to be in the history books.'

'I'm pleased for you, Marianne,' Luisa said. 'Really I am.'

'Of course you are,' Marianne said, snippily. 'I can tell by the way you're so happy to make my life difficult just when I actually need you.'

'I'll help find another assistant during my notice period,' Luisa said. 'I'm sure there are plenty of candidates—'

'You know what, don't bother. I don't want you back,' Marianne said. 'I expect you to return any company property and paperwork by the end of the week. Otherwise, consider this the official termination of our association.'

'Oh,' Luisa said. 'Well, in that case—'

Marianne hung up and, just like that, Luisa found herself out of gainful employment for the first time in her adult life.

Chapter Eight

On Tuesday morning Luisa got up at her usual time and was half way through her regular morning routine when she realized that she had no job to go to. She froze in the middle of brushing her teeth and stared at herself in the bathroom mirror, suddenly terrified. What had she done?

'This is the start of something wonderful for you, Luisa,' Owen had declared, when she'd called the night before to tell him her decision. 'I just know it. Reuben would be so proud.'

She'd been as buoyed by his enthusiasm as by Joanna's. Between them they had made it seem as if Luisa had made the best decision, the *only* decision. But now here she was on the morning of her first day as her own boss and *Oh my God*, she thought, with full horror, *What was I thinking?*

It was insane and ridiculous, but she couldn't go back. She'd been as polite as possible to Marianne, but that bridge was well and truly burned. The only thing for it was to sit down and find a place to start.

'I've already got the legal team on it and they'll be in touch in due course when they need your input with regards to the legal charity what-not,' Owen said, during a phone call where she'd had to disguise just how close she was to all-out panic. 'For now, focus your energies on what you're good at. Don't worry about anything else. Get that garden going.'

Luisa stared out of the window from the kitchen table, her coffee growing cold. *Get that garden going.* As if it were that simple. Luisa thought of the utter wasteland for which she was now responsible and the panic began to return, accompanied by a clench of terrible grief. If Reuben were here . . .

If Reuben were here, he'd be getting on with it.

She *had* trained for this, Luisa reminded herself. That training might be over a decade in the past, but still. She'd spent the last eight years watching Marianne create garden after garden. Besides, hadn't Lady Caroline liked those fledgling designs she'd done for Feldspar Hall? Luisa *did* know how to do this. She just needed to remember how. There had been a time when she'd imagined doing exactly this for a living. Surely that part of her must still be there somewhere?

Luisa spent the morning making lists and thinking about what she'd seen at the site during her first visit. She looked on Google Earth, the aerial image giving her a basic idea of the layout. The old factory wall loomed over the far end. That would have to come down – it would cast too much shadow, and besides, it looked as if it was unsafe and ready to fall anyway. The rest of the site was a mess of rubble and weeds. Luisa saw that her first task would be to knock down the wall and scrape everything back to earth. There it was, she realized: a place to start.

Luisa zoomed in, looking at the rest of the square. There were a few terraced houses, some more empty plots, the small knot of abandoned shops and the pub she'd noticed before. She located the 'gym' building, which was one of the largest on the street. She glanced at the clock on her screen. It was late morning, so both Cas and Harper would be in school. She tried to imagine the huge man who had stopped to see if she needed help standing suited and booted at the front of a classroom and couldn't. Luisa thought again about the building he was sinking his own money into, the club and kids he had spoken about with such quiet conviction.

At lunchtime she got a call from the garage to say that they were bringing back the Defender. The Land Rover had been their late father's, who had died only the year before, another loss for which Luisa had not been prepared. Driving it made her feel closer to him than looking at photographs ever did. Once Luisa had waved the garage guys off she made herself a sandwich, eating it quickly in the kitchen as the radio burbled in the background. Then she set off on her second trip down the Cumbrian coast in just three days.

This drive to Collaton was in stark contrast to her previous visit. The rain had given way to a low winter sun that glowed against the breaking banks of cloud and the rolling waters of the Firth. Snow lay on the high fells and the chill in the air scoured Luisa's nose as she breathed it in. The trip took about an hour and Luisa arrived at the site at around three, parking the Defender in exactly the same place as she'd put the BMW on her first visit. This time when she pushed her way onto the site, it was with proper kit, which included a pair of work gloves, her trusty old Leatherman and a tape measure. She'd also got her iPad – not the one that she'd used when she worked for Marianne, but her own older generation model.

Luisa began to make more notes, mapping the site. The tarmac would provide a useful hardstanding for the skips that would be required for the initial clearing of the rubble. The fence would need to be better secured, at least while the work was being carried out. Luisa worked quietly, fully absorbed in the task at hand as time slipped away. She considered how best to begin engaging the locals. She had no entry point, no way in. Except . . . that wasn't entirely true, was it? She *had* met a couple of people who lived here.

Thinking of Cas and Harper again made her look over to the double doors of the boxing gym. To her surprise, Luisa saw that they were open. She checked her watch – it wasn't yet four o'clock, but then it was an after-school club, wasn't it? It made sense that there would be someone there straight after school finished for the day. She looked around again, an idea forming in her mind.

Chapter Nine

She'd been prepared for the noise of frenetic activity but instead Luisa was met with near silence as she entered the gym's shabby corridor. There was just the singular, fast rhythmic *thwack* of leather hitting leather – no raised voices, no raucous teenage laughter. She reached the door to the main room and stopped in her tracks.

Casimir Pattanyús was the only figure in the room. Dressed in a white vest, black shorts and white trainers, he stood at one of the punchbags set at a right-angle to the door, turned slightly away from her. His weight on its floor plate was keeping it in place as he pummelled seven shades of hell out of the fading red leather. Luisa couldn't tell if he was angry or whether this was merely what he looked like in action. She stepped into the room but hung back, unwilling to interrupt an intense training routine. The speed and power with which his gloves smashed into the bag was astonishing and, if she were honest, a touch mesmerizing. Luisa knew she'd be burned out after throwing two punches of the intensity she saw him pitch, but Cas seemed in no danger of stopping to take a breath. Sweat beaded on his neck, over his bare arms and between his shoulder blades.

A split–second later he lost concentration, jerking his head around to look at her. The battered punchbag flipped back towards him.

'Oh!' Luisa took a step forward, seeing what was coming.

Cas just barely managed to get his hands up, stopping the bag before it could smash him in the face. He let it go and stepped off the plate, breathing hard.

'Luisa MacGregor,' he rasped.

'I'm so sorry. I didn't mean to interrupt.'

Cas started loosening the ties on his gloves as he came towards her. 'It's fine. I didn't expect anyone to walk in. I usually lock the door when I'm here alone. I must have forgotten.'

'Is there no club tonight?' Luisa asked, looking around the otherwise empty room. 'I expected it to be in full swing.'

He came to a stop before her. Luisa was shocked to find that she had to work hard not to let her gaze stray from his face and then had to stop herself blushing at this realization. She never noticed men, or at least not in this way. Hadn't for a long time, not since—

'Club runs from five-thirty until eight,' he told her, oblivious. He shucked the gloves and picked up a water bottle that waited beside a sports holdall he'd left on the floor.

'Really? That seems like a late start for an after-school club.'

Cas downed half the contents of the bottle in two swift gulps and gave her a wry smile.

'The more of the evening they spend here, the less time they have to cause trouble elsewhere. Besides, the kids have to eat. When I first opened this place I tried to give them that too, but I couldn't persuade anyone to fund it, and ...' He shrugged. 'Well, to tell you the truth it's hard enough just finding the rent most months, let alone anything else. In any case,' he added, indicating the punchbag, 'it gives me a chance to work out the day's frustrations, which means I'm more likely to be in a good place to deal with the kids when they get here. They can be a challenge.' Cas rubbed the towel over his face as he added, 'Anyway, not that it isn't nice to see you again, but I didn't expect you to come back to my door. Is there something you need?'

Luisa glanced over at his office. 'Can we sit for a few moments?'

Cas slung the towel around his shoulders with a nod. 'Sure.'

'The thing is,' Luisa began, as they took the same seats as the last time she'd been there, 'I've decided to take on the project. The one I told you about.'

'Right,' he said, clearly a little surprised. 'Well ... then I suppose congratulations are in order?'

'Yes, it's ...' Luisa looked away, suddenly feeling emotional. Saying it aloud to a stranger was somehow more potent than telling friends and family. 'It's quite a big thing for me. I've quit my job, so for the next few months, this is going to be my whole focus. I want to give it my best shot.'

Cas smiled. 'Well, good for you. And good luck.'

She laughed a little. 'Thanks. I'm going to need it. Anyway, look – the reason I wanted to talk to you is that I'm going to need an office. I was thinking about renting a Portakabin, but that's going to take up space on the site, so it'd be better to find somewhere else, preferably very local.'

Cas leaned back in his chair. 'Somewhere around here? There are plenty of empty places to choose from. One of the shops on the other side of the square? Or the pub, perhaps?'

'Actually,' she said, 'I was thinking about this place.'

Cas stared at her. '*Here*? The gym?'

Luisa nodded. 'It's perfect. It's close to the site, it's easy to secure and it's enough for what I need.'

'I'm pretty sure you're aware it's already occupied.'

'Yes,' she agreed. 'But for how long? You just said yourself that keeping up with the rent is tough.'

She saw his jaw clench in restrained anger.

'That's it, is it? You walk in here, take one look around and bam – "Nice, I'll take it, goodbye gym"?' he asked, his tone dark but steady. 'I get that you're used to handing out money to get whatever you want, and I'm sure the landlord would bite your hand off, but as far as I'm concerned the answer is a straight no. Now, I've got a mountain of marking to do before the kids get here, so please just . . .' Cas held out an arm, indicating the door.

'No,' she said, a little surprised by his outburst. But

then, as usual she hadn't approached this correctly, had she? *That was why Reuben always handled this kind of thing*, Luisa reminded herself, with a slight pang.

'No?'

'Please just hear me out, Mr Pattanyús. It won't take long.'

He stared at her for another minute. She stared back. Luisa felt no threat from him, but her heart ticked up a beat or two.

A second later Cas gave a curt nod.

'I don't want to take this place away from you,' she said. 'Of course I don't. My project is about helping the community, not taking from it. What I want to suggest is a . . . a timeshare, I suppose.'

'What do you mean?'

She looked out of the office window for a moment, at the empty, quiet space beyond. 'You said yourself that the kids aren't here until five-thirty. This place is empty a lot of the time. Here's my idea: the project can use it during the day. The club gets it in the evening and at weekends, same as always. Nothing has to change for you. Most of the time you won't even know I've been here. There might be the odd overlap or a delivery or two that needs storing for a few days, but,' she nodded at the ample space outside his office window, 'I don't think it'd be hard to find a corner for that, would it?'

Cas rubbed his chin, having the good grace to look a little ashamed. 'A timeshare?'

She smiled. 'What do you think?'

'I can't lie,' he said, with a sigh, 'splitting the rent would be . . . a godsend.'

'Ah,' Luisa said, 'well, actually, if you agree, the charity will pay the lease on this place up front for a year and the club . . . would not be expected to contribute to that expense.'

Cas blinked at her as if he thought he hadn't heard her correctly. 'We'd carry on exactly as before . . . but rent free?'

'Yes.'

'Why would you do that?'

'Why *wouldn't* I?' Luisa asked. 'Like I said before, I think we're trying to do similar things, just in different ways. I need space, this place is perfect. It's no skin off my nose if we can make sharing the amenities work. If the charity assets I've got to use for the garden will help you too, so much the better.'

Cas stared at her. 'I don't know what to say.'

She tipped her head to one side, watching him. 'Say yes.'

'I can't help but feel that there must be . . .'

'. . . a catch?'

'Yeah. Call me ungrateful,' he said, 'but you're telling me you're going to give me everything I need to keep this place running for another year, just like that, and there's nothing you want in return?'

'Well, I wouldn't say *nothing*.'

She saw him brace himself, as if expecting the worst. 'Okay . . .'

Luisa smiled. 'I want you to help me, Cas. You and

71

your kids. It's going to be a huge job. I need to get people interested in helping me build this garden quickly or I'll be finished before I've even started. You know this area better than I ever will. You know the community. I need your help to get to know it, too.'

He let out a breath and she watched some of the tension drain from his shoulders. Then a frown passed across his face.

'I can do that,' he said. 'And you already know you've made me an offer I can't refuse. But still . . . I've still got one condition to saying yes.'

Chapter Ten

Later, Harper leaned in the doorway of his office, arms crossed as she watched Cas dumping stuff from his desk into a cardboard box. She'd been late and had turned up with a smudge of oil on her face, which meant she'd done a couple of hours at the garage instead of the coursework she'd promised him she was keeping up with. He wondered if she'd had time to eat before coming. Harper should have been around to help with the younger ones first thing as part of her 'community service', but Cas didn't have the heart to call her out on her tardiness. Not today, not when things were finally looking rosier than they had for a long time.

'I can't believe you're letting this woman just waltz in here and take this place away from us,' Harper said, with a bitter edge to her voice.

'She's not taking it away from us,' Cas told her, opening a drawer and staring briefly at the accumulated detritus within. 'She's doing the exact opposite.'

'Then why are you having to move out of *your* office?'

'Because Ms MacGregor is going to need it more than I do,' he said, deciding to tip the entire contents of the drawer into the box and worry about it later.

'I don't want her here,' Harper said, her voice as resolutely stubborn as her stance. 'We don't *need* her here.'

'Actually, we really do.' Cas opened the flaps of a new box. 'She's the one that doesn't need us. Harper, in another two months I'd have been out of money to pay the rent and this place would have been empty anyway. She's doing us a favour. More than a favour. Without her, the club wouldn't be able to carry on.'

Harper made a dismissive sound. 'You'd have found a way. You always do.'

He smiled slightly at this display of a faith he wasn't sure he deserved. Cas wondered what Harper would think if she saw the deficit in his bank balance.

Harper shifted to look back out into the gym. Two of the kids were sparring in the ring, a few others were paired on the punchbags. 'It won't be the same.'

'Change is inevitable,' Cas said, mildly. 'How we deal with it defines how well we adapt to life.'

The girl rolled her eyes. 'Who are you, Yoda?'

'No,' he said. 'If I was, that sentence would have sounded more like—' He took a breath to deliver the line in the broken syntax of a fictional alien sage, but before he could start Harper held up both hands.

'Don't,' she said. 'Just . . . don't.'

There was a brief moment of amusement between them,

predicated on an unspoken but obvious joke about Cas's age and equivalent sadness, quickly subsumed by the cloud that resettled over Harper's face.

'There's something else you need to know,' he added. 'It's about your community service hours.'

Harper's face hardened. 'What about them? I'm already helping out here. And I thought you were going to make me paint the old people's home down the road or something.'

Cas sighed. 'I did suggest that to them, but—'

'Don't tell me, let me guess,' Harper said, bitterly. 'They don't want a thief near the old folk and their wallets, right? Even though it wasn't money I nicked. Even though it was just *pens* from—'

'Harper,' he said. 'It doesn't matter what you were stealing or why.'

She crossed her arms and leaned against the doorjamb, rolling her eyes. 'Whatever.'

'That attitude isn't helpful and you know it.'

Harper sighed. 'Are we done? I've got to show the littles some new moves. I promised.'

'Just a minute. I've found a new way for you to work out your hours. A better way. I want you to help Ms MacGregor get her garden up and running.'

Harper glared at him. 'That's a joke, right? You're trying to be funny?'

'Nope. I'm completely serious. We agreed that you owe the community a hundred hours of service, didn't we? Well, Ms MacGregor needs all the help she can get. It's perfect.'

Harper looked disgusted. 'No. I won't do it.'

'Why not?' Cas asked. 'Think about it. It's around the corner from home for you. It's doing something beneficial for your neighbours, and it's practical. You might learn some new skills. I think it's a great opportunity—'

'No,' Harper said again, hotly. 'I won't work for that rich bitch. You can send me to jail before I'll say yes.'

'Bit dramatic,' Cas pointed out. 'And don't use language like that about another person.' He pointed at the sign on the wall behind her. Harper didn't turn to look. 'And I really don't understand your reticence. Even if you don't like Ms MacGregor – and I honestly can't understand why you wouldn't – you'll be working on behalf of the charity, not her personally.'

'How am I supposed to find the time to build a garden?' Harper asked. 'Do you want me to drop out of school? Or do you think I can do it in my sleep? Because between the garage and this place and homework, I don't have time to *think*!'

'Time is going to be an issue wherever you end up doing those hours, Harper, and quite frankly, that's your problem to work out. Actions have consequences. Learning that is the whole point.'

Harper shook her head, face defiant.

'I'll speak to the school,' Cas suggested. 'We'll arrange for some of your free periods to be spent in the garden. During the holidays you can spend more time here.'

'I could just drop out,' Harper said. 'A-levels are a waste

of my time anyway. I'd be better off getting a job. If I'd had one I wouldn't have been stealing in the first place, would I?'

'You're already working at the garage, though, aren't you?' Cas asked.

'Yeah, but only when Carl's got extra work he needs help with. He can't rely on me for more because of school – which I'm only still at because *you* wanted me to stay on,' she reminded him, bitterly.

'I know it feels like a waste of time right now,' Cas said, going back to an argument they'd been having weekly for at least a year. 'But it's just two years and you're almost through the first one already. You could achieve so much if you just . . .'

'. . . didn't live in this no-hope town?' she supplied.

'If you just . . . *applied* yourself a little more.'

Harper shook her head. 'You have never sounded more like a teacher than right now.'

'That's because it's true.'

'Yeah?' she said, her voice rising a little as she threw up her hands. 'Let's say I pass with flying colours – then what? Life just magically turns into unicorns crapping rainbows and pound coins?'

'Harper—' Cas warned.

'You know what would happen, Mr P? A big fat eff all.'

'Harper,' he said, more sharply this time, although privately he reflected that a year ago she wouldn't have bothered to censor her language, which was at least a little progress.

'*This* is what's true,' she said. 'I'd still be stuck here but I'd be even worse off because instead of showing the garage that I'm worth taking on full time, they'd have got tired of me telling them I can't come in when they need me and they'll have found someone else. I'll be stuck here *and* without a job. That's why it's not worth it. What's the point of me having qualifications if I don't have a *job*?'

'If I thought there was a better path for you, I'd recommend it like a shot,' Cas told her. 'And you're right, a full-time job at the garage wouldn't be the worst outcome in the world for you. I just don't want to see you throw away all your future potential too soon. You could do great things, Harper. I know it. I want you to open doors, not close them. Right now, A-levels are the best way for you to do that.'

Harper set her jaw. Cas knew there was a fine line between pushing her to do better and losing her completely. But of all the kids he'd had come through those double doors he had never felt as sure as he did that Harper Dixon could have a bright future if only she made the right choices, had the right chances.

'Look at it this way,' he said, into her sullen silence. 'Since I'm not shelling out for this place, I'll have more money to use for other things.'

Harper blew a short strand of hair out of her face. 'Well, lucky old you.'

Cas put down the pile of books he had in his hands and leaned on the desk. 'If you do this – if you agree to help Ms MacGregor with the garden, I have an incentive for you.'

'Oh yeah?' Harper asked. 'Like what?'

'You've passed your driving tests, haven't you?'

Harper smirked. 'Like you even needed to ask? Passed both first time about five minutes after I could apply.'

Cas nodded. 'I've been thinking about this for a while. My old car is still sitting on my parents' driveway. It hasn't run in years, it's a banger and it will need doing up. But we both know that you can do that, probably with your eyes closed, so here's the deal. If you commit to helping Ms McGregor . . . you can have the car.'

Harper went very still. 'What?'

'You can fix it up. Once it passes the MOT – the garage should be able to help with that, right? – I'll tax it for you. I'll even put something towards the insurance,' he pointed at her, 'which I would not be able to offer if not for Ms MacGregor's generosity, so you should think about that.' Cas could just imagine what Annika would say if she knew about this idea, which was why he had no intention of telling her. Ever.

The girl still hadn't moved. 'Why would you do any of that?'

'Because I have faith in you, Harper. And frankly, my parents are getting antsy about my old rust-bucket making them look bad to the neighbours. Giving it to you is cheaper than getting a breaker to come and take it away. Since that place around the corner closed they have to come too far.'

Harper's face took on a suspicious look. 'What kind of car is it?'

'A Mini Cooper.'

'A *Mini*?' she said, aghast.

'It's one of the old ones, the proper ones! It's a classic!'

'That's one word for it. You won't let me say the others.'

'Hey, if you don't want it—'

'No,' Harper said, hurriedly. 'I do. I do want it.'

Cas smiled. 'Good. Then we have a deal?'

There was a slight flush of excitement on the girl's cheeks, which Cas knew she was trying to hide behind her usual carapace of stoicism. He felt a flash of guilt that an old car so decrepit that no one would even bother to nick it seemed like such an opportunity to her.

'Deal,' Harper said, seriously.

Cas nodded and resumed packing up his desk. 'Good. Now give me a hand with these boxes, would you?'

Harper stood there for another minute, watching him with narrowed eyes.

'Harper?'

'Sure,' she said, finally moving. 'I was just trying to imagine what you must have looked like behind the wheel of a Mini.'

Chapter Eleven

Harper went home that night in a kind of daze. A car. Sure, it was currently off the road, and from Mr P's description it sounded as if by rights it should be consigned to the scrap heap. But still, it was a car and she didn't need to look at it to know she'd be able to fix it, even if it was a total rebuild. She was a born engineer, that's what Carl at the garage said. Harper's own bones might as well have been made of car parts, that's how well she understood vehicles: as if they shared something in common, as if they came from the same place. Working on a car was where she felt at home, which was why the hours she put in at Carl's Auto Repair flew by. Out of all the small horizons of her life, there were only two places she ever actively wanted to be, and that was the boxing gym and the repair shop.

She preferred the older cars best – the ones that, when they went kaput, you didn't just plug into a computer to find out what was wrong. The ones where you had to get into their guts, had to really listen to them to know how to put them right. Maybe it was just that she had an innate feeling for how things should move in order to work in a world where so many things were often so hopelessly out of alignment. It felt good to know how to *fix* something.

Harper opened the front door into a quiet house and when she shouted up the stairs she heard her brother call back. He'd been subdued since the incident at the corner shop, although where Max was concerned that was a relative term. Harper was just thankful there had been no more trouble.

'I'm making dinner!' she called, because he dealt with life best when he had time to prepare. 'It'll be ready in half an hour!'

She didn't bother looking into the front room, as it was obvious that their father wasn't home. Harper didn't know where he was and didn't care. The house was invariably a better place to be when she and Max had it to themselves. She went upstairs, changed out of her gym gear and went into the bathroom. On the windowsill was a neat line of plastic pots with soil in them. They weren't plant pots – instead they had clearly been salvaged from the recycling. Yoghurt pots, mainly, one of Max's favourite snacks, although he would only ever eat the lemon flavour. A few years ago she'd gone through a battle with him over the fact that it was not healthy to eat only lemon yoghurt at every meal. In desperation she'd ended up powdering a multi-vitamin pill into the one he ate for breakfast, until she'd realized it was a texture thing, and if she pureed peas or broccoli he would at least eat them in small quantities, especially if she included a slice of lemon that he could squeeze on top. After a while, she'd introduced mash, and that worked too. Harper ate a lot of meals that involved pureed peas and mashed potato. Yoghurt, too. Although never the lemon ones.

Harper poked experimentally at one of the pots of dark earth and then saw a neatly written label pegged into the one at the end of the line. *Cosmos bipinnatus*, it read.

She went downstairs to the kitchen and started cooking. Max didn't like meat, which was fine because she could rarely afford to buy it anyway and she had issues with mass production, so their diet was mainly vegetarian. Harper went to the fridge, hoping that their father hadn't consumed everything inside it. Tonight she was lucky: the remains of the macaroni cheese she'd made the night before were intact and there was still milk left in the bottle. At one point Harper had considered installing another fridge in her own room – to which she'd fitted a lock years before – so that she could be sure the thieving bastard wouldn't leave them with nothing. She hadn't, though, chiefly because that would have increased the electricity bill.

Max appeared in the doorway of the kitchen and Harper knew that if she checked, it would be exactly thirty minutes since she'd told him it was half an hour until dinner. You couldn't be imprecise with Max.

'How was school today?' she asked, once they were seated with their plates of macaroni cheese and pureed peas.

'Okay.'

'What did you do at lunchtime?'

'Went to the library.'

Harper had already known what the answer would be, but this had become a ritual for them. Besides, it led on to part of the conversation that was actually always different. Max read books like they might disappear in the blink of an eye. 'What are you reading today?'

Her brother had been studiously separating the macaroni from the cheese sauce, leaving the pasta in a neat pile on the side of his plate, but now he paused for a second. He was caught in his own routine now, because this was how their evening meals always went and if he didn't answer, the routine would be out of whack. Harper didn't call him on it, just carried on eating as she waited for him to work it out.

'About plants,' he said, eventually.

'I saw the pots in the bathroom,' she said. 'What are they?'

'Flowers,' Max said and then, macaroni successfully excised from his meal, finally began to eat.

Harper didn't ask where he was planning to put them when they grew. She'd learned to pick her battles and she'd work out how to approach that war when they came to it.

'Can you eat a couple of spoons of the pasta?' she asked, nodding at his plate. 'Like last night? Just two, that's all.'

Max screwed up his nose. He did it, though. He did it for her.

They were just finishing up when there was a brusque knock at the door. They both froze, looking at each other for a moment. No one ever came to visit.

'Put the plates in the sink and get your yoghurt,' Harper told Max as she got up. 'I'll be back in a minute.'

She pulled the kitchen door shut behind her as she went into the hallway. Harper opened the front door to find a woman that she recognized but did not know standing on the doorstep. She wore a long, burgundy-coloured quilted coat and was holding the remains of a broken terracotta plant pot. She was in her sixties, with an air of perpetual unhappiness that was at this moment overlaid by annoyance. Harper looked at the broken plant pot in her hands with a sinking feeling.

'Look,' she said, before Harper had a chance to say anything, 'I know that boy doesn't mean any harm but this is the second time I've caught him stealing out of my garden. And now,' she gave the pieces of pot a meaningful little shake, 'it's vandalism, too.'

'I'm sorry,' Harper said. 'I didn't know—'

'If he'd just asked me, I probably would have given him cuttings,' the woman went on, as if Harper hadn't spoken. 'Or shown him how to do it and let him take them himself. But he doesn't speak, he just sneaks around making a mess. I found him out there with a trowel and a bucket, nicking my bloody compost!'

Harper's mind went back to the yoghurt pots in the bathroom, the dark soil covering the seeds. It hadn't even occurred to her to wonder where Max had got it from. Earth was just earth, wasn't it? Under your feet, under everyone's feet, everywhere. Except – she glanced up the dark street, at the concrete, brick and tarmac – it wasn't actually, was it?

'I'm sorry,' Harper said again, her hand tightening on the door. 'I'll pay for the damage.'

The woman suddenly squinted at her, frowning. 'Sorry, love. I didn't mean to go off on you. Just frustration, that was. It's not your responsibility. It's your dad's.'

She didn't mention their mum, Harper noticed. Around here, everyone knew everything, and yet still no one had a clue.

'He's not in, though, is he?' the woman guessed, glancing at the darkened windows.

'He's at work,' Harper told her. It might be true. Last she heard, their dad had got some shifts somewhere out on the industrial estate. That was a few weeks ago now, though, so who knew.

The woman sighed. 'Well, I thought you should know. It's not that I want to make life more difficult, but – well, we've all got our struggles.'

'We'll replace everything,' Harper said. 'Tell me what he took and I'll make sure you get it back. I promise.'

Their visitor smiled then, tiredly, as if all the energy she'd gathered to get her to their doorstep had dissipated now that she'd said her piece. 'You don't need to do that. But I can't help feeling that you really should get that boy some help.'

Harper felt the cold prickle of fear creeping up her neck at that word. *Help.* Just one more thing out of alignment in the world, that something that should offer hope could mean the exact opposite.

'He's fine,' she said. 'He's got me.'

The woman's gaze flicked to the darkened windows of the front room again. 'Yes,' she said. 'But who do you have, Harper?'

Harper felt the fear transforming into anger. What did this woman know, coming here to stick her nose in over a bloody broken plant pot and some missing dirt? *No, please, do tell me again how hard your life is.*

'I don't need some sad little busybody telling me how to live my life,' she said. 'Why don't you just leave us alone? I've said sorry, I've offered to pay for the damage. It's not my fault if you've got so little in your life that you have to bully a little kid to get yourself off.'

The woman's face closed, like a shutter going down. Her lips pursed and she turned away. 'I'm just trying to help,' she said. 'Because believe me, there are plenty who aren't as patient as I am. My pots aren't the only ones he's ransacked.'

Harper waited until the woman had stepped out of their yard and onto the pavement and then slammed the door shut, hard. The bang echoed into the night. Harper leaned her forehead against the closed door, shutting her eyes, breathing hard. *One good day*, she thought. *Can't we just have one good day?*

She turned around to find Max standing in the light of the open kitchen doorway. Behind him she could see their dinner things, already washed and left to dry beside the sink. His head was down and Harper knew without asking that he had heard everything. He said nothing about it and neither did Harper. What was the point?

'Have you got homework?' she asked, instead.

He nodded.

'Better go do it then, eh?'

He scurried past her and up the stairs. She heard his bedroom door close, very softly.

It was after midnight when their father got home, blind drunk. Harper knew this because she was still doing her own homework. She heard him stumbling around but didn't take any notice until he began working his way up the stairs. Usually he'd just pass out on the sofa in whatever he was wearing. She put down the pen she'd been making notes with and listened to the commotion rolling its way nearer, step by uncertain step. He was angry about something, that much was clear, but it wasn't until she heard a drunken fist pounding against Max's bedroom door that she cared.

Harper was out of her seat and on the landing in a second. She'd debated whether to put a lock on Max's door when she'd fitted the one to her own, but wasn't convinced that the positives of him being able to lock himself in outweighed the negatives.

'Stop it,' Harper said. 'Right. Now.'

Her father looked up at her out of bleary eyes. He wouldn't come at her, she knew that. He'd tried it once and she'd thrown a punch hard enough to make sure he never did it again. She'd made it clear that if he ever went for Max what he'd get in return would be ten times worse.

'Talk in t'pub. What that boy's been up to. Tell 'im,' the

drunk snarled, lucid enough to form words in anger, 'if I ever hear he's been thieving plants again, I'll—'

'You'll *what?*' Harper asked, her voice very quiet and extremely clear.

Her father sneered at her, then tried to land one last pathetic thump in the direction of Max's door before heading for the bathroom. Harper knew what was coming next but there was nothing she could do about it. The bathroom door closed and she stood in the hallway, waiting. She heard the strangled roar, heard the first yoghurt pot thumping against the wall, then the next. She waited until the noise subsided and then returned to her room, though she didn't go back to her homework until she heard her dad making his unsteady way down the stairs. She entertained the brief hope that maybe he'd fall and break his neck, but he didn't.

Silence reigned after that. She didn't bother going to knock on Max's door, she already knew he wouldn't answer. She considered going to clear up the bathroom, could imagine what a state it was in. She had to finish this essay, though. She had to keep up her end of the bargain with Mr P. Because once she had a car, she and Max could go anywhere they wanted.

She'd clean up the mess in the morning, because there was no one else to do it.

Chapter Twelve

'The first thing we've got to do,' Luisa told Harper, 'is clear the site. That means taking down that wall, clearing the rubble and scrub and ripping up a lot of the tarmac.'

They were standing inside the gate. Since Harper had arrived a few minutes earlier she'd kept her arms crossed and her jaw set, just in case she hadn't already made it abundantly clear to Luisa that she was there under duress.

'Oh yeah?' Harper said, her voice dripping with insolence. 'And I suppose you're expecting me to do that with my bare hands, are you?'

'Of course not,' Luisa said. 'I've got two skips booked to arrive tomorrow and a JCB coming first thing on Thursday morning. What we need to do today is clear enough of the tarmac for the skips to stand on. I've already made a start – look.' Luisa waved at the pile of debris she'd assembled.

Luisa had left Carlisle before seven o'clock that morning and had arrived for her first full day at her new desk to discover a handwritten note from Cas. *Welcome to Collaton*, it said. *Anything you need, let me know. Harper has a lesson first thing but will be with you by 10.30am. She'll need to be back at school by 1pm. Let me know how it goes. Best, CP.*

Now here Harper was and Luisa was no longer sure she'd made the right decision when she'd agreed to allow the girl to work with her. At the time an immediate extra pair of hands had seemed like a godsend and besides, helping a troubled teen was surely a way 'in' to the local community, but Harper's spikes were on full display today. She clearly resented having to be there and had obviously taken an active dislike to Luisa herself.

'I've got you some heavy-duty gloves,' Luisa said, holding them out to Harper. 'And look – I've started up a timesheet to log the hours you're here in the garden. That way we can make sure you're not cheated out of your time, okay?'

If Harper was grateful for this, she didn't show it. She just took out her phone and looked at the time. 'I got here ten minutes ago,' she said, 'and you've got me for two hours so I'm setting a timer. Let's get on with it.'

With that, Harper stalked away and started ripping up brambles as if they'd done her a personal wrong. Luisa sighed and joined her. She'd been hoping that they could strike up a conversation that would give Luisa a few insights into the local area, but Harper kept up a stony silence, answering anything she was asked with brief, curt replies. When her only answer to Luisa's offer of coffee was 'nope', Luisa gave up. Still, at least by the time Harper's alarm went off there was a decent stretch of the tarmac that had been cleared – enough for the two skips to stand side by side on level ground.

'I'll be back for another two hours tomorrow,' Harper said. 'Same time.'

'I've got something else I need your help with,' Luisa told her.

Harper crossed her arms defiantly. 'I've already done two hours today. I've got more important things to do than help with your crappy little poor-people garden.'

Luisa shrugged. 'Fine. I thought it'd be an easy way for you to work a few more hours off your community service from home, but if you'd rather not . . .'

She turned away, busying herself with the pile of detritus. It was already enough to half-fill a skip.

'All right, all right,' Harper groused. 'Go on then. What do you want me to do?'

Luisa turned back. 'Have you got a computer at home?'

'Yeah,' Harper said, suspiciously. 'I've got one on loan from school for coursework. It's ancient, but it works. Just about. Why?'

'Mr Pattanyús is letting me host a public consultation in the gym on Saturday night. I'm hoping it'll help engage the local community. I need a flyer that we can give out, inviting people to attend. Could you do that?'

Harper frowned. 'Depends. How fancy does it have to be?'

'Doesn't have to be fancy. A5, Black and white, no

pictures. Simple text with the time, date and information about what the meeting's for.'

Harper considered. 'How many hours is it worth?'

'Two?'

'Yeah, right. Try four.'

'Three and that's my final offer. Or we can forget it and I'll do it myself.' Luisa could probably do that anyway and in under an hour, but she needed to find some way to win the girl over or the next ninety-eight hours in her company were going to be painful.

Harper huffed a sigh. 'Fine. You'd better tell me what you want it to say, though.'

Once Harper had gone Luisa worked on her own for the rest of the day, deciding to clock off when the light failed at four o'clock. She wrote a note and left it on the desk that Cas had established for himself in the corner of the main gym room. *Harper's a hard worker. She was helpful, thanks. Best, LM.*

Luisa and Harper were both at the site to see the JCB start work at 8am on Thursday morning. They kept a safe distance as the first load of rubble was scraped from the ground and deposited with an almighty racket into one of the skips that stood close by. The sight made Luisa feel strangely emotional – that one swing signified such a magnitude of hope and effort. She remembered the first conversation she and Reuben had ever shared about the idea, the seed that had germinated between them and then had been stunted by his awful, untimely death. At the time she'd had no inkling that it could ever be revived again, or that it would be down to

Luisa to try to make it work, alone. *If only he could be here to see this*, she thought. *If only—*

'We've got an audience,' Harper told her, over the noise of the digger continuing its work. She nodded towards the fence line.

Luisa turned to see curious faces beyond the wire, watching. She smiled. This was exactly what she'd hoped for.

'Time for these,' she said, pulling out the flyers she'd printed out that morning from her bag and holding them out to Harper.

Harper griped but took the leaflets and headed for the gate. As Luisa watched her go a figure standing at the distant corner of the fence caught her eye. Even at this distance his size made him unmistakable. She smiled and waved, unreasonably pleased when Cas waved back as she began to make her way towards him. They'd not seen each other since the day he had cleared out his desk to make room for her – Luisa had kept her word and made sure she was out of the office every evening by the time the club was due to start.

Instead, their tenuous conversation via scribbled note had continued. Every morning she had come in to find a fresh note on her desk with the answer to whatever question she had left the night before. There was something about this nebulous communication that appealed to Luisa, though she couldn't pinpoint what.

'Hi!' she said, jogging to meet him, the wire of the fence between them.

He smiled. 'Hi yourself.'

Cas was wearing a sharply pressed charcoal grey suit, white shirt and navy tie, his face clean shaven. Luisa detected a faint tang of cologne. She was surprised by his appearance and realized that she always thought of him as he'd been that night he'd almost ended up with a punchbag in the face because of her: standing on that plate in a sports vest, throwing punches with the most astonishingly defined arms she'd ever seen. It wasn't until that second that she recognized quite how embedded that image had become in her mind.

She cleared her throat.

'Shouldn't you be at school?'

He nodded and held up a sheaf of papers that had been tucked beneath one arm. 'I should indeed. Had to come by and pick up these, I forgot them last night.' His gaze drifted over her shoulder, towards the digger still at work behind them. 'Looks like you're hitting the ground running.'

'Well, whatever we end up doing with it, the space will need clearing first,' she said. 'I'm glad to see you, actually – I've got a big favour to ask. It's about Saturday – the meeting? I wondered if I could persuade you to come. I know it's the weekend and you're probably busy . . .'

'It's fine. That's the deal, right?' Cas smiled. 'I'll be there anyway for the club's afternoon session. It finishes at three so I'll stay and help you set up.'

'Thanks,' she said, relieved. 'You're bound to know at least a few of the attendees. If I'm honest, I'm looking at you as a bit of an ice breaker.'

'Happy to be of service in any way I can.' Cas glanced

across at the continuing work. 'I'm sorry but I've got to go, I'm already late. Good luck today.'

'Bye – and thanks,' Luisa added to his retreating back. He turned and threw her a brief gesture that was somewhere between a salute and a wave, slightly awkward in a way that seemed entirely at odds with his stature. It made her smile.

There came an almighty crash from behind her. Luisa turned to see the old factory wall tumble to the ground in a plume of dust, as if it had been no more than a sandcastle standing before a high tide.

Harper was gone by midday but Luisa and the JCB driver, Nick, kept working. Spectators came and went – at one point a small group assembled on the other side of the fence at the far end of the site and seemed to be discussing something. Luisa went over to say hello and hand out more flyers, but the group dispersed as she approached, apparently unwilling to talk.

Luisa had already decided to retain as much of the downed factory wall as possible for reuse elsewhere. As Nick continued to rip up cracked concrete, Luisa began to haul and stack the chunks of sandstone into a pile beside the two skips. It was back-breaking work and she would have loved to have a team of volunteers to help her (or even, the thought crossed her mind, the singular but mountainous form of 'Mr P') but there was only her, so she might as well buckle down and get on with it.

The light was failing by mid-afternoon and Luisa was

exhausted. She went over to where Nick was scraping up the last of the broken red stone and waved him to a standstill.

'Let's call it a day after this one,' she said, over the sound of the idling JCB engine. 'We'll start again early. Think we can get some of the tarmac up tomorrow, too?'

Nick glanced over her head towards the car park end of the site. 'Sure thing,' he said.

He was about to start up again for his last load when Luisa spotted something amid the rubble. She held up her hand for him to pause so that she could take a closer look. Clambering over the last of the wreckage, she crouched, trying to work out what the bright flash of yellow was that had caught her eye. Luisa realized as she reached for it that a battered bunch of flowers had been caught beneath the collapsing wall. They were chrysanthemums, wrapped in clear cellophane, squashed but not faded – they obviously hadn't been there long. Luisa straightened up as she held them in her hand, looking at the ground on which they had rested. Had they been against the wall? If they had, who had left them there and why?

A feeling of unease skittered across Luisa's aching shoulders. She placed the flowers back amid the rubble.

Chapter Thirteen

That evening and the following day Luisa tried to research the factory site, kicking herself for not doing so before. Had there been some historic tragedy of which she should have been aware before she stomped all over the place? That would explain why someone would leave what seemed like a memorial on the spot where the old wall had stood. She could find nothing, however. She left Cas a note asking him if he knew why anyone would leave flowers on the site, but he wrote back to say there was nothing as far as he knew. When asked, Harper simply shrugged, which could have meant that she didn't know or that she wasn't prepared to say. Either way, Luisa was still entirely in the dark when Saturday and the consultation came around.

When Luisa reached Collaton that afternoon she dragged the box of equipment she'd brought with her out of the car and walked into the gym to find Cas and a handful of the club kids busily wiping the dust off a stack of old plastic chairs. Pop music played tinnily from a small digital player propped up on Cas's desk, combining with the general laughter to echo around the space.

'Hi, everyone,' Luisa said with a smile, her heart lifting to receive a chorus of 'hellos' back. 'Well, I didn't expect to find such a hive of activity! Thank you.'

Cas got to his feet from where he'd been kneeling on the floor, smiling too. 'This is what you get when you ask for help in Collaton.'

'It's a good job I brought supplies, then, isn't it?' she said, putting down the box and pulling out a packet of Jammy Dodgers with one hand and chocolate Hobnobs with the other, both of which were met with whoops of approval. Luisa had actually meant them for after the consultation but no matter – she'd passed a corner shop on her drive in, so she could get more if they were needed.

With the additional help it didn't take long to clean and set out the rest of the chairs. Luisa tried to commit the names of the kids to memory – there was JC, a boy of about thirteen already tall enough to seem at least a couple of years older; Sally, ten or thereabouts; Siddig, the quietest of the group ('A difficult home life,' was Cas's explanation later, 'but he's got a hell of a left hook. A real dark horse'); and Mo, who at a huge, brooding fifteen was the kind of teen that would have made Luisa hold her bag tighter if she passed him in the street but who worked harder and faster than any of them.

'Harper will be back later,' Cas told her. 'She had things to do this afternoon but she'll be here before the consultation starts.'

'Great,' Luisa said. 'Would you mind if I pin some things to the walls?'

'What, and spoil our beautiful décor?' he dead-panned.

'Would it help if I promised to make sure I return it to its current state?'

'Please don't,' he laughed. 'Come on, I'll help you. What have you got?'

'Mr P?' Mo said, from behind them. 'I've got to go now. Is that okay?'

'Sure, Mo. Thanks for your help, all of you.'

'Yes, thank you so much,' Luisa said. 'I really appreciate it. And don't forget – I'd love to see everyone at the consultation, and your parents. I'd love to hear what you'd like to see in the garden.'

There was a general shuffling of feet and looking at the floor, accompanied by collective mumbling as the kids sidled out.

'Did I say something wrong?' Luisa asked, once she and Cas were alone.

Cas smiled a little. 'No. But none of them have a particularly good relationship with their parents. Mo lives with his grandmother because he got kicked out last year. Sally doesn't get on with her step-dad and spends as much time as she can outside the home. Siddig is in foster care with six other children with whom he hasn't managed to gel.' He shrugged. 'If they had a better time at home they probably wouldn't come here in the first place.'

'Right,' Luisa said, her heart sinking. 'Which means I've

managed to put my foot in it again through sheer assumption and ignorance.'

He nudged her arm, a playful gesture that took her by surprise. 'Don't be so hard on yourself,' he said. 'That's what I'm here for. Come on, MacGregor, no slacking. Or are you expecting me to do all your hard work for you?'

His teasing made her smile and she wondered if this was how he dealt with difficulties with the kids, too. Cas's general demeanour was far warmer than his bulk suggested at first glance.

She took out one of the cardboard poster tubes she'd brought with her from home, sliding out the large sheet of paper within. 'I thought it'd be a good idea to have some representation of the sort of garden I think we can achieve out there,' she said, unrolling the first of four large-scale colour pencil illustrations depicting a garden design that progressed through the four seasons.

'Wow,' Cas said, as he helped Luisa pin the first to the wall and then stepped back to get a better look. 'Did you have these done especially for tonight? They're great.'

'No, actually,' Luisa admitted. 'There wasn't time to do fresh designs – at least not on this scale, although I have produced a few digital sketches. These are pretty old, to be honest – they were part of my final undergrad degree show.'

Cas looked at her. 'You did these?'

'There's no need to be so surprised.'

'Not surprised,' he said. 'Impressed.'

Chapter Fourteen

By the time everything was set up it was almost 5pm. The flyer had said that the consultation would start at five o'clock, but there was no sign of anyone arriving. Not even Harper.

'Perhaps no one's going to come,' Luisa fretted, as Cas made her a fresh mug of instant coffee.

'They will.'

They had left the double doors open and now footsteps sounded in the corridor outside. Harper appeared in the doorway, glancing around at the empty space with her eyebrows raised.

'Great turnout,' she said. 'Glad I came, no way you would have coped without me.'

'Harper,' Cas said, in a warning tone.

Harper shrugged off her ubiquitous black backpack and dumped it beside the refreshment table, nodding at the plates of biscuits. 'Can I have one?'

'Sure,' Luisa said, noting the dark circles under the girl's eyes.

Luisa had convinced herself that no one was going to turn up when the sound of voices and more footsteps echoed towards them. Four people appeared in the doorway, led by a woman wearing a long, quilted burgundy coat. As she came into the room Luisa was aware of a small reaction from Harper. She wondered if the two knew each other.

'Hello,' Luisa began, speaking collectively to the group. 'Welcome, it's so good to see everyone. I'm Luisa MacGregor. Thank you for coming, I'm looking forward to getting to know you, and—'

'I just came to say my piece,' the woman in the burgundy coat said, bluntly, as she took a seat in the front row. 'But I'll do you the courtesy of listening to what you have to say first. I've got five minutes and then I have to go.'

Everyone else sat down too, including Cas and Harper, who chose seats towards the back.

'Oh,' Luisa said, a little taken aback by the woman's brusque tone. 'Well, I'm hoping that I can involve all of you in the project, to make sure the garden fits the desires and needs of everyone in the area. That's why I wanted to hold this consultation, so that I could have a chance to meet local people, explain what the aim of this project is and gauge the direction we should take moving forward. This project is about building something for—'

More footsteps echoed in the corridor outside, along with the sound of heavy tramping feet and loud voices. Five young men entered the room, all elbows, swagger and loose clothes. Luisa felt rather than saw both Cas and Harper react, as the group's leader, a thin man of about twenty with straggling dark hair and a thin moustache, strode into the room. He cast Cas an insolent grin. On his cue the little posse made a meal of seating themselves, the noise and commotion turning the heads of the rest of the few attendees. Luisa didn't want to judge by appearances but they really didn't seem like the sort who would willingly spend time in a garden. Still, who was she to say?

'Thank you all for coming,' she said, directing a bright smile at the gaggle of young men. 'It's so great to see such interest in the project.'

'Oh, we're interested,' the group's leader drawled, to sniggers from his crew. He slouched elaborately in his chair, legs spread in front of him.

Luisa tried to get back to her talking points, aware that her five minutes were rapidly ticking away, but the lads continued to shift and whisper loudly among themselves.

'At its most basic, the aim of this project,' she said, loudly, indicating the illustrations Cas had helped her pin to the wall, 'is to build a garden that the whole community—'

'Wouldn't mind having a private *chat* with her, actually,' Darren mock-whispered, drawing more cackles from his boys. 'Might be nice to try a bit of mutton for a change, eh?'

Cas got to his feet and the lad was out of his chair in a second, shoulders up, hands spread as Mr P strode towards him.

'Yeah, big man?' he challenged. 'Think you're hard enough to take all of us, do you?'

'You're trespassing, Darren,' Cas said. 'Get out before I call the police.'

Darren sneered at him, his lads attempting to loom around Cas, but since only Darren himself came anywhere close to Cas's height their pale faces just bobbed around his shoulders like weeds searching for light.

'Leave,' Cas said, his voice very low and very steady, his face set like granite. 'I mean it. How do you think it'll go down with your parole officer if the police get a call from me?'

Darren kept his stance for a moment, leaning into Cas as if to prove he was not afraid of the weight advantage. He sucked his teeth and grinned and then peered past Cas to where Harper was still seated, staring studiously at her feet.

'All right, Harps?' Darren said, raising his voice. 'Long time no see.'

'Get out,' Cas repeated. 'I won't tell you again.'

'You'd better watch out, Big Man,' Darren told him, with a dangerous edge of quiet to his words. 'Things around here are going to change, you get me? Probably better if you went home.'

There was no discernible reaction from Cas. He stood there, a monolith: unmoved, immoveable.

Darren gave a sudden, nonchalant smirk. 'Come on, lads,' he said, still with his face close to Cas's. 'We've got better things to do.'

A moment later the group had gone, shoes loud on the floor, insolent voices echoing from the walls. For a moment after they'd gone there was silence. Then one by one the rest of the attendees also stood, preparing to leave.

'Look, I'm sorry for the disruption,' Luisa said, over the sound of chairs and feet. 'But really, if you could just spare a few more minutes—'

It was no good. The consultation was over before it had really begun. In two minutes the room was empty apart from Luisa, Cas and Harper. No one had taken any of the questionnaire sheets that Luisa had printed out and left on every chair.

Harper shifted for the first time since the chaos had begun. 'I've got to go.'

'Harper,' Cas called after her as she stood, hooked up her backpack and headed for the door. 'It would be great if you could stay and help—'

The girl didn't listen. A moment later she was gone, too.

Luisa tried to gather her scattered thoughts, a little stunned. How had everything turned into such a disaster so quickly?

'Who *was* that?' she asked Cas. 'What did you call him – Darren? You obviously know him.'

Cas rubbed one hand over his eyes. 'I'm sorry. His name's Darren Dixon. He's an old student of mine, he's ... got a long-standing problem with me.'

'What kind of problem?'

Cas shook his head. 'It doesn't matter. What matters is that little display just then had nothing to do with you and everything to do with me and I'm truly sorry. He wanted to rattle his sabre in my face, that's all, wanted to let me know he's back and he wanted an audience. He must have seen the flyer.'

'Back?'

'He's been away for a while. In prison.' Cas shook his head. 'I didn't know he was out, actually. It must be very recent.'

Luisa surveyed the room. How was she ever going to make this happen if she couldn't even get through a single consultation? Reuben would have had everyone in the room eating out of his hand in minutes, no matter how angry they'd been, no matter who they were. But Luisa? No, not Luisa.

'I can't do this,' she said, the realization hitting her the way that wall had come down out there on her useless waste-land of a site. 'I'm never going to be able to make this work.'

Cas moved closer and rested one large hand on her shoulder. He squeezed gently, unwittingly easing a muscle that had been aching for days. Luisa took a breath, unmoored by the unexpected comfort.

'Don't say that,' he said. 'You'll get there. This is just a set-back, that's all. Look, why don't you go home? I'll clear this lot up. Grab your stuff and I'll walk you to your car. Everything will seem better tomorrow.'

'No,' she said, as he dropped his hand. 'This is my mess. I'll clear it up.'

Cas smiled a little. 'Well then, we'll do it together. And for what it's worth, I think we should leave those up there.'

He indicated to her sketches on the wall. 'Who knows, maybe more people will come in looking to talk to you about the project who couldn't make it tonight. Anyway, they brighten the place up.'

Chapter Fifteen

When they finally left the gym, the night had drawn in. Darkness pooled between the cars and the narrow strips of houses as Cas walked Luisa to her car.

'Can I give you a lift home?' she asked, but he shook his head.

'Thanks, but it's not far.'

'What did that Darren guy mean,' she asked suddenly, 'when he said you'd better go home? Aren't you from here?'

'I am. Cumbrian born and bred. I grew up in Whitehaven. My parents are still there.'

'Then what did he mean?'

'My name, probably. That's enough to make the worst sorts of people show themselves nowadays.'

'Casimir Pattanyús,' Luisa said, thoughtfully. Cas liked the way his name sounded in her voice. 'That first night we met you told me it was Hungarian.'

'That's right,' Cas said. 'Both my mother and my father were refugees from Hungary in 1956, when the Soviet

Union invaded to crush the revolution. A lot of Hungarians came to Cumbria and their families were among them. They settled here and met when they were both at school.'

'That must have been tough,' Luisa said, 'starting an entirely new life in the wake of fleeing a war. Having to leave everything and everyone they knew behind them.'

'It was,' Cas agreed, 'but the people here were welcoming. Even the most remote villages took in families, who ended up working on the farms or in the mines up on the fells. Some Hungarians went back when the situation at home improved, but others made their lives here permanently. Raised their children and became part of the community.'

'I never knew that, and I grew up in Carlisle,' Luisa said. 'There's always so much history hidden in a place. It's so easily forgotten. That old factory wall, for example. I'm no closer to knowing who left those flowers on the site or even why. But it obviously means something to someone.'

'Sorry,' Cas said, with a wince. 'If Darren hadn't turned up looking for me you might have been able to get your answer.'

'Not your fault,' Luisa told him, although a shadow of anxiety passed over her face. 'I don't like that you've got someone like that harassing you, though.'

Cas smiled. 'You don't need to worry about me. Although I like that you do.'

He'd said the words before realizing quite what was in his mind. Luisa looked a little surprised. They stood looking at each other for another moment.

'Well,' she said. 'I'd better go.'

He nodded. 'I'll see you next week?'

Luisa let out a breath. 'Not sure. Maybe I should knock this on the head now.'

He slid his hands into his pockets. 'You won't do that.'

'No?'

'No. At least – I hope you don't.'

She smiled a little sadly. 'Night, Cas. Go safe.'

'You too.'

She got into the Defender and a moment later was pulling away from the kerb. He saw her glance back at him in her rear-view mirror. The intermittent orange glow of the sparse street lamps lit the Land Rover in silhouette until it turned a corner and was finally gone from sight.

In the wake of her leaving, a sense of melancholy settled over Cas. He pushed it away. He was tired, that was all, not to mention discombobulated by the sudden re-emergence of Darren Dixon in his life. He wondered whether he'd been right to tell Luisa that she had nothing to worry about and decided that it was true. Sure, Darren seemed to have developed even more of an arrogant swagger in the wake of his incarceration, but it was Cas himself that the younger man had a problem with. It always had been. There was no way he had any interest in the patch of wasteland that had brought Luisa to Collaton. That display tonight had merely been Darren showing off to his mates. He had always liked to imagine himself as a leader. It was why he'd ended up going head-to-head with Cas in the first place. Cas always seemed to bring out the worst in lads like Darren. It was his size, he supposed. They knew he could flatten them without trying and they didn't like it. Never mind that Cas wasn't a violent man and worked hard not to seem threatening to anyone, especially not the students in his care.

Cas started his walk home, thinking of Luisa's images of a fictitious garden. For a moment he tried to contemplate the scrub he'd just walked past transformed into a scene like that, but despite his best efforts he just couldn't reconcile the idea with the reality. He wanted it to work, he really did. He wanted to see – and for others outside its confines to see – that Collaton wasn't just a waste of time, a forgotten corner of the world that had nothing to offer to anyone. But there was so much accumulated dust between this place and the sun, so much decay and neglect. Look at Darren. How hard had Cas tried with him? He'd been a smart boy with plenty of promise. But it had been too late even before Cas had started and now it was very clear that Darren had gone too far down that path for Cas to offer a way back.

Still, he thought. *If anyone can do this, it's Luisa MacGregor.*

He caught himself. For all Cas knew, in six months' time the weeds would be back and she would be gone again, having moved on to somewhere new, somewhere easier. In fact, after tonight he'd be surprised if she came back at all.

Around him, February had given way to March but the air still held an icy chill. He wondered briefly if he needed to keep an eye open. He wouldn't put it past Darren to pop out of the night's long shadows and have a crack at him, especially if he had his little posse with him to back him up.

Cas was passing the block of flats on the corner when a movement caught his eye. It only took a glance for him to see that it wasn't Darren, or any of the young men who had invaded the gym earlier in the evening. This figure was much smaller. There was something familiar about the boy standing on the other side of the street. It took Cas a moment to place him. Then he realized it was Harper's younger brother, Max. Cas had met him a couple of times. The first had been the single time that Harper had brought him to the club. The second had been when he and Harper had left the gym together at the end of a session and found Max outside, waiting for his sister. On neither occasion had the boy spoken to Cas, which Harper had explained away as her brother being shy of strangers. Cas knew enough about Harper's home life to know that she was her brother's main caregiver, a subject he'd tried to address with her on several occasions, only to be firmly and unequivocally shut down. There wasn't a lot else that Cas could do. When Max got to high school, Cas would be better able to monitor the situation with a view to offering help – although, by then, Harper herself would have left.

'Max?' Cas called across the dark street. 'Hi!'

The boy froze, staring at him.

'It's Mr Pattanyús,' Cas went on. 'From Harper's school? I run the boxing gym.'

Max looked around, his sudden movements frantic, as if

he were afraid of being seen talking to Cas. Then he moved backwards into the shadows. The street was so dark now that he faded completely from Cas's sight, until he wasn't sure Max was still there.

Cas remained there for a moment, contemplating what had just happened. Then he started walking again, heading for home. As he passed out of the street where he had seen Harper's brother another movement caught his eye. Two friends stood at the outer circle of the uncertain light cast by a flickering orange street lamp. For a second Cas thought they were talking, passing the time in a town with nowhere else for the young to hang out, but as he thought this he saw that one of them was already hurrying away, hood up, head down, while the other leaned back against the wall behind him. Waiting.

Cas kept walking, but this incident troubled him and he couldn't put his finger on quite why. It finally occurred to Cas that he was still thinking about Darren, who hadn't been much older than Max when Cas had first become aware of him. As much as Darren's later behaviour angered Cas now, as dangerous a man as he'd become, he'd been just a boy once. At what point would someone have needed to step in in order to change the course of what had come later?

He was still thinking about Max Dixon – worrying, really – when he turned the key in the lock of Annika's flat and pushed the door open on to an unusual silence. He'd asked her if she'd wanted to come to the consultation that evening, whether she might consider helping out at the garden. She'd given him a strange look, as if something had finally occurred to her. Cas hadn't had time to ask her what was wrong, had assumed they could discuss it when he got home.

In some ways it turned out he was right.

Annika appeared at the end of the hallway, her face beautiful even though she wore no make-up, even though her expression was serious.

'We need to talk,' she said.

Chapter Sixteen

The past couple of weeks had been a nightmare for Harper. In the aftermath of her father destroying the bathroom, Max had gone into some weird kind of withdrawal. She'd tried to make it better. She'd said that with her next pay packet from the garage they could buy proper pots and a bag of compost and whatever seeds he liked. She'd told him that he could use the window ledge in her bedroom as well as his own. But Max had just absented himself, as if he'd stepped out of the world and locked an invisible door behind him for which no one else had a key. Even when he was in a room with her he wasn't really there. He kept disappearing and Harper didn't know where he was going. It didn't help that she was home less and less too, because she'd begged Carl for more work at the garage, even if all she was doing was scrubbing oil off the concrete floor, so that she could afford to start doing up Mr P's old rust-bucket of a Mini and rent the space it was currently taking up in the garage's car park. Harper kept thinking that she should just give up, that she should put Max first and be with him every minute she could, but how else was she going to get him out of here?

Tonight when she reached home, the house was ominously quiet. Harper shrugged off her jacket and hung it on the hook. She was heading for the kitchen when something on the stairs caught her eye through the banisters – a smudge of dark soil. Harper backtracked to examine the mess more closely. The streak took in several steps, as if something had been dragged up or down the stairs.

Harper continued up to the landing, following a grubby line of marks that led to Max's closed door. She knocked, but got no answer. It was a stated rule that Harper never, ever went into Max's room without permission. That was his space alone and she knew it helped him to know that. Something was off, though, and Harper felt it with a certainty that coiled a thick rope of unease around her heart. Had Max stolen from their neighbours again? The thought made Harper feel sick, because it would only take one of them to call the police or social services and things would fall apart. Harper already felt as if she were only just holding everything together.

She bit her lip for a second and then reached out in one swift movement to open Max's door. Harper glanced down the stairs as if her brother might suddenly appear, but the house remained silent. Flicking on the light revealed a room far neater than anyone would expect for a nine-year-old. A desk just like hers held school books and a cup full of pens. Other books filled the shelves beside it. Max's duvet had been straightened on his bed. It was what was stacked beneath the window that really drew Harper's gaze, though. There she found the source of the dirt: four sacks of garden compost, piled one on top of the other. Beside them were an array of plastic plant pots that looked new. Some had labels holding stacks of them together, which she recognized came from the hardware shop in the middle of town that in spring doubled as a garden supply centre.

Harper couldn't work it out. Had Max stolen them? She couldn't imagine how. What would he have done, picked up a sack and run off with it? She couldn't see how he'd be able to do that once, let alone four times in a row. But he didn't have any money; she knew that because she hadn't given him any for the past week, hoping that would prompt him to talk to her in order to ask for some.

'What are you *doing*?'

The voice behind her was shrill and came from Max, who had returned home and made his way to the top of the stairs without her hearing him.

'Why are you in my room? You're not allowed in my room!'

'Max—'

'Get out!' he shrieked at her. 'Get out, get out, get out!'

'Max—' Harper held out her hands to her brother but he swatted them aside, shoving through the door of his room and then turning to push her out. 'Wait. Where did the compost come from? Where did you get it?'

'Get *out*!'

'*No.*' Harper stood squarely in the doorway, holding the door open so that he couldn't slam it shut. She was stronger than him but she had rarely, if ever, showed down against her brother like this. 'You have to talk to me. You have to tell me where you got that stuff. Who does it belong to?'

'*Go away!*'

'Max, this is important. Did you steal it?'

'It's mine!'

'Max, please.'

'It's mine,' he screamed. 'I earned the money for it and a friend helped me get it from the shops because you're too horrible to even do that because you don't want me to have my own life and I hate you, I hate you, *I hate you*! Get out of my room, right *now*!'

In her shock Harper let him shove her out. A second later he slammed the door in her face, so hard that the wall shook. Then she heard something being dragged across carpet – his desk as he barricaded himself in.

Harper stood staring at the door. Max rarely said so many words in one go and he'd never said he hated her before. He'd often been angry with her, yes, but not like this. As lopsided as they were, she'd always thought he understood that they were a team. Harper and Max against the world. She'd do anything for him, he knew that. Didn't he?

'Max?' she tried, but there was no answer. Eventually she gave up and went back to her room, her head spinning as she contemplated what else her brother had said. He'd earned the money? How? Doing what and for whom? And who was this friend who'd helped him get this stuff to the house? One of the kids from school? Even with two kids carrying a sack of soil between them she couldn't see how that would work.

Harper sat down at her desk and rubbed a hand over her face, feeling empty and defeated, too tired for the unfocused rage that knotted itself into her gut.

The next morning after a sleepless night, she tried to talk to Max again, but he wasn't having it. He wouldn't look at her when he came downstairs at half past eight, already dressed to go out.

'Where are you going?'

Her brother pulled on his shoes and then his coat, resolutely refusing to meet her eye.

'Are you going to have some breakfast before you go?' she asked. 'I got some more yoghurt yesterday. I had an idea, actually – how about I mash a banana in a bowl and you try putting the yoghurt on top of that? I bet that'd taste good. Maybe add some honey?'

At this Max shot her a look of pure dislike. 'I'm not a baby.'

Harper swallowed, tugged by the riptide of a sea suddenly threatening to drown her. 'I know. I just—'

'I'm going out.'

'Where are you going?'

'I don't have to tell you anything. You're my sister, not my mum.'

'Max.'

'Leave me alone, Harper,' Max said. 'Get your own life for a change.'

He slammed the door behind him. She heard his footsteps echoing across concrete, then the creak of the metal gate. Then nothing.

Harper stood in silence for a moment, trying to process what had just happened, then headed for the coat rack. Loud snores emanated through the door of the front room: their father, too heavily asleep to have heard the altercation between his kids. Harper rushed to put on her boots and coat and then followed her brother out of the door, determined to find out where he'd gone and who had put those words in his mouth, because what she'd seen a few minutes before sure as hell hadn't been Max.

She looked up and down the street to see him disappearing into an adjoining road and ran to catch up. When she reached the corner she saw Max already at the far end. He was standing on the kerb, waiting as another kid on a bike raced towards him. Harper watched – was this the friend that Max had talked about? She wanted him to have friends, she really did, even if they ended up making him want to say things to her in the way he just had.

As Harper went to follow, a car slid up to the kerb beside her, music pounding from the open window.

'Well, well, well,' said a voice. 'You grew up, you filled out, didn't you?'

Harper felt all the skin on the back of her neck prickle.

She looked down to see Darren leaning on his arm out of the open passenger window of the car. She would have happily gone the rest of her life without ever seeing the unmitigated creep that was her cousin ever again. He was wearing dark glasses and a cap as if he was the sort of hard nut gangster he could only dream of being. He'd tried to feel her up once. She'd only been thirteen at the time. She'd broken three of his fingers. He'd played it off and he'd never tried anything like it again, but Harper wasn't fool enough to think he'd forgotten, much less forgiven, any more than he'd given up on his ridiculous beef with Mr P.

Darren had been way ahead of her in school, but the story of what happened between her cousin and Mr P was legendary. She'd wondered, sometimes, which of the scars on the teacher's arms were from the knife that Darren had been carrying. Darren had said that Mr P had started it, that he'd *tried* something, but the school's CCTV told a different story and anyway everyone knew that Darren had always had a problem with Mr P. Mr P had been completely cleared of any wrongdoing, while Darren's behaviour had escalated until he'd landed himself a stretch in prison that Harper wished had lasted far longer than it had. Why had he come back here? Why couldn't he have gone somewhere else? Why couldn't *she* go somewhere else?

'Fuck off, Darren,' she said.

'Aw, don't be like that,' he said. 'Can't blame a man for looking. I've not had much opportunity recently, you know that.'

Her skin crawled. Her cousin was exactly the sort to think that having been inside was some sort of badge of honour, as if he'd earned something, as if it made him *worth* something. Harper started walking away but the car kept pace with her, that idiot lackey of Darren's behind the wheel creeping along beside her like the bug he was.

'That was your little brother, yeah?' Darren asked, conversationally. 'I remember him. Cute kid. Smart, too, right?'

Harper stopped dead. The car stopped, too. 'You stay away from him.'

Darren was out of the car in a flash, standing over her with an expression that should have been a smile but wasn't. He might have been scrawny, but he was tall with it. The driver door opened and his mate joined him, thin and weedy, mean because he had nothing else going for him.

'Think you can give me orders now, do you?'

Harper decided there and then that no, she wasn't afraid. Not of this waste of space. Never.

'It's not an order,' she said. 'It's a warning. It's the only one you'll get. Stay away from my brother or you'll get worse than last time. Remember that, shit for brains? When a thirteen-year-old girl broke your weak little fingers?'

Darren didn't seem cowed in the slightest. Something glittered in his eyes. 'It's about time you showed some respect, Harps,' he said, softly.

Harper laughed in his face. 'Show me hell freezing over,' she told him, 'and I'll show you some respect.'

Max had vanished. Harper turned on her heel and left Darren where he stood, huffing like the mouth-breather he was.

Chapter Seventeen

'You look beautiful, Jo,' Luisa said. 'Really.'

Jo made a daft face at herself in one of the bridal shop's many full-length mirrors. The gown was white satin, the neckline scooped so her shoulders were bare, the skirt full to the floor from the cinched waist. Around her the opulence of the shop's décor was beautiful, tumbling artificial blooms and swags of pale draped fabric.

'We will take this in a little here,' the shop owner was saying, busying herself at Jo's waist, pinching fabric tight against her body. 'You have such a tiny waist. This style suits you very well.'

'Right,' Jo said. 'Let's go with this one. Done. Dusted. Hooray!'

Measurements taken and further appointments made, they found a café for lunch and collapsed into their seats as if they'd run a marathon, not spent a morning staring at dresses.

'I'm so relieved that bit's over,' Jo muttered, as she poured a much-needed cup of tea.

'Don't say that,' Luisa said. 'This is supposed to be fun.'

'I know it is,' her sister sighed, 'but I'll just be glad when it's done with, to be honest. It's such a fuss and over what? It's just one day!'

Luisa stayed silent as she poured her own tea.

'What's the matter?' Jo asked.

Luisa looked up at her sister. 'I'm just worried that the reason you're not enjoying the wedding planning is because you think you can't because of me,' she said, voicing what had been on her mind for weeks now. 'And I don't want that. I'm fine, Jo, really. I'm so happy that you've found Neil, the two of you are so perfect together, and—' She stopped at the look on Jo's face. 'Jo? What is it?'

Jo blew out a breath. 'Do you really think we're perfect for each other?'

Luisa blinked. 'Well – yes, because ... you are. Or at least, it seems that way to me. Why – are you having second thoughts?'

Her sister stared into her teacup. 'I don't know if it's second thoughts, exactly. I love Neil, I really do. You're right, he's wonderful and funny and we share a lot of the same values and the same interests ...' She trailed off.

'So ... what?' Luisa prompted, gently.

Jo leaned back in her seat and raised both hands, releasing a sharp breath that puffed out her cheeks. 'I don't know ... *inevitable*?'

Luisa frowned. 'I'm not sure what you mean.'

Jo shook her head. 'I'm not sure what I mean either. I do

love him. I do. It's just sometimes ... I wonder if it's the wrong kind of love. We were friends for ages before we got together, you know that. Now we've been together for ages too and I'm thirty and he's thirty-two and we're both settled in our careers and here I am choosing a stupidly expensive wedding dress and bloody *swags*, and ... I don't know, sometimes it feels as if this is just another step we're taking in a pre-planned life.'

'You feel like you're settling?' Luisa asked.

Jo looked away, out of a window streaked with a sudden shower of rain. 'Maybe? Or not settling so much as *settled*. It's all so ... comfortable.'

Luisa stroked a fingernail along the polished silver of the little teaspoon beside her cup. She wondered what it would have been like to have Reuben in her life long enough to reach that kind of comfortable, that kind of settled.

'I'm sorry,' Jo sighed, as if she might have read Luisa's thoughts. 'I know this is selfish. I think—' She stopped herself, bit her lip.

'You think – what?' Luisa asked.

Jo took another sip of tea. 'I think I still keep holding onto how you and Reuben were,' she said. 'My older sister and the perfect man who cared about the same things as she did. I saw how in love you both were, how well you worked together. It was more beautiful than any teen romance I could have read at that age. It made me want that. I'm just afraid, I suppose. I thought I'd found that with Neil, but what if I'm wrong?'

Luisa felt herself grow cold. That same old pain opened up in her chest, along with a type of jealousy she'd never felt before, certainly not for her sister. For the sheer luxury of Jo being able to sit here like this, talking this way. That she had a *choice*.

'Love doesn't always come accompanied by fireworks, Jo,' Luisa said, keeping her voice steady, trying to quell a little spark of anger. These were just wedding jitters. Jo deserved to have them, same as everyone else, but still. 'It's naïve and foolish to think it does. I envy you what you have with Neil. You get to spend the rest of your life with a person you love, a person who loves you, and—' She stopped. 'I wouldn't throw that away for anything, not if I could help it.'

Jo reached across the table and caught Luisa's hand, squeezing it hard. 'I know. This is just cold feet. I'm just being stupid and I do know how lucky I am. I do! Ignore me. I'm sorry.'

After a moment Luisa slipped her hand out from beneath her sister's and picked up her tea, but it had begun to grow cold. The room seemed dimmer, somehow. There was a throb in Luisa's chest, a little pulse of anger inside her heart. It wasn't even aimed at Jo, not really. The world was a cruel place. But then Luisa knew that already, didn't she? Far too well.

'I wish,' Jo said, then, 'that I could find someone for you. I worry that you're still alone, Lu. It's not right.'

This was not a new conversation between them. Luisa had explained over and over how she felt, that she already knew she'd never find what she had with Reuben again, that the idea of trying filled her with dread and, yes, with fear, too, despite the years of therapy. Life was fragile and fickle; love could be devastating. 'I'm happy how I am.'

'You're not happy – how can you say that?' Jo asked.

'Sometimes I am,' Luisa said. 'And when I'm not, I'm fine. I think that's the same as most people, Jo.'

'You're surviving, that's all. It's not enough.'

'Are you saying you don't think a person can be happy and fulfilled if they're not in a relationship?' Luisa asked, with a touch of acid to her tone. 'I think you'll find yourself in some hot water if you are.'

'Of course I'm not,' Jo said. 'I'm not talking about the whole of humanity, Luisa, I'm talking about *you*. You have such a capacity for *love*. I want you to be with a guy who makes all your nerve endings tingle at once. Someone who makes your heart hiccup and your knees weak.'

Luisa couldn't stop the sudden image of Reuben that instantly surfaced in her mind, nor could she quell the fresh burst of pain that came with it. She shut it out, annoyed at herself and steadily growing furious with her sister.

'I've already had that once,' she said. 'And it was wonderful, but I don't need or expect that again.'

'Do you hear yourself?' Jo asked. 'You're not even forty! What happened to romance? What happened to being swept off your feet?'

'I told you, I'm *fine* the way I am,' Luisa said, roughly. 'And anyway, that's not what real love looks like.'

'It did for you, once. I just want you to have that again, Luisa. I don't want your heart to stay locked away for the rest of your life just because you're afraid of being hurt like that again.'

Luisa stared at her sister, hard. '"*Just because*"?'

Jo shook her head, looking pained. 'I'm sorry, that didn't come out right. I just meant—'

'I know what you meant, Joanna,' Luisa said. 'And you don't know a damn thing about it.' She got up, intensely glad they had come in separate cars. 'I'm going.'

'Luisa, please don't—'

Luisa walked out, leaving her sister calling frantically for the bill. She got into the Defender and slammed the door behind her. She was shaking, hating the tears she could feel threatening. Better to hold onto the anger that was there, stave off a collapse that would prove as useless as it was debilitating. Years ago, she'd have ended up curled in a ball for the rest of the day, perhaps the rest of the week, but she was better now. She just needed to stay busy enough to ride it out.

It was the Tuesday after the disaster that had been the garden consultation. She'd decided to take a few days to step back and regroup. Today was supposed to be about Jo and the wedding, a welcome break. Now, Luisa didn't want to think about spending the afternoon at home. She started the car and headed for Collaton, instead. Maybe she wasn't wanted there, and perhaps saying yes to taking on the site had been a terrible mistake, but at least it would keep her busy today.

When Luisa pulled up in the square it was to find that Nick had finished and gone. Half the tarmac had been peeled from the ground like the skin of an atrophied orange. In its wake had been left dry, dead dirt that hadn't seen sunlight for decades. It looked like the surface of the moon.

Apart from the work gloves that were in the Defender Luisa wasn't dressed for the site — she was wearing a cream silk blouse over skinny jeans tucked into tan suede boots. It was an outfit that definitely wouldn't survive a few treks through the desiccated earth that had been exposed by the JCB, but right then Luisa was too worked up to care. She pulled on the gloves and passed through the gate to start collecting the chunks of tarmac and broken concrete that the digger had missed, hefting them up and slinging them into the skips, barely pausing for breath. Lift, walk, throw, repeat. Lift, walk, throw, repeat.

'Hey,' said a voice, sometime later. 'Luisa? Everything okay?'

It was Cas. He was standing in front of one of the skips, dressed in his gym gear, watching her with a quizzical expression.

'I called from the gate,' he explained, when she stopped, 'but you didn't seem to hear me.'

Luisa realized she was out of breath when she tried to reply but the words caught in her throat. She slung the chunk of debris she had in her hands past Cas and into the skip, catching her breath.

'Sorry,' she said, looking at her watch to see that it was

only three o'clock. 'I was miles away. What are you doing here? It's a bit early for school to be over, isn't it?'

'My last class of the afternoon has work experience this week. Meant I could slope off early.' Cas glanced around. 'Looks like you've got your work cut out here. I'll give you a hand.'

'You don't have to do that,' Luisa said. 'Don't you want to go and pummel a punchbag before the kids get here, or something?'

He picked up a block of stray concrete twice as big as any she could lift herself and glanced at her, amused. 'I'm pretty sure this could work out any frustrations just as well.'

Luisa blew her hair out of her eyes. 'Well,' she said, 'that's what I'm counting on, anyway.'

'Oh?' he said. 'Want to talk about it?'

'No,' she told him and then added, 'Come on, Pattanyús. *Now* who's the one slacking?'

He grinned at her and then slung the chunk of debris in his arms into the skip with a resounding crash. 'Like that, is it, MacGregor?'

She shrugged, giving him a grin of her own as she hoisted up another heavy chunk of tarmac and headed for the skip again. 'Don't dish it out if you can't take it, right?'

They went on working. The sun was setting a little later now, the temperatures of March beginning to rise as the year drew on. It'd be planting season before she knew it, Luisa thought. By rights she should already have seeds starting indoors.

'I'm glad,' Cas said, as they met at the skip for the dozenth time.

'About what?' Luisa asked.

He gestured at the empty parcel of land. 'That you haven't given up. I was a little worried that you weren't going to come back again after Saturday night.'

Luisa looked at her hands, buried in her thick work gloves. There were smudges of dirt all over her jeans and her blouse was sweaty and ruined. She sighed. 'I'm still not sure that wouldn't be the right thing to do,' she said. 'It's pretty clear that no one wants me – or my ideas – here.'

'No one?' Cas repeated. 'That's not true.'

She looked up at him. The shadows were beginning to lengthen, pooling across his face, making the break in his nose more pronounced and the expression in his dark eyes hard to read. After a moment Cas looked over her head towards the road and then lifted his fingers to his lips to emit a piercing whistle that made Luisa wince.

'Ow.'

'Sorry,' he said, with absolutely no trace of remorse. 'But the cavalry's arrived.'

There came the sound of feet and murmuring young voices – some of the boxing club kids arriving for the evening's session.

'Mr P?' called Mo, through the fence. 'That you?'

'It's me, Mo. Come on, you lot,' Cas called to them. 'Ms MacGregor here needs some help. How about it?'

'Sure, Mr P,' Mo said, an assent that was echoed by

133

the other kids who followed him through the gate. 'We can do that.'

Cas turned his smile on Luisa. 'See?' he said. 'It's a start. Acorns into oak trees, right?'

When Luisa checked her phone before beginning the drive home that night there was a text waiting for her from Jo. *I'm so sorry*, it read. *I love you. Will we be okay?*

Luisa rubbed a grubby hand over her face. The garden work had scrubbed away her anger, leaving her merely weary, aching and tired.

I love you too, she texted back. *Of course we will.*

Chapter Eighteen

As March warmed and gave way to April, Luisa oversaw the delivery of twenty tons of topsoil and another ten tons of good-quality organic fertilizer. By the time both had been spread, what once had been a wasteland looked more like a ploughed field ready for planting. Harper helped here and there but in the main Luisa rotavated it herself, driving herself to exhaustion as she worked the heavy machine back and forth over the land to mix the soil and manure.

There had been no improvement in relations with the local community. She'd set up a dedicated email contact, produced a placeholder page for a website with details and also tried more flyers, pushing them through letterboxes herself when Harper declared herself too busy. She even stopped people in the street whenever she saw them passing. Nothing did any good. She was met mostly with indifference but occasionally there was low-level hostility, too. According to Cas, who had quizzed the kids to see if they knew where the anger had come from, it had to do with the old factory wall.

'There's talk that it shouldn't have been knocked down,' Cas explained late one afternoon, after he'd arrived at the gym to see Luisa hauling the heavy rotavator across the fresh earth. 'That it should have been left up out of respect.'

'But out of respect for what?' Luisa asked. 'I can't find any record of any tragedy happening here. I even contacted the local historical society to ask, but they didn't know anything either. The wall was unstable, it was going to fall sooner or later anyway. Would it be better for this place to look steadily worse than for me turn it into a garden?'

Cas shook his head. 'I don't know any more than you do,' he said. 'I'm sorry. That's just the scuttlebutt the kids have told me, but how accurate it is I don't know. The bottom line is, some people just don't like change.'

'Or outsiders with big ideas?' Luisa suggested.

He laughed a little. 'There's maybe a bit of that going on too, yeah.'

'I have to keep going,' Luisa told him. 'If I wait until I can work out how to win everyone around to the idea, I'll miss planting season. I'm going to be cutting it fine as it is. Onwards and upwards, as they say.'

She liked the encouraging smile he gave her. 'Good. That's the spirit. Do you know what you're going to do next?'

Luisa smiled back. 'I do,' she said.

'Trees?' Harper said, when Luisa arrived a few days later with the Defender's trailer stocked with a very small forest's worth of three-year-old saplings.

'Fruit trees, to be exact,' Luisa said as she jumped out of the Defender. 'I've got four apple, four pear, four plum and four cherry.'

'That's your big plan?' the girl asked. 'You're going to turn this place into an orchard?'

'Partly. If we espalier them, it'll disguise some of the fence and still leave plenty of room in the centre of the site for the rest of the garden.'

Harper looked at her blankly. 'Espalier?'

Luisa made a spreading gesture with her hands held out flat, her fingers splayed. 'It means to train the branches against a framework. We can use the fence as the support. Help me get them out, would you?'

Luisa dropped the back of the trailer and climbed aboard to begin handing the saplings down to Harper. They were quite tall already, reaching as high as Luisa's chest. The branches of each little tree had been fanned out against triangular arrangements of bamboo sticks. They looked like a peacock's tail feathers, if those tail feathers had been stripped to the shaft.

Harper hefted down the first pot as Luisa handed it to her. Once it was on the tarmac the girl looked doubtful. 'They look pretty dead to me. Think you might have been scammed.'

'They'll start putting out new growth soon enough, you'll see,' Luisa told her. 'It's why it's important to get them in the ground now, though. They should really have gone in at the end of last season, so we can't wait any longer.'

Once unloaded, Luisa and Harper started digging holes, spacing them out beside the fence and making sure to allow enough room for the trees to spread and grow.

'All right,' Harper said, shoving her spade into the ground with a determined stab once she'd finished the last hole. 'What's next, then?'

Luisa looked at her watch. 'That's your two hours pretty much up,' she said. 'You can leave the rest to me, if you like.'

'Nah, I can stay a bit longer,' Harper said. 'I told school I had to take my little brother to a dentist's appointment.'

'But you don't?'

'Nope.'

'Why did you do that?'

The girl shrugged. 'What do you care? Do you want the help or not? Because if not, I'll head over to the garage and work on the car instead, it's no skin off my nose.'

Luisa sighed. 'I'm not sure Mr Pattanyús would be very happy with me if he knew I was colluding in you bunking off school.'

Harper smirked. 'Dunno about that. He seems pretty *happy* with you every time I see you two together.'

Something about that flippant statement made Luisa's stomach do an unexpected somersault. With horror she felt her cheeks threatening to burn. 'What do you mean?'

The girl's moment of levity was gone, replaced once more by impatience. 'Look, do you want me to stay and help with these sticks, or do you want to stand around gossiping? I've got time for one, but not the other.'

Luisa sighed. 'Your help would be great, thanks.'

Harper nodded. 'Let's get on with it then. What's next, putting them in the ground?'

'We need to water the holes first. It's called "puddling in". We fill each hole with water and let it drain away to make sure there's enough moisture in the ground.'

Harper looked around. 'Where do we get the water from?'

Luisa grimaced, knowing how what she was about to say would go down. 'Well, I've ordered a couple of rainwater tanks but the supplier can't deliver them until next week. For now, we're going to have to go analogue.'

'What's that mean? You've got a hose?'

'I wish,' Luisa admitted. She pointed to four galvanized buckets that were waiting by the skips. 'The nearest tap is in the gym.'

Harper stared at her as if she'd grown a second head. 'You have got to be joking.'

Luisa shrugged. 'You could always go back to school, tell them the dentist cancelled?'

Harper cursed under her breath and stalked across the tarmac to pick up a pail in each hand.

'This is only temporary,' Luisa told her, as she followed with the other two buckets. 'The tanks will save us having to do this every time we need water.'

'Whatever,' Harper grumbled. 'Let's just get on with it.'

By the time they were done with filling the last hole, the water they'd put into the first had drained away. Luisa had watered each of the saplings well before she'd driven out of the nursery, but there was another step before they could be taken out of their pots and sunk into the waiting earth. She went to the Defender and pulled a plastic sack out of the back.

'We need to put a scoop of this into each hole,' she said.

'More fertilizer?' Harper asked. 'Didn't you spread a load of shit just last week?'

Luisa ignored the subtle dig. 'This is a more direct mode of helping the plants.' She opened the sack and showed Harper the contents, which looked like miniature white cat litter.

'What is it?' Harper asked.

'Mycorrhizal fungi. It's a natural fertilizer derived from the rootstock of fungus. It helps the roots communicate the nutrients in the surrounding soil more directly into the tree's roots. It'll promote healthy growth.'

'Fungus?' Harper said, incredulously.

'Yup. This soil is going to take years to improve, even with the manure. This will help the trees to take.'

'If you say so,' Harper muttered, reaching for the scoop that Luisa held out.

They left the bamboo training sticks the saplings had come with in place. As they set each tree in the ground, Luisa showed Harper how to tie them and the bare branches back against the rusted cables of the fence, fastening each with a cable tie loose enough to allow for growth. Beside the thin trunks they added the name tag for each tree. *Beauty of Bath*, *Egremont Russet*, *Beurre Superfin*, *Fondante d'Automne*, *Excalibur*, *Mirabelle*, *Bigarreau Napoleon*.

'They sound like the fancy names for race horses,' Harper observed with a slight grunt as they lowered the last sapling into its hole.

Luisa laughed. 'They do a bit.'

Once the trees were in place the pair stood back to admire their work. There wasn't much to look at considering the effort they'd both exerted. The saplings looked like bare sticks poking out of the ground. Luisa could feel Harper's silent dissatisfaction radiating like heat from the girl's customary cross-armed stance.

'They'll grow, you'll see,' Luisa said. 'We just need to keep them well watered until they settle and they'll be off like greyhounds. Or race horses ...'

'We've got to water them again? This is insane. *You're* insane.'

'Once the tanks are here it'll be much easier,' Luisa pointed out. 'And anyway, this is the Lake District – it rains here all the time, doesn't it? Once they're settled it'll only be in dry spells that we need to water.'

Harper shook her head. 'Yeah, because global warming and climate change definitely aren't a thing, are they?' she said. 'You do remember what happened last year, right? Record heatwave, weeks of drought? They're already saying that we're probably going to have that again this summer. Two tanks aren't going to be enough to keep these trees watered in those scorching temperatures, let alone whatever you stick in the rest of this place. What are you expecting people around here to do, spend their time taking water out of their taps and hauling it out here to keep this place going? Who's going to want to do that? Who's going to have *time* for that? And anyway, how is that good for the environment?'

They were both quiet after this sudden tirade. Luisa had to admit that she hadn't thought that far ahead, but Harper was right. Water could definitely be a problem in the long term.

'It's something I need to think more about,' Luisa agreed. 'In the meantime, I'll order more water tanks for when it does rain. How about that?'

Harper scooped up her buckets again. 'Whatever. In another sixty hours it's not going to be my problem. Right now, I'm doing two more trips to water in your precious trees and then you're on your own.'

Chapter Nineteen

'Right,' Luisa said. 'This is where it really starts.'

'I thought we'd already done that with the trees?' Harper asked.

It was the first week of April and they were standing together inside the site gate again, looking at the expanse of bare earth. Every last piece of debris had been cleared. Luisa had finished giving it one last fine rake over herself the day before. It was ready to become . . . something.

'Well, yes,' Luisa agreed. 'But this is where it will begin to take shape properly.'

'All right,' Harper said, in a deliberately bored voice. 'Whatever it's going to be let's get on with it, yeah? I haven't got all day. Carl's found me a new clutch for the Mini. I'm going to fit it later.'

Luisa took out her iPad, flipped it open and held up the image on the screen. Harper squinted at it. The sketch showed the garden site, bisected neatly down the middle from where they were standing to the trees at the far end by a pathway.

'You're planning to build the yellow brick road?' Harper asked, with a shrug.

Luisa laughed. 'Kind of. Only ours will be red.' She nodded at the semi-neat square of reclaimed sandstone salvaged from the downed factory wall. 'I thought we could use some of the materials we have here.'

'To do what, exactly?' Harper asked. 'Looks to me like you're planning to build a path to nowhere.'

'We'll be dividing the garden into different zones, or areas,' Luisa explained. 'For starters – flowers on one side of the central path, vegetables on the other. There'll be a grassed area too, see? And there's plenty of room for other suggestions – when we get some from the community.'

'Right. Whatever,' Harper said, still with no trace of interest. 'Just tell me what to do and I'll get on with it.'

'What we really need,' Luisa said, as they started unloading equipment and materials from the back of the Defender's trailer, 'is to find a way to engage more volunteers. We can't do this all ourselves.'

'Well,' Harper said, 'soon enough that's not going to be my problem, so . . .'

Luisa sighed, failing to hide her exasperation. 'I wish I knew what I'd done to upset you so much, Harper.'

'You haven't upset me.'

'I clearly have,' Luisa countered. 'Trying to talk to you about anything is like pulling teeth. What is it about me that you dislike so much?'

Harper shrugged. 'What do you care whether I like you or not?'

'Because I like you,' Luisa said, pointedly. 'Attitude and all. You're a hard worker even when you're stuck doing something you don't want to be doing and you've clearly got a sharp mind. I completely understand why Mr Pattanyús is so convinced you've got a bright future, so if I've upset you, I'd like to know why – and to fix it, if I can. Is it just that you don't like my garden idea? If that's what the problem is, I'd really like to talk to you about why. Maybe it'll give me an insight into why other people around here are equally angry with me.'

Harper was diligently looking away from her, although Luisa got the sense that something in her words had struck a chord. She was silent for so long that Luisa wasn't sure she was going to say anything at all. Luisa was just about to turn away and get on with the job at hand when the girl spoke.

'I guess no one around here gets why they should be used as free labour,' Harper said, her voice as blunt as a chisel. 'But that's rich people all over, right? Why pay for what you want when you can con someone into giving it to you for free? Maybe that's what people think.'

Luisa frowned. 'Is that what *you* think?'

Harper shrugged, her jaw set, angles all jagged.

'Harper,' Luisa didn't even know where to start. 'I'm not *rich*.'

'Yeah, right,' the girl said. 'Everyone sails around in a

spanking new car and spunks handfuls of twenty-pound notes as they buy up half a town because they've had a great idea for a hobby.'

Luisa tried to work this out. She remembered Harper's attitude the first time they met. 'Are you talking about the BMW?' she demanded. 'That wasn't mine, Harper. Have you ever seen me in it since? That's my sister's company car, she let me borrow it that weekend because mine was off the road. Which I also didn't buy – my dad left it to me when he died. I didn't buy this land either, it was a gift from someone for the charity – which, by the way, I didn't even *want* to start with. They had to talk me into taking this project on. As for the money I gave you for patching the tyre, well—' Luisa gave a laugh and stopped short.

Harper glanced at her with a frown. 'What about it?'

Luisa shook her head. 'I only realized how much I'd handed over when I went to get petrol on the way home,' she said. 'I'd meant to give you forty pounds but I suppose my fingers were still cold and I took out too many notes without realizing. Eighty pounds is a lot of cash for me, too, Harper. Especially now. I gave up my job to make this project work. The money for it . . . well, that's not mine either and it's not going to last forever. It wouldn't cover paying for the months of labour it's going to take to turn this place into a garden, that's for sure.'

There was a silence in which Harper looked at the scuffed toes of her shoes. 'I didn't know that,' she said, eventually. 'About someone giving you this land, I mean.'

Luisa sighed. 'Why would you? Why would anyone? That's what the consultation was for. To explain. To show that I want to involve everyone. The point is to build a garden together that will be for people who live here, not for me.'

Harper shrugged. 'You asked. That's what I've got. I mean, look at this place. All I see is a big field of mud and a load of work.'

Luisa realized that Harper was right. Just because Luisa could see the potential in this place didn't mean to say that everyone else could. Besides, she was a born gardener – to Luisa, spending time with soil and plants had once been a gift in itself. But that wasn't the case for everyone, was it? What she needed to do was get people involved, to prove that the process itself could be enjoyable, not merely the end result. But how could she do that without getting people involved? It was a Catch-22 situation and her six months were ticking away.

Luisa blinked as the flash of an idea occurred to her. She pulled out her iPad and looked at the calendar.

'Easter!' she said.

Harper frowned at her. 'What?'

'Easter weekend. It's two weeks away.'

'Yeah? And?'

'And we need to order a sack or two of seed potatoes.'

Harper eyed her as if she'd gone completely insane. 'If you say so,' she said.

'Traditionally, Easter is when potatoes are planted,' Luisa

explained. 'Good Friday, to be precise. We can turn that into a way to get people involved. Make it an open day. We'll call it ... a Potato Planting Party. People can come along and we'll give them their own seed potato, which they can plant themselves. We'll have little labels for each one that we can put names on so that they can keep coming back to check on the progress of their plants, and then when they're ready to lift they can do that themselves, too. I think if we pitch it right it could really encourage people to come into the garden and help, especially kids and parents. What do you think?'

Harper made a face, which looked to Luisa like reluctant agreement. 'Yeah,' she said. 'That might work.'

Luisa bit her lip. 'I've left it late to get the potatoes chitted, though,' she said. 'I'll have to ring around and see if anyone's got some that are already started off.'

Harper was giving her another weird look. 'I really don't understand half the things that come out of your mouth.'

'Ah ha,' Luisa said, 'well, stick with me, young padawan, and soon the student will become the master.'

Harper narrowed her eyes. 'Was that a *Star Wars* joke? No wonder Mr P's got a thing for you.'

Luisa coughed. 'What?'

The girl seemed oblivious to Luisa's sudden embarrassment – although it was equally possible she was entirely aware and just didn't care. 'He's always spouting that stuff, too. Quotes and that. It's sad.'

'No, I meant—' Luisa stopped herself, shook her head. 'Never mind.'

Harper looked out at the site again. 'Are we going to build this path, then?' she said, with a heavy sigh. 'Or is it just going to be a free-for-all where you let these potato planters tramp all over the place?'

By the end of the day they had set out the path boundaries, a three-foot-wide strip temporarily edged by twine fixed in place by beanpoles. The next day they would lay edging and several inches of sharp sand, into which the reclaimed stone could be paved.

'I've got to go,' Harper said at lunchtime, looking at her watch. 'I've got to get back to school.'

'That's fine,' Luisa said, passing her the iPad so she could mark her hours. 'Thanks for your help today.'

Harper noted her time on the spreadsheet and passed it back. 'Do you want me to do a flyer? For the Potato Planting Party?'

Luisa was surprised. This was the first time Harper had volunteered to do anything for the garden.

'Thanks,' she said. 'That would be great. Let's make it the Bank Holiday Monday — I don't want to offend or exclude anyone who has religious commitments on the Sunday. Ten in the morning to four in the afternoon, do you think?'

Harper nodded. 'All right. I'll do it tonight, then. See you tomorrow?'

Luisa smiled. 'See you tomorrow. Thanks for today, Harper. You've been great.'

She watched Harper heft her bag over her shoulder and walk swiftly away, and wondered if she were imagining a slight thawing in her attitude. She looked at the iPad and saw that in the past few days Harper had worked another ten hours off her community service. She hoped her plan for Easter weekend worked, because she couldn't imagine how she would be able to continue without even the reluctant Harper there to help her.

Luisa went into the empty gym and called around as many garden centres as she could find. Several had seed potatoes that were already beginning to sprout, and so would probably be chitted enough by Easter weekend if she picked them up straight away and had somewhere to set them. That got her thinking about what else the site needed – a greenhouse, for a start, as well as a shed where she could store equipment like forks and trowels. She didn't want to take up space in the gym permanently, however accommodating Cas insisted on being.

She retrieved a piece of scrap paper, intending to leave him a note about the Potato Planting idea. Then she paused, pen in hand, remembering that little throwaway dig of Harper's. *No wonder he's got a thing for you.* Luisa was a little dismayed to feel her heart flip over on itself again at the memory. It was ridiculous, of course, nothing but the thoughtless statement of a thoughtless teen. Cas had been helpful and supportive, but it didn't equate to anything more than that. She wondered suddenly if he had a partner, and if not why not, and then was horrified at herself for that thought even crossing her mind.

Luisa screwed up the piece of paper and tossed it into the bin beside her desk.

Chapter Twenty

'Right,' Harper called, straightening up from beneath the Mini's bonnet as she stuck her wrench in her top pocket and wiped her hands on her already grease-stained overalls. They were three sizes too big – hand-me-downs from Carl himself. She'd had to trim the legs off so she didn't keep tripping over her own feet and the waist had been pulled in with bulldog clips she'd 'borrowed' from the office. 'Give her a try, then!'

Carl was behind the wheel, the driver-side door wide open. It was after hours, but he'd let her stay late to work on the car because she was so close to this first proper test.

'Go on,' Harper urged, peering around the open bonnet.

Carl clambered out of the car. 'I can't, Harps,' he said. 'She's your car. You've got to be the one to do the honours.'

Harper grinned as she swapped places with her boss, sliding into the driver's seat, wiping her hands again before she touched the steering wheel (*as if the Mini isn't going to need a full top-to-tail clean anyway, the total piece of junk*, she thought, with more affection than it should be possible to feel for an inanimate object).

'Okay,' she said, with a deep breath. 'Here we go . . .'

Her heart was beating as if she'd already gone three rounds in the ring as she pulled out the choke and turned the key. The Mini gave a spitting sound, the engine turning over but failing to start.

'Try her again,' Carl said. 'She just needs a bit of encouragement.'

Harper tried the key again. Another chug, followed by another, and then—

Vroo-ooom!

The engine started. The Mini emitted a faint plume of smoke from her exhaust as it blew out the last of whatever dust had accumulated in it over its years of inactivity, then settled into an almost-gentle purr.

'Yes!' Harper shouted with a wild whoop of laughter, thumping her hands on the steering wheel. 'Yes, yes, *YES!*'

Carl shut the door and then leaned down to grin at her through the open window, nodding his head towards the garage's entrance.

'Go on, then,' he said. 'Take her round the block once, see how she runs. Don't go any further, mind, we don't want you getting points on your licence before she's even had her jabs, do we? And for Pete's sake, keep it under twenty!'

Harper nodded, too overwhelmed by the moment to speak. She eased the Mini out of the garage's doors and across the tarmacked forecourt to the entrance before carefully pulling out onto the street. Harper turned left, onto the usual route they used to road-test cars they'd worked on in the garage. Since she'd got her licence Carl had occasionally let her be the one to do the road tests – but this immediately felt different. This was *her* car! Sure, it was a beater – it didn't even have a uniform colour, because they'd had to replace a couple of door panels and the bonnet and she couldn't afford a re-spray. It was tiny and old and looked both of these things and yet Harper couldn't keep the grin off her face as she turned left again, pulling onto another street.

This was *her* car.

This was her *freedom*.

Well, as long as it passed its MOT, of course, and there were a few more things that needed taking care of before they could even try that. But it was running far more smoothly than she would have expected. The tyres were good, she'd checked each tread herself. Lights were functioning, indicators were good, exhaust had stopped chugging out smoke. No odd knocking, no rattling, no whine of a fan belt about to go.

She was still grinning when she pulled back onto the garage's forecourt in front of Carl and switched off the engine.

'Well,' Carl said, 'how does it feel?'

'*She* feels great,' Harper told him, patting the Mini's roof as she climbed out of the car. 'I didn't want to come back!'

Her boss laughed. 'Sounds good. You've done an amazing

job, Harps, really. You're one hell of a mechanic, you know that?'

'Thanks, boss,' Harper said, embarrassed by the praise. 'It was everyone, though, really. Couldn't have done it without all the guys – and you.'

Carl slapped her on the back. 'That's teamwork,' he said. 'No one's an island. I've never had a harder worker than you, Harper. Wish I could have you around more.'

Harper looked at him, a flicker of hope dancing through her chest. 'I could give up school,' she suggested. 'If you could give me a proper job?'

'I can't do that, Harps,' Carl said. 'For one thing, I'd have to lay one of the other lads off to afford it. Anyway, as good as you are, you still need training. I'm sorry.'

Harper looked at her semi-clean hands. 'Yeah. I get it.'

Carl leaned against the wall for a moment, sticking his hands in his pockets. 'Here's the thing, though,' he said. 'I've been thinking about how else we might make it work.'

Harper looked up at him. 'Really?'

'There might be a way for me to take you on as an apprentice here and give you practical training while you're also attending college part-time.'

Harper found herself shifting from foot to foot. There must be a 'but' here somewhere, mustn't there? There always was when things started sounding good.

'I'll have to look at how to get this place set up with an apprenticeship scheme,' he went on. 'But if I can make it work you could be the first student we take on. You can study up at Carlisle or down at Barrow for the exam stuff. Everything else you can do here. You've got a real way with cars, Harper. And I'm not going to lie, we need some fresh blood. Kids who can learn and understand all the new tech if we're going to survive. It's going to be coming thick and fast in the next few years. What do you think?'

She swallowed, suddenly unable to breathe properly. What did Harper *think*? She thought all her Christmases had come at once.

'I say where do I sign?' she said, trying not to sound as if the entire rest of her life depended on the outcome of this conversation.

Carl chuckled and straightened up. 'Not so fast, Verstappen,' he said. 'First you've got to make sure you get the grades you need for the course and I've got to work out where the money from the scheme is supposed to come from, because I don't have it.'

'Oh,' Harper said, kicking herself. Of course it wouldn't be that easy. 'Right.'

'Here's the deal,' Carl said, shepherding her out of the workshop and setting about rolling down the lock-up. 'I know life isn't a bed of roses for you. Keep your nose clean, stay out of trouble, stay in school, finish your A-levels and get the grades you need for one of those courses – and we'll work out how to make this happen. You'd be an apprentice for two or three years. By then Eddie will be ready for retirement and I'll be looking to take someone on full time, full wage. How does that sound?'

Harper couldn't help the grin that broke out on her face. 'Sounds good.'

Carl slapped her on the shoulder. 'Excellent. Now I've got to get home. The baby's not been sleeping. Ava must be tearing her hair out by now.'

For days afterwards, Harper was on cloud nine. Sure, she had to finish out another year of school, which was rubbish, but she was already at the top of her classes. She believed Carl when he said they'd work out a way to make it happen. She'd looked at the grades she'd need to get onto a Mechanical Engineering course. Harper knew she could get them, easy as breathing. All she had to do was keep going. A few more weeks and she'd be done with the garden project: she'd no longer owe anyone a thing. She could concentrate on school and getting Mr P's car into decent working order, because with it on the road she could get to and from college.

Finally, she thought, *everything is coming up roses. Everything is going to be okay.*

She spent the whole of Saturday at the garden site, helping to set the path of bricks into the sharp sand that Luisa had lain herself the day before. It was going to take hours, but for once Harper didn't mind. If she stayed there all day that'd be another six hours at least off her community service.

'Harper! Great to see you!'

It was Mr P. He walked onto the site like the Pied Piper of Hamlin, the club kids straggling along behind him as he strode through the gate.

'Mr P,' she said. 'No club today?'

He looked over to Luisa, who was busy heaving bits of brick into a wheelbarrow, and gave her a wave. 'Thought the time would be better spent if we helped you two out,' he said. 'How are things with you? I feel like it's been a long time since you've been to the club.'

'Fine,' she said. 'You know – busy. But good busy.'

'Yeah?' Mr P smiled. 'I'm glad. Do you think you might have time to come back for a few sessions over the Easter holiday, though? We miss you. And I could do with your help in the run-up to our exhibition day in summer.'

Harper actually smiled at that. 'Maybe. No promises, okay? But maybe.'

He grinned. 'I'll take it. For now.'

The day was actually fun, especially with Mr P and all the kids there. Chaotic, yes, but fun all the same. Luisa was even happy to let the littles help out, despite the fact that Harper had to reposition every single brick that one of them put down, just to make it straight. Still, what did that matter? She could see how happy the kids were to feel included, to be part of what was going on. Maybe this whole garden idea wasn't completely stupid after all.

It made Harper wish that she could have brought Max with her to help out, too, but he'd never have been able to deal with all the raucous noise that went with the day's activities. Besides, he was still avoiding her. Thinking about her brother and the current state of their relationship was enough to put a dent in Harper's good mood, but then she considered that, in a year, things would be better. She'd be at college, she'd be training properly. She smiled to herself just thinking about the fact that there were now possibilities where before had just been a black void of nothing.

'Penny for them?'

It was Luisa. She knelt down in the soil beside Harper, but Harper shook her head. 'Nothing.'

'Well, thanks for your help today. Look at what we've managed so far already! I thought it would take us far longer.'

Harper looked up and, sure enough, they were more than half way along the winding route of the path they had set out over the previous days. The red bricks, broken and uneven as they were, had come together to make something complete, attractive.

'It looks really good,' Harper said, surprised.

'It does, doesn't it? I'm so grateful for your help, Harper.'

Harper shrugged. 'I have to be here,' she pointed out.

Luisa laughed. 'I know. But that doesn't make me less grateful. Right, I'm going to send JC and Siddig off to the corner shop to get ice creams. Any preference?'

'Ice cream?' Harper asked, incredulous. 'In April?'

Luisa shrugged, looking up at the sky. 'The sun is out! Anyway, that's what the kids decided they wanted. You can have something else if you want.'

'No,' Harper said. 'A Cornetto would be good. Strawberry. Thanks.'

Luisa got to her feet. 'Good choice. Classic.'

She went to walk away and Harper was filled with the sudden, unexpected need to say something. 'Luisa?'

She stopped and looked back at Harper. 'Yeah?'

Harper got up and dusted off the knees of her jeans. 'The person who didn't want you to knock down the factory wall. I think I know who it is.'

A look of surprise crossed Luisa's face. 'Oh?'

'I think her name is Kath. She was at the consultation – she was the one who said she wanted to say her piece but then left when . . . when Darren did his thing?' Harper took a breath. 'She's one of my neighbours. I mean, I don't know exactly where she lives, except that it's one of the yards that has pots in it.'

Luisa took this in for a moment. 'Do you know why she didn't want the factory wall to come down?'

'No,' Harper said. 'Sorry.'

Luisa gave her a smile. 'Thanks, Harper.' She took a breath and then said, 'Hey, come and look at this, would you?'

Harper followed Luisa across the empty earth to one of the saplings they'd put in. She crouched down beside it and pointed. Harper bent to see what she was pointing at and saw a small green leaf just beginning to sprout.

'Some of the others are putting out new growth already, too,' Luisa said. 'They're obviously happy here. Isn't that great?'

Harper felt herself smile. 'Yeah,' she said. 'Yeah, it really is.'

Luisa got to her feet again. 'Thanks for letting me know

about your neighbour. I think I'll go and see if I can get her to talk to me.'

Harper frowned. 'Really? You're not going to finish the path?'

Luisa dusted off her hands and looked back across the site. 'I think you can handle it on your own, can't you? You've got this little team of willing volunteers. Just tell them what you need. I'll try not to be long.'

'Me?' Harper said, doubtfully. Luisa was leaving her in charge? Although she wasn't really, of course. Mr P was here, wasn't he?

'Sure,' Luisa said. 'And don't let Mr Pattanyús slack off. Ice cream first, then back to work, okay? Crack the whip if you need to.'

Harper stared at Luisa in surprise. Luisa gave her a wink and set off towards the gate, calling for the boys as she pulled her wallet out of her pocket.

Chapter Twenty-one

Luisa didn't know what house she was looking for, but Harper had given her the name of the street and had said that there were pots of flowers in the front garden. She traversed the road from one end to the other before beginning to knock on doors. There were only a handful of homes that fitted Harper's description. The first three doors she knocked on were a bust – the first there was no answer at all, the second and third were not the right people and looked at Luisa as if she might be vaguely insane.

The fourth house she called on had a small front yard full of neatly kept plant pots flourishing with the massed colourful heads of winter pansies interspersed by tulips preparing to bloom. One pot looked as if it had been blown over by the wind – shards of broken terracotta and dark soil had been swept up and piled beside the low fence that divided the property from next door. Luisa wondered if the broken pieces were being kept for use as drainage in a new pot.

She knocked on the door and stepped back, slightly nervous as footsteps echoed towards her.

The door opened and there she was. The woman who had come to the consultation apparently ready for a fight, but who had ended up leaving without either hearing what Luisa had to say or expressing her own thoughts. They stared at each other for a second, the woman's face creasing in a deep frown. She was wearing a pair of navy slacks and a cerise pink jumper, the pink a sharp pop of bright colour against the drab backdrop of concrete. She fitted well with her flowers.

'Hello,' Luisa said, awkwardly. 'I'm sorry to bother you. I'm Luisa MacGregor, from—'

'Yes,' the woman said. 'I know who you are.'

'I'm sorry to seem rude,' Luisa said. 'But is your name Kath? Harper Dixon told me—'

'It's Mrs Larkspur,' the woman said, still stony faced. 'Was there something you wanted? I need to get on with making my husband's lunch.'

'The thing is,' Luisa said, 'I get the impression that you're offended by what's happening on the factory site. That wasn't my intention. I'd like to find out why, and whether there's something I can do to remedy the situation.'

A man's voice called from somewhere inside the house. 'Kath? What are you doing out there?'

'Nothing, Arthur,' she called back over her shoulder, holding the door a little closed as if wanting to shield the owner of the voice from Luisa. 'Look, I really don't have time for this,' she said. 'I've got to go.'

'I'm sorry for calling without warning,' Luisa said. 'Would there be a better time? Can I come back?'

Mrs Larkspur sighed. 'Why? Really, I don't know what you want from me.'

Luisa looked around the small front yard, at the vibrant bursts of colourful flowers, so well looked after. 'What I'd love is for you to be involved in the garden,' she said. 'You've obviously got green fingers and that's really what the project is about – giving people here a chance to grow what they want in a space they can think of as their own. Doesn't that appeal?'

'Kath!' called the voice again. 'Are you there?'

'Look—' the woman began, clearly harried.

'It's you who left the flowers against the factory wall, isn't it?' Luisa asked quickly. This clearly wasn't the right time but if Luisa didn't say what she'd come to say now there probably wouldn't be another chance. 'I didn't find them until we had already removed the wall. I've tried to locate information about why someone might put them there but I couldn't find anything. I'm sorry if that was upsetting for you, it would never have been my intention. But we've retained the sandstone and I wondered what you thought about using some of it in a memorial garden—'

'*Kath!*' It was a shout this time, loud and sudden enough to make the name's owner jump. 'I need you *now!*'

'I've got to go,' the woman said, shutting the door in Luisa's face. The burble of voices continued inside, rising and falling as Luisa walked away.

*

Luisa tried to hide her disappointment as she headed back to the garden square. It was her own fault for doorstepping someone who had already shown themselves to be hostile. It was obvious that Kath Larkspur had her own problems. Still, it weighed on Luisa that the garden had detractors before it had even really got started.

'Hey, Miss MacGregor!'

She looked up at the shout, which was echoed by several other voices. It was Sally, waving to her from the other side of the site fence. The girl was sitting cross-legged on the tarmac where the skips had stood, eating her ice cream. The rest of the kids were congregated around her, doing the same. They variously waved and shouted as Luisa made her way into the garden.

'Hey everyone,' she said. 'Good ice cream?'

'Great!' was the general consensus.

'Thanks for your help today,' she went on. 'Will you come to the Potato Planting Party next week? I'll have a potato for each of you, and a name tag!'

There was another chorus of yeses as Luisa looked at them sitting on the ground. She made a mental note that however the garden panned out, there would be a need for ample seating incorporated into the designs if she wanted to encourage people to visit. She looked across the site to where Cas and Harper were still working, patchworking the bricks to make the last short stretch of path.

Cas looked up with a wide smile as she approached and Luisa was beset by a strange sense of déjà vu, a vague notion of a memory flitting through her mind. It unsettled her – she had no history with this man or this place, so how could there be any sense of remembrance for her here? She shook it off, though it lingered, nebulous in her periphery as she returned the smile.

'Harper's just been telling me some amazing news,' Cas said, his enthusiasm written across his face. 'Haven't you?'

Luisa looked at the girl, who shrugged and looked away as if determined to maintain her cool nonchalance, though there was the slight hint of a smile on her face.

'Come on,' Cas urged. 'Tell Luisa about it.'

'Why would she care?' Harper countered. 'It's got nothing to do with her.'

Cas raised his hands in slightly exaggerated exasperation. 'Trust me. She'll be happy for you, same as I am.'

Harper rolled her eyes. 'Carl at the garage is trying to set me up on an apprenticeship scheme at his place,' she said, 'once I've finished school.'

'That's fantastic,' Luisa said. 'Really, Harper, what great news. I'm so pleased for you.'

'There, you see?' Cas said. 'It's brilliant, Harper, I'm so proud of you. Assuming you want to do it?'

Harper's cheeks had taken on a faint tint at Cas's words. 'Yeah,' she mumbled. 'Yeah, I do. If Carl can make it work.'

'Is there anything we can help with to make that happen?' Luisa asked. 'If he needs references for you, I can do that.'

Harper gave her a strange look. 'What sort of reference?'

'Well, sometimes schemes like that want assurances that

they're taking on students that will put in the effort,' Luisa said. 'I'd be happy to write one for you that explains what a hard worker you are and how helpful it's been to have you working with me.'

'Right.' Harper frowned a little, as if she wasn't sure what to say to that. 'Thanks. I think mostly I have to have the right A-level grades, though.'

'Ah ha,' Cas said. 'Does that mean . . .' He wiggled his eyebrows at her, a comical expression that made Luisa laugh.

Harper sighed, but there was a smile hiding beneath the impatient exhale. 'Yeah, yeah. What do you want me to say? That you were right? Well, there you go, Mr P. You were right. Staying on at school is the right thing to do and I'm going to make sure I get the grades I need. Okay?'

Cas grinned. 'I was hoping for "You're a genius, Mr P, and I'm sorry I never acknowledged that before", but sure. I'll take "Okay".'

Harper shook her head and looked back down the brick path that hadn't existed when they all arrived this morning. 'We did good work today.'

The boxing club kids had finished their ice creams and were fooling around at the other end of the garden, their laughter echoing over the bare earth as they played some variation of tag.

'We really did,' Luisa agreed.

'What's next, then?' Harper asked. 'What else needs preparing for your weird Potato Planting Party thing?'

'Well,' Luisa said, hiding her surprise. 'I've bought a

greenhouse. That way on the open day we can get people planting other seeds, too, and start them off indoors. I'm going to pick it up tonight. It would be great if we could get that up as soon as possible – it's at least a two-person job, though, so I will need help.'

Harper dusted her hands off. 'Fine. What about tomorrow?'

'Sunday? I've already had you all of Saturday, I don't want to take your whole weekend.'

Harper shrugged. 'I'd rather get it done,' she said. 'Next week's the last week of school. I want to make sure I'm on top of everything before the Easter break.'

Luisa glanced at Cas, who grinned and crossed his arms.

'Okay,' Luisa said. 'Tomorrow it is then. Thanks, Harper.'

Chapter Twenty-two

A bright, sunny Sunday morning found Luisa on her way to Collaton early, having arranged to meet Harper at the site at nine. Her phone rang as she drove and Luisa glanced at the name on the screen to see that it was Harper calling. She smiled and tapped her Bluetooth earpiece.

'Harper!' she said. 'I'm on my way. Hope to be with you by nine o'clock. It feels like a proper spring day, doesn't it?'

Her cheerfulness was met by a pause.

'Harper? Are you there?'

'Yeah,' came the girl's voice. 'Look – I'm sorry, but I can't make it today.'

'I— Oh,' Luisa said. 'Right.'

'I'm sorry,' Harper said. 'It's just that when I checked I realized I've got a stupid essay due *before* Easter. I've been working on it all night but it's still not finished, and if I don't—'

'Of course,' Luisa said, immediately. 'I'd far rather you get that assignment delivered.'

'You won't be able to put the greenhouse up without me, though, will you?'

Luisa glanced in her rear-view mirror at the rented trailer attached to the back of the Defender and the protected greenhouse panels that were secured there. It had taken her and a guy at the depot she'd collected it from to load it the previous night.

'Don't give it another thought,' Luisa said. 'School comes first. I understand, Harper. Don't worry.'

There was another pause. 'Thanks. I just . . . I don't want to mess this up. Not now.'

Luisa smiled to herself. 'I get it. And I'm completely behind you. Okay? Anything I can do to help, let me know. If you want me to talk to Mr Pattanyús about cancelling the rest of your community hours, I will.'

'What?' Harper said. 'But then you wouldn't have me helping you in the garden, would you?'

'No,' Luisa said, 'and to be honest that would be a problem for me. You've been such a great help. But your education is more important, especially with this apprenticeship on the horizon. I mean that.'

There was another silence. 'Thanks,' Harper said, again. 'Really. Thanks. Don't talk to him yet, though. I'll see you soon, yeah?'

Luisa smiled. 'Good luck with the essay.'

After they'd hung up, Luisa debated what to do. She was already well on her way to Collaton. Harper was right, though, she didn't have a hope of putting up the greenhouse on her own. Luisa thought about who else she could call to give her a hand. She could ask Joanna, but it was Sunday and it would mean her sister having to drop whatever plans of her own she might have.

Luisa suddenly wished she had Cas's number, but they still hadn't exchanged them. Instead the notes between them had continued at least once or twice a week, or more if they hadn't crossed paths in person for a few days. Sometimes Luisa thought Cas only left her a note because there was something about the elusive communication he enjoyed as much as she did, to the extent that now when she tore off a corner of paper or turned over a discarded envelope to scrawl a reply she felt slightly illicit, though if pressed she would not have been able to explain quite why. It all felt a little bit like flirting, despite the fact that there was never anything even vaguely salacious in their exchanges. It was far more likely to be something along the lines of *Could I have the key to the bathroom supply cupboard, please?* or *When was the last meter reading taken?*

An image presented itself to her, one that had seemed to have become fixed in her subconscious, no matter how hard Luisa tried to scrub it from her mind. It was Cas as he'd been the second time they'd met, when she'd stopped in the doorway of the gym to see him pummelling that punchbag into oblivion with a power that was frankly mesmerizing. Not her usual style at all but perhaps that was the explanation: he was so unlike anyone else in her life, that was all. And it was impossible not to notice how attractive he—

Nope, Luisa told herself, cutting off that thought before it could grow to fruition. *No. Definitely not ever going there. Stop it.*

Still, even as she tried not to think about Cas, Luisa was taken back to that strange sense of déjà vu she'd experienced as she'd looked at him the day before. Except this time it wasn't Cas in the memory, it was Reuben. Reuben, with his hands in the soil of a garden, looking up at her with a sunny smile on his face and the clear light of affection in his eyes.

It hadn't been a memory of Cas, of course it hadn't. It had been Reuben. It was just that in her mind, just for a moment—

A frisson of fear poked at her heart, a sensation bordering on panic.

No. Not going there, either.

She slammed in the CD that was hanging out of the Defender's ancient player and within a couple of minutes was belting out 'Livin' on a Prayer' at the top of her lungs. She sailed into the square at Collaton with the window down despite the chill, hammering out 'You Give Love a Bad Name' as loudly as her voice would allow. She was still singing as she killed the engine and nearly jumped out of her skin when a large figure appeared beside her open window. Luisa let out a yelp.

'*Slippery When Wet*?' Cas enquired, into the sudden silence, a warm spark of laughter in his eyes.

'What are you *doing* here?' she exclaimed, one hand over her hammering heart.

171

He grinned. 'I thought you and Harper might want an extra pair of hands.'

She realized she was still staring at him. He looked good. He smelled good too, that same hint of aftershave she remembered from the day they'd first broken ground on the site.

Luisa undid her seatbelt and pushed open the door as Cas stepped back. She jumped down onto the tarmac, regretting the loss of the extra height the car seat had given her. Luisa shielded her eyes from the sun as she looked up at him.

'You really didn't need to come,' she said. 'I've already taken up too much of your weekend.'

'It's fine. There's a club session later anyway. I thought Harper would already be here, actually.'

'She just called me to say she couldn't make it after all. I was already half way here so I thought I'd come anyway.'

Cas looked at the dismantled greenhouse languishing in the trailer. 'You can't manage that by yourself.'

'No,' Luisa admitted. 'But I figured if I can at least unload it, I can find some way of putting it up in the week.'

Cas patted the trailer. 'I can give you a hand.'

Despite herself, Luisa felt something turn over in the pit of her stomach. 'Oh no,' she said, 'I can manage well enough on my own.'

'I don't doubt it,' he said, 'but I'm here now, aren't I?'

She opened her mouth to find another excuse but Cas was already heading for the gate, opening it so that she could drive the trailer inside. Luisa admitted defeat and hopped back behind the wheel to start the engine. The music roared into life again.

'Bon Jovi,' he muttered, loud enough for her to hear as she drew level with him, the look in his eye teasing despite the shake of his head. 'Really?'

She stuck her tongue out at him. It made him laugh and Luisa wished she wasn't as happy to see him as she was.

Chapter Twenty-three

Cas turned to help Luisa with the last panel only to find that she'd already lifted it from the flat-bed. He'd already known she was a grafter, but this morning she'd impressed him anew with her willingness to get her hands dirty, to do the hard work. Woe betide the person who underestimated this woman. The thought made him smile. Coming here had been a good idea, he congratulated himself. Since the final disintegration of his relationship with Annika he'd been renting a spare room from his friends Chris and Becky while he sorted out a new place of his own. As lovely as they both were and as far back as the friendship went, he hated the thought of getting in the way and outstaying his welcome, especially on a Sunday morning. At least doing something useful stopped him from wondering how he'd managed to screw up his life quite so spectacularly.

'I figured,' Luisa said, straightening up from putting down her load, cheeks flushed and a little breathless from the effort, 'that as well as the potato planting we could get people to plant other seeds, too. It's still a bit early to put things straight out, though.'

Cas surveyed what they'd just wrestled out of the trailer. 'Hence the greenhouse.'

'Hence the greenhouse,' she agreed.

'Sounds like you've got it figured out,' he said.

She blew out her cheeks. 'Do any of us ever have that? Mostly I still feel as if I'm just muddling along, hoping for the best.'

Cas smiled. 'Well,' he said, 'that's not how you seem from the outside, believe me.'

She didn't answer, looked away from him instead. He wondered where she'd gone in that moment. After another beat she turned back, blasting him with another of those smiles that Cas kept finding himself thinking about. *At least, he told himself, you don't have to feel guilty about that anymore.*

'Thanks for the help unloading,' she said. 'We can leave the panels where they are now, I think they'll be safe enough.'

'Why don't we just put it up today?' he asked.

'Really, Cas, that's not necessary,' Luisa said. 'I know how precious your time must be. I don't want to eat into it. Especially not on a Sunday morning.'

'Ah,' he said, 'but you are forgetting – it's Easter holidays soon.' Cas gave an exaggerated sigh of relief. 'In four short days I'll be free to do whatever I want for two whole weeks.'

Luisa rested her hands on her hips and smiled up at him. He realized that it would take a lot for him to get bored of seeing her face, that smile. 'Wonderful! Are you going anywhere?'

'No,' he said. 'Well, originally I was supposed to be going to Greece for a week but that ... didn't pan out.' He'd endured a brief and painfully spiky text conversation with Annika in which she'd told him that they were cancelling too close to the date of their holiday date to get much back, so she'd decided to go anyway. He didn't actually regret the break-up, but still, the edges were sharp. It was a sense of something failed, broken. 'I've nothing else planned at the moment. Besides ...'

Luisa tipped her head to one side, a quizzical look on her face.

'What?'

'I actually didn't come down here to help this morning. Or not just to help, anyway. I came to bring you a present. Being able to help was just a happy accident.'

She looked astonished. 'A present? For me?'

Cas waved a hand expansively. 'Well, it's for general gym use really.' He laughed at her puzzled expression. 'Come on, it's inside. I'll show you. Then we'll get this greenhouse up.'

She followed him into the gym, clearly mystified. When she saw the box waiting on the desk in her office, Luisa stopped dead, looking up at him in amazement.

'You bought me – us – a coffee machine?' she exclaimed.

'Ah – well, no,' he confessed. 'I didn't buy it, or at least not recently. My ex wants to get a new one for her place so told me to take this one when I packed up my stuff. It's going to be a while before I actually have a kitchen to put it in. I figured you'd have more use for it than me.'

Luisa seemed to go very still somewhere in the middle of him talking.

'If you don't want it, it's fine,' he offered. 'I'll take it to one of the charity shops in town. I just thought—'

'Oh no,' she said, looking up at him with a quick smile. 'It's really kind of you, Cas, to think of me. Of us,' she corrected herself, with an uncharacteristic awkwardness that he didn't understand. 'I just hadn't realized – I'm sorry, about – that your relationship ended recently.'

'Thanks,' Cas said. 'But it's fine. It was a long time coming. We tried to make it work for far too long. It seems ridiculous, now, that we let it go on the way we did, but there you go. It happens, doesn't it? Shall I make us a coffee?'

They took their full mugs back out onto the site and began work on the greenhouse. Cas was unsurprised when Luisa pulled a fully equipped toolkit from the back of her Land Rover, including what was clearly a well-used Makita drill.

'You've obviously done this before,' he said, as they set the frame in place.

'I'm pretty handy when it comes down to it,' she told him, hefting a six-foot girder with shocking ease. 'I like to think that in the event of an apocalypse, I'd be quite proficient at shelter-building in extreme circumstances.'

He laughed. 'I'll bear that in mind.'

Later, once the greenhouse was up, she insisted on buying him lunch to say thank you before the club session began.

Cas took her to his favourite chippy and they sat on the old harbour wall to eat, watching a lone fishing trawler chug its way through the waves. The Irish Sea was steely grey and turbulent with the changing tide. Though the sun was bright, there was a chill in the breeze. Luisa didn't seem to notice.

'I don't know enough about you,' she said, and made him relate his history to her while watching him through a veil of wind-blown hair that he kept having to stop himself from brushing back from her face.

'What made you want to be a teacher?' she asked.

He thought for a moment, looking back at the years he'd spent in the classroom. 'I'm not sure I really did want it, to begin with.'

'Well then,' she said, 'what did you want to be?'

He shrugged. 'A boxer. And I was good – up to a point. But then my dad got sick for a while. He had cancer when I was a teenager.'

She frowned. 'I'm sorry.'

'It's fine – he recovered and has been cancer-free for years now. But while he was sick I had priorities other than boxing. Dad and Mum needed me close, not spending all my time training or travelling to and from bouts. I didn't resent it. Time just ... passed me by. And I've always been a practical sort, so when I had to find a career – teaching made sense, I suppose.'

'Well, the school is lucky to have you, clearly,' she said. 'As are your students.'

Cas looked out over the water, shrugging off the praise. 'They deserve it,' he said. 'There are so many I see coming through the doors of the school and the gym with so much potential that's just ... thwarted before they even get past school age, and not through any fault of theirs. Sometimes I wish I could wave a magic wand to give them all a chance, even if it's just one. Sometimes I wonder, if I could make just one thing easier for each of them – what would that do?'

'You *are* giving them a chance,' Luisa said. 'At school and at the gym.'

He looked at her with a smile. 'Luisa. The gym only still exists because of you. If you hadn't come along when you did, I'd have run out of money by now. It would just be one more failed idea.'

'You'd have found a way to keep it going, with or without me,' she said. 'You're not the type to give up.'

He smiled at that, screwed up the paper his lunch had come in into a tight ball. 'I guess we have that in common,' he said.

'What makes you say that?'

Cas looked over at her. She had turned towards him, shifting to sit cross-legged now that she had finished her meal. She was scooping her hair back from her face with both hands, the glint of sunlight on the waves diffusing against her skin in an unearthly glow.

'You told me that you've given up your job to get this project up and running. That's some commitment. What's driving you?'

Luisa dropped her hands into her lap and turned her face in profile, looking out at the expanse of sea that stretched away from them into the haze of the horizon. For a while she was quiet.

'I told you it wasn't just me, didn't I? The charity idea. To begin with,' she said. Her voice was flat, as if she was purposefully keeping the emotion out of it. 'When it started—' She broke off, took a breath.

'Hey,' Cas said, reaching out a hand and touching her lightly on the arm. 'Sorry. I didn't mean to upset you.'

Luisa turned to look at him and her smile was now a sad one, an old one, as if it had been there for a long time. 'You didn't,' she said. 'The charity was an idea that my late husband and I came up with, when we were both still at university. But he died before—' She looked away again, pressing one hand against her chest as if holding her heart in place. 'Sorry. He's been gone a long time now. It shouldn't be this hard to think about.'

'You don't have to apologize,' Cas told her, quietly. 'Do you – want to tell me about him?'

She turned to look at him again, surprised.

'If you don't, I understand,' he said. 'But if you do . . .'

Luisa twined her hands together in her lap for a moment and then smiled. 'His name was Reuben,' she said, 'and before I met him I thought the idea of soul mates was absurd. But we just seemed to click, immediately, like we'd known each other for years. We were . . .' She trailed off, and then shrugged, as if there was nothing more to say. 'Anyway.

Everyone said we were too young to get married, but we had great plans for what we were going to accomplish together. We were just so happy, nothing was going to stop us. We got married on Christmas Eve, the year we both started our Master's degrees. But then a few months later, during one summer break, we took a holiday, climbing in the Alps. It was supposed to be our "proper" honeymoon, because we hadn't had time to have one straight after the wedding.' Her breath became sharper, her sentences shorter. 'We were both experienced climbers. It wasn't anyone's fault. But something happened. I still don't really understand what. We – we both fell. Reuben ... Reuben was hurt. I couldn't help him. I couldn't move. I couldn't *do* anything, I couldn't—' Cas watched as Luisa swallowed, hard, the motion shivering up her throat. 'No one reached us for ... well, for too long.'

'Luisa,' Cas said. 'I'm so sorry.' It was inadequate, but what else could he say to a revelation so terrible?

She glanced at him, trying to smile. 'It was a long time ago now. Recovery was hard, both physically and mentally. My life changed, in so many ways. I lost my life partner and I left my career behind before it even started. It took me a very long time to learn to cope with Reuben's death, but I did, eventually. It's been raw again recently, though, what with this sudden opportunity to try the project again. I keep thinking that Reuben should be here to do this with me. I keep thinking that—' She broke off again, shook her head. 'Really, I don't know why I'm burdening you with all of this. As if you don't already have enough on your plate without listening to me whinge.'

'Hey,' Cas said, 'I'm always happy to listen to you whinge.'

She laughed a little then and the melancholy of the moment passed into something lighter. Cas smiled at her laughter, realizing that it would make him happy to hear more of it. He'd like to ask her out, in fact, but she'd just told him of a past so tragic that she was still feeling the after-effects many years later and just being here had reopened the wound. *Not the right time*, he told himself. His split with Annika was too recent anyway. Even without that, would it be a good idea? Probably not. Luisa had sunk everything she had into this place. That's how dedicated she was to the Collaton Garden Project. The last thing he'd want to do is make her feel uncomfortable either at the garden or at the gym.

They walked back to the square and Cas waited as Luisa pulled the Land Rover out through the gate again and locked it shut behind her, passing her the key through the open window. With her in the Defender they were eye-level. For one insane moment he imagined leaning forward to kiss her. He took a step back, slid his hands into his pockets instead. *Bad idea*, he chided himself. *Very bad idea.*

'Thank you for today,' Luisa said.

'Any time,' he told her, and he meant it.

Chapter Twenty-four

Easter Monday dawned bright and clear. In fact, there had been no significant rain since the greenhouse had gone up. Luisa had spent the week carefully watering the fruit tree saplings by bucket, thinking about how right Harper had been to point out this issue. She had no idea how to solve it apart from to hope for rain in the near future. The weather reports were already suggesting that this could be the driest April on record. A comedian had made a dark joke about rewriting children's songs to fit an era of ecological disaster. It had stuck in Luisa's mind, a throwaway joke that wasn't throwaway at all.

The Collaton site was empty as she arrived in the square. This was as Luisa had expected and yet still it filled her with trepidation. If today didn't work then surely nothing would. She may as well give up.

You're just tired, she told herself. It had been a long week in which, without Harper's help, Luisa had realized exactly how much there was to do even in a garden that had yet to become anything other than dirt. Watering had been a large part of that, hauling those buckets back and forth to keep the orchard saplings alive. It was worth it to see the little trees sprouting leaf after leaf, but still. It had made her think again of Reuben. If he was here—

Luisa stopped herself there. No point dwelling on the past. She was having to remind herself of that a lot lately.

She unlocked the garden gates and left them open. Inside the greenhouse was an A-board she had painted up herself and now carried out onto the street to welcome attendees.

Collaton Community Garden

Easter Monday

Potato Planting Party

Come and plant your own potato!

All welcome!

Free event 10–4

She was carrying the folding tables she'd bought specifically for the day out of the greenhouse when Harper appeared in the open gate. She was dressed in her usual head-to-toe black.

'Harper!' Luisa called, absurdly relieved to see her.

'Hey.' The girl dumped her backpack inside the greenhouse and immediately picked up one of the folding tables. 'Sorry I'm late.'

'You're not. It's good to see you, though. How's the week been – did you get your essay finished?'

Harper glanced at her with a brief look of surprise, as if she wasn't used to being asked these kinds of questions. 'Yeah, just about. Thanks.'

'And now you've got two weeks off?'

Harper actually smiled. 'Well, if you can count a thousand assignments and a ton of reading, then yeah, I've got two weeks off.' She grew serious for a moment. 'I'll try to fit in more hours here, though. To make up for the last week.'

'You don't have to do that,' Luisa told her. 'I'm just grateful you're here today. It might have been me on my own all day, otherwise.'

'Nah, others will turn up,' Harper said, briskly, beginning to lift out the boxes of seed potatoes that Luisa had sourced for the event. She frowned slightly. 'I did try to get my little brother to come along, but . . . he didn't want to, sorry. Mr P is bound to turn up, though, isn't he, and loads of the kids from the club, too, probably.'

Luisa ignored the slight flutter in her chest at Harper's easy reference to Cas. In truth she wasn't sure whether he would appear today. Part of her was hoping he would and another part of her hoped he wouldn't. She had felt this way since they'd put up the greenhouse. It wasn't that anything bad had happened. The opposite, in fact. It had been easy to spend time with him and since that day Luisa had found herself thinking about it on more than one occasion. The second time he'd floated into her thoughts unbidden Luisa had felt a spark of shock. She'd registered what it was with a kind of horrified fear that she absolutely refused to acknowledge or contemplate. Instead, she had returned to the boundaries she had set all those weeks ago when she'd told Cas how they could make the timeshare of the gym building work. Luisa used the space during the day, made sure she left before the club began, and tried to squash the little skitter of disappointment she felt every time five o'clock came around and Cas had not appeared in the doorway of the gym.

As for Cas, he seemed to have stopped popping in early, no doubt plenty busy with his own affairs. The result was that they hadn't seen each other for the past week.

'I don't know about that,' was all she said to Harper, aiming for a levity she didn't feel. 'It's the holidays now, isn't it? They might all be away.'

She busied herself with the information boards she'd produced – A1, they would stand on the tarmac beside the tables and explain to visitors what the aims of the garden were. There was also a call for volunteers, a poster of its own in bright, bold, eye-catching colours.

Harper didn't seem to detect anything in Luisa's tone. 'I did do some research about the watering thing.'

Luisa stopped what she was doing and looked up, surprised. 'Really?'

Harper shrugged. 'Yeah. There hasn't been any rain, has there? It made me think so I just did some googling and stuff.'

Luisa hefted out another box of potatoes. They had sprouted well in the warmth of the greenhouse, putting out little shoots in their eagerness to grow. 'What did you learn?'

'Well, the only real way to get water on tap from the source is to drill a borehole,' Harper said. 'But that would cost a lot.'

Luisa screwed up her nose. 'No other options?'

Harper leaned on one of the tables. 'Kind of.'

'What do you mean?'

Harper shrugged. 'I'm interested in ecology and stuff. I know, it's weird what with me being a petrol-head, but—'

Luisa smiled. 'I don't think it's weird. We're all more than one thing. If we weren't, we'd be boring, one-dimensional people, right?'

Harper gave her a look that might have been suggesting that she already thought Luisa was exactly that, but didn't say it. 'I read somewhere once that when you've got a problem where you're lacking something, you need to look at what you've got too much of and work out whether there's a way to get the thing you need from the thing you don't,' she said, instead. 'It doesn't always work, but it makes you think clearly about what you have, about what you need and about what you waste. It's also a way to look at a problem from a completely different perspective.'

Luisa listened carefully. It was the most Harper had ever said to her in one go. 'Sounds pretty smart,' she said, wary of interrupting the girl's flow.

'Maybe. Anyway, I really hate people wasting food. I mean, there's loads of crap happening in the world, I know, but that really gets my back up. Like, it's not that hard to just not be wasteful, is it? There are people who can't afford to eat but other people can't be bothered to use what they have? How is that okay? But still, so much food ends up in the bin and then in landfill. Tons of it. *That*'s what we've got too much of. And that got me thinking, because that's where there's water. Right? There must be loads of water in that thrown-out food that also ends up at the dump. Not just in old fruit and veg, either, but *everything*. And sure, it goes back into the ground eventually, but it takes all sorts of stuff that probably shouldn't be going into the soil with it, right? Pesticides and crap. Chemical preservatives. Oil. All sorts.'

'I'd never thought of that,' Luisa admitted. 'Do you think it would be possible to extract that water first, somehow?'

'Yup,' Harper said. 'Actually someone's already worked out how.' She took out her phone and thumbed into her Google app before holding it up.

Luisa leaned over and looked at the webpage. It was for an industrial compactor unit that reduced food waste by extracting the water.

'Wow,' Luisa said. 'I've never seen anything like that before.'

'It's not perfect,' Harper said. 'It's for indoor use only. It's about space-saving more than anything else, because commercial kitchens have to pay for waste collection, so this way they can fit more in their bins. The unit compacts the food by extracting the water, which saves space. I guess you could use the water to flush a toilet or something, but you'd need a way to purify it properly if you wanted to use it for, like, drinking or cooking or whatever. But it proves it can be done, doesn't it?'

'It does,' Luisa agreed. 'There must be a way to make it more user-friendly, mustn't there? Cheaper, for a start.' The price tag on even the smallest unit was upwards of £10,000.

'I guess so,' Harper said. 'No idea how, though.'

'I bet you could work it out,' Luisa told her. 'Design a waste food recycling unit for the garden that produces clean water as an end product.'

'Me?' Harper said, with an incredulous laugh. 'I wouldn't even know where to start.'

Luisa shrugged. 'Sure you do.' She waved at the phone Harper still held. 'Take what you've already found and use it to invent something better.'

'Yeah,' Harper said, 'because I've got such a lot of spare time on my hands, haven't I?'

Luisa was about to acknowledge the point when they heard a noise behind them and turned to see a group of kids coming through the gate. Some Luisa recognized as belonging to the boxing club, but others she didn't. Cas wasn't with them.

'Showtime,' Harper said.

Chapter Twenty-five

The next couple of hours passed in a whirlwind as Luisa showed the kids how to plant their potatoes. First they marked out long lines with twine so that each plant would grow with plenty of defined space between the drills, making them easier to reach without trampling when it was time to harvest. Harper was in charge of helping people choose a potato and labelling it with their name and the variety.

'When the leaves start appearing, we'll begin to earth them up,' Luisa explained, raising her voice so that the little group could hear her over the slight breeze that rustled over the empty site. 'That means gradually making a mound around the plant. That helps to keep the potatoes closest to the surface from exposure to sunlight, which would make them go green. Has anyone here planted potatoes before?'

There were a few raised hands. 'My grandma has an allotment in Worki'ton,' said Mo, who had brought along his younger brother and sister as well. 'We go to help.'

'Excellent! Then you'll know exactly what to do. It'd be great if you could help some others.'

The planting party got under way. Luisa spent most of the next couple of hours on her knees in dry dirt, only getting to her feet to greet new arrivals. It still wasn't quite the turnout she'd been hoping for, but it wasn't nothing.

'What about watering?' Mo asked, crouching down beside her as Luisa helped a young mother called Hayley show her toddler how to gently cover a Maris Piper with soil.

'We'll leave that until the end,' Luisa said, 'because otherwise—'

There was a collective cheer from the boxing club kids. Luisa looked up and saw Cas laughing and waving to his students as he approached. She ignored the sudden, irrational flutter in her chest and focused on brushing dirt from tiny hands.

'You're late, Mr P!' Siddig shouted. 'Did you oversleep?'

'Yeah,' Mo shouted. 'You're always telling us off for that, Mr P! You should set an alarm.'

'I did not oversleep,' Cas called back, entering into the spirit of the jibes. 'I do actually have a life away from you lot, you know!'

There was more good-natured jeering at this apparently incomprehensible idea, as well as a few 'Oooohs', as if Cas had said something racy. Cas waved to Harper but headed for Luisa, dropping to a crouch beside her.

'Hi,' he said, with a smile. 'I understand this is the place to come if I want to plant my own potato?'

Luisa laughed. 'That's right. I didn't expect to see you today.'

He shrugged a little, eyes warm. 'I wanted to see how things were going.'

'And plant a potato.'

'And plant a potato,' he agreed. He looked at her for moment as if he were assessing her face and then said, 'You've got dirt, here.' He reached out to brush it off himself and then hesitated, as if thinking better of it. He indicated the smudge on his own cheek, instead.

'Oh,' Luisa said, faintly embarrassed, although by the end of the day she'd surely be covered in dust from head to toe. She wiped her cheek with the back of her hand and got to her feet, stumbling a little on the uneven ground. Cas reached out to steady her and she grabbed his hand as she regained her balance, then realized what she'd done and let go, feeling unreasonably flustered, annoyed with herself.

'It's a good turnout,' he observed after a moment of slightly awkward silence.

'It is,' Luisa said, 'although I was hoping for more, if I'm honest.'

Cas looked past her towards the site entrance. 'Well, here's a few people now.'

Luisa turned to look and saw the familiar but not particularly welcome sight of Kath Larkspur standing just inside the gate. She was flanked by three friends – Luisa thought they were probably the same people who had accompanied her to the first consultation. None of them looked very friendly.

'Oh no,' Luisa muttered.

'Trouble?' Cas asked.

'Maybe,' she sighed. 'At the very least I suspect I'm about to get a dressing down I could do without.'

'Ah, well,' Cas said. 'Keep your chin up and don't let 'em see you're afraid, that's my advice.'

She looked at him with a spark of amusement. 'That's how you deal with your classes, is it?'

He grinned widely. 'Always. Works every time.'

Luisa felt unsettled all over again and this time it wasn't because she'd nearly ended up flat on her face at his feet. He was wearing a white shirt that he'd left open at the neck and faded blue jeans – he looked good, happy and relaxed. *Get a grip, for goodness' sake*, Luisa told herself. She turned away, towards the new arrivals.

'Maybe you could help Harper with refreshments?' she called back to Cas, over her shoulder.

'Will do.'

Luisa approached Mrs Larkspur, preparing herself for the worst. If she was going to be shouted at, it was probably best to get it over and done with. The woman stood inside the gate, looking around. The friends she had come with drifted towards the tables and the information boards as Luisa got closer.

'Mrs Larkspur? Hello again.'

The woman's gaze reached Luisa. She looked tired rather than angry, Luisa realized. She pulled a folded piece of paper from her pocket – one of the flyers that Luisa had posted through letterboxes in the area, including hers.

'You're persistent, I'll say that much for you,' she said.

Luisa risked a smile. 'I thought it was worth a try,' she said. 'We didn't really have much of a chance to talk last time we met.'

The woman nodded. She indicated the ribbon of new-from-old path that had been set into the soil. It'd had a decent workout today and was beginning to look more bedded-in. 'You've used the old stone for that?'

'Some of it,' Luisa admitted. 'The wall simply couldn't stay standing, it was too unstable, but I wanted to incorporate it into the garden somehow. There's more left over that could be used for something else.'

'A memorial garden, you said.'

'That was one idea, yes. But any suggestions are welcome.'

Kath Larkspur returned her gaze to Luisa. She was quiet for a moment, assessing. 'I owe you an apology,' she said then, abruptly. 'For how I behaved, that time at the gym and at the house. There's no excuse for rudeness.'

'Oh,' Luisa said, surprised. 'There's no apology necessary. I'm only sorry for whatever it was I did that caused upset. I waded in without knowing a lot about the area, I know that. I should have been more circumspect and done more research.'

The woman looked again to the bare corner where the factory wall had once stood. 'You didn't do anything much, to tell the truth. I knew that old wall would come down sooner or later. It were just a shock when it finally did, that's all. My old granddad used to work here, you see, when the place was still up and running. It were my grandparents raised me, mostly. My grandma and I used to walk up and meet him from work when he'd finished his shift. They're both buried in the cemetery up Whitehaven way, but the bus that I used to take up there to visit them doesn't run so often anymore. It's too far to walk, especially since I can't leave Arthur for long now. That's why I started bringing flowers here instead. It seemed like the next best thing.' She issued a sigh and then changed tack with barely a breath. 'Arthur doesn't mean to be difficult. I don't think he realizes how he's being. It's just that since the accident he's in pain and frustrated and sometimes he takes it out on whoever's closest. I wouldn't want you to think badly of him, though. He's a good man.'

'Well, perhaps once the garden is a little more established, he'd like to visit,' Luisa suggested. 'I'm keen to make sure it's accessible to everyone.'

Mrs Larkspur looked at her again and gave a slow nod. 'That might work, what with it being so close. Anyway, your memorial garden idea – that's a good one, I think. Can't just be me who'd appreciate it.'

'No, I'm sure you're right.' Luisa smiled. 'Perhaps we can talk about what you think it should look like? I'd love a chance to discuss ideas. Any help you can offer would be appreciated.'

'All right,' Mrs Larkspur agreed. 'I can't stay long, though. I'll have to get back soon.'

'Have you got time to plant a potato?' Luisa suggested. 'There are plenty left.'

Mrs Larkspur actually laughed at that. 'Can't remember the last time I planted a tattie,' she said. 'Did you know that folk around here have been trying to get the council to set up allotments for years?'

Luisa blinked in surprise. 'No, I didn't. Really?'

'Oh yes. And honestly, seeing this patch of land now, it beats me why none of us thought about trying it right here in the first place. I suppose it's easy to get blind to what we see every day. To me this has always been "the factory", even as it crumbled into dust, all except that last blessed wall. But change is inevitable. There's nowt any of us can do about that except steer it good or steer it bad, and I know which I'm on the side of here.' Kath nodded towards the group of people she'd come with. 'Come on, let me introduce you to some of my friends.'

Behind them the sudden roar of an engine echoed across the site. A black car, something sleek and fast, turned into the square. It was flanked by motorcycles, four of them, one at each of the car's wheels. The riders were all in black, too, their helmet visors closed and as impenetrable as the carapaces of beetles. Luisa watched warily as the car sped around two corners of the square and slid to a halt outside the open garden gates. The motorbikes continued to circle the square, the noise from their engines deliberately deafening. The car window opened, one smooth motion that lowered it to the tune of the pounding bassline emanating from within.

Luisa recognized the driver. It was the same man who

had interrupted the first garden consultation in the gym. Darren. Darren Dixon.

No one inside the garden said a word. Darren didn't get out of the car. He sat there for a moment instead, a slow smirk spreading across his face as he looked past Luisa and Kath. Luisa turned to see Cas, standing beside Harper. Both of them were impassive, though Harper's jaw was jutting in silent fury and abject defiance. Luisa could see the tension radiating from Cas, too, as he and Darren glared at each other. Darren reached up, took the stub of his cigarette from between his lips and flicked it to the ground before sliding the window closed again. The car's engine revved and the bikes completed their turn of the square to flank it again as it sped away in a flurry of dry dust, a cacophonous and absurdly performative motorcade.

In the wake of its departure, silence reigned over the garden. Luisa shut her eyes briefly. She knew what would happen next. Everyone would leave. The day – and as a result the garden, most probably – would be over, in the same way that first failed consultation had been.

She felt a hand on her arm. It was Kath Larkspur.

'Ignore them,' the older woman advised, the look in her eyes steely. 'Give that sort an inch and they'll take a mile. Wastrel cowards, the lot of 'em. Show me where you're thinking of having this memorial spot.'

Chapter Twenty-six

It was weird, Harper thought as she made her way home, but the day had been fun, right up until that loser had shown up. Darren. What did he *want*? To pretend to be the big man he never would be? Had it been for her benefit, or for Mr P's? Maybe neither, she mused. Her cousin was the sort who just wanted to show off to an audience – any audience.

Harper stopped at the corner shop to top up the meter key with her week's wages from the garage. She was glad she'd be able to fit a few more hours in over the next couple of weeks. The Mini was nearly finished but she still needed to pay for the MOT and put money aside if she was going to have any hope of affording petrol.

On her way out again she paused in front of the rack of magazines. The ones about gardening – pale colours and curly fonts in their titles – all had images of pastel roses and blowsy peonies on their covers. One had a little packet attached to its front. THREE FREE BULBS WITH THIS ISSUE! shouted the banner strapped across it. Harper picked it up and went back to the counter to pay for it, thinking that it would give her a reason to talk to her brother. He'd been distant for weeks now and Harper had yet to work out where he'd been going those times he disappeared without a trace.

'Max?' she called, when she reached home, a familiar ritual that hadn't waned despite her brother's determined silence in the wake of his last, terrible meltdown at her expense. She waited at the bottom of the stairs for a moment but couldn't be sure if he was even in.

Harper put the key into the meter, then went into the kitchen and dumped the magazine on the table. For a moment she leaned over it, squeezing her eyes shut. She didn't know what to do. Things with Max were the worst they had ever been. She had a terrible feeling that he was spinning away from her faster and faster. She didn't know how to stop it, how to bring him back into her orbit, how to return their relationship to the little binary system they had always been. She didn't even really make dinner for him anymore. He'd suddenly decided he could do it himself. She'd tried to talk to his school but they said they could only consult with a legal parent or guardian, and if Harper opened a can of worms by explaining how incompetent their dad was it would be game over.

A door slammed above her head and suddenly there were Max's footsteps running down the stairs. Harper's heart lifted as her brother came into the kitchen.

'Hi!' she said. 'Shall I make dinner? Oh, hey – look, I got you a present! It's got free bulbs with it. I thought that at the weekend we could go and get some compost and pots and plant them together?'

Max glanced at the magazine and his expression turned into one of disdain. 'They're tulip bulbs.'

'Okay,' Harper said, cautiously, not understanding his ire.

'They have to be planted before winter,' he told her, as if she were the most stupid person in the world for not knowing this simple fact. 'They can't go in until autumn now.'

'Oh,' Harper said. 'Sorry. Well, maybe the magazine will be useful anyway?'

Max brushed past her and went to the fridge, opening it to pull out a yoghurt. It was then that she realized what he was holding in his hand.

'Where did you get that?' she asked, shocked at the sight of her brother with a mobile phone.

He put it in his pocket and backed away from her as if she might take it from him. 'My friend gave it to me.'

'What friend? The same friend who got you the compost?'

Max gave a half shrug and turned away to get a spoon from the drawer. He tore open the yoghurt and practically inhaled it. Harper felt a sinking feeling in the pit of her stomach.

'Max, please tell me. Where did you get the phone?'

Her brother finished the yoghurt and dumped it and the spoon in the sink without rinsing either. Harper wondered briefly if someone had switched Max with an imposter. She tried to catch his arm as he passed her again, tried to make him stop and talk to her, but he shook her off and as he did so the phone peeped – a text message coming in.

Max took off for the front door as if he were a dog answering a whistle. Harper followed. As Max shoved his feet into his shoes Harper wrenched open the door to see a familiar black car standing outside the gate with its engine running and its boot open. A figure she recognized was decanting sacks of compost from the car's trunk, hefting them over the garden wall into a pile on the grey concrete oblong beyond.

'*Darren?*'

Her cousin looked up with an oily smile that flicked the cigarette between his lips up towards his nose. He dropped the last sack of compost into place and plucked the sagging roll-up from his mouth with two yellowed fingers.

'Harps.'

Max ran past her, heading for the car. When he got there he pulled open the passenger door and jumped in.

For a second Harper was frozen in shock. Then she plunged through the gate and reached for the passenger door handle, but Max quickly slammed down the lock. He stared up at her through the window, his jaw jutting defiantly, his eyes cold and angry.

'Max,' she said. 'Get out of the car, right now.'

'He can't do that, little girl,' Darren said, slamming shut the boot and coming around the side of the car to stand in front of her. 'I'm a good boss, see, I'll even come to pick him up, but I don't like lateness. He's got to go to work.'

For a moment Harper couldn't breathe. 'Max is working for *you*? Doing what?'

Darren gave an indulgent smile. 'Don't get your knickers all twisted, now. He's just a lookout.'

'He's only nine!'

'I'm ten in two months!' Max yelled, his voice muffled from inside the car.

Harper felt the colour drain right out of her face. 'Let him out of the car,' she said, unsteadily. 'I won't let you do this, Darren. I won't let you use him. I'll go to the police, I'll—'

Darren leaned towards her, threat leaking from every pore. 'Oh, will you now? Well then. I guess they're going to find out a few things about you too, then, eh? How light your fingers are, for a start. And maybe how that creepy paedo teacher of yours always goes out of his way to get you off. I've always thought it weird, the way he hangs around with little kids every free moment he's got. There's got to be a reason for that, right? A reason why he's so keen to help out? Especially if it means aiding and abetting criminal behaviour in the young. Sounds pretty dodgy to me.'

Harper clamped her teeth together so firmly it hurt. She couldn't believe this was happening. She'd tried so hard to keep Max out of all kinds of trouble. Darren had taken it all apart without even having to try.

'Please,' she said, and hated the sound of herself begging, had promised herself she'd never beg for anything from anyone. 'Please, Darren. Just leave Max alone. Please.'

Darren sighed heavily and shook his head, as if this boon

was beyond his power to give. 'But he's got a debt, Harps, that's the thing. I've been helping the little gadgie out, haven't I?' He nodded at the pile of compost sacks. 'That's not even the tip of the iceberg. And there's the phone, and—'

'I'll pay the debt,' she said. 'Just tell me how much it is. I'll get you the money. As long as you promise you'll never talk to Max again.'

'No!' Max screamed from inside the car, fists against the glass, angry breath misting the window. 'He's my *friend*! He's *family*!'

Darren grinned again, attention fixed on Harper. 'It's not that kind of debt, Harps,' he said, cheerfully. 'You can't pay it back. It's got to be worked off. That's the deal we have, isn't it, lad?'

'Yeah!' Max yelled back. 'I want to work for Darren! I *want* to!'

Darren shrugged, spreading his hands. 'There you go,' he said, as if the matter was done with. 'Willing workers. You can't beat 'em.'

'I'll do it,' Harper said, and as she said the words she felt something falling away from her, very fast, and thought it was probably that sudden, ridiculous spark of hope she had so recently harboured for herself and for the future. As if there had ever been a future for her other than the one she was staring at right here, right now. 'I'll do it, Darren. I'll be better at it, you know I will. I'm smart, I'm quick. I know the area like the back of my hand. Max,' she nodded towards the car window, but couldn't bear to look at her brother's face and see the hate there, aimed at her, 'he's carrying too much baggage. He's already been in trouble at the shop and he's nicked stuff from the neighbours. They'll notice him if he's hanging around where he shouldn't be. But me? No one ever takes any notice of me. And even if they did ... well, like you said. Mr P can get me off anything. Right?'

Darren gave another smile. It was a slow one this time, as if he knew he'd won something monumental. Harper suddenly wondered if this hadn't been his game the whole time, as if this hadn't been the whole point of befriending Max in the first place. Not that it mattered, not now.

Darren reached out and opened the car door.

'Out you get, Max,' he said. 'You've been replaced.'

'No!' Max wailed, real tears on his cheeks. 'This is *my* job! You're *my* friend.'

Darren looked down at him, any trace of joviality gone. 'Get out of the car before I *make* you get out of the car.'

'Don't talk to him like that,' Harper said. 'Max—'

Max undid the seatbelt and got out of the passenger seat, sobbing. 'I hate you!' he screamed at both of them. 'I hate both of you!'

'Yeah, yeah, kid,' Darren said, bored now. 'Tell someone who gives a shit.'

'Max,' Harper said, reaching for her distraught brother, not wanting to leave him like this. He batted her hands away and ran towards the house, slamming the door shut behind him. Even from the path she could hear the heavy thump of his feet on the stairs. She went to go after him, but Darren grabbed her arm.

'Where do you think you're going?'

'I need to check on him.'

'Get in the car,' Darren said, his face hard. 'Didn't I tell you things were going to change? You're on my time now. You'd better learn to respect that, fast, or I'll make sure you – or someone you care about – pays for it.'

Chapter Twenty-seven

The broad beans sprouted first, vibrant green shoots curving eagerly out of the rich compost of their pots. Everything else caught up quickly, reluctant to miss out on a minute of growing now the season was under way. The sugar snaps and the mange tout were soon rampant. Even the brassicas were keen. Cauliflower, kale, broccoli, Romanesco – they brought out their first true leaves far more quickly than Luisa would have expected, as if wanting to show their support for this venture in leafy, verdant terms. Then there were the courgettes, which had started slowly but were now threatening to take over the shelves on which they sat. They'd have to be repotted and kept in a little longer; it was too soon for them to go out yet.

There were flower seedlings, too, perennials that would pepper the garden's decorative beds with years of returning colour if they were looked after properly. There were wallflowers and antirrhinums – the latter were being recalcitrant, but then snapdragons were always slow. The phlox were making up for it, throwing leaves out every which way. The delphiniums were already up, too, and would soon be long spears making for the sky. Someone had brought a series of rose cuttings that they said were from a friend's Lady of Shallot. They had started as bare twigs dipped in a touch of the mycorrhizal fungi and stuck in pots, but just in the past week or two had shown signs of growth, tiny buds of fresh green against the older, darker branches. Later there would be faster-growing annuals to plant, too. The seed packets were there, ready and waiting for once the earlier plants had been transplanted, leaving a little more room under cover for fresh seedlings.

Every morning Luisa came into the greenhouse and took a moment to marvel at how much each plant had grown since the day before. She'd forgotten the wealth of joy that was contained in so simple a thing as a seed you had put into the soil and cared for beginning to grow.

'Everything's really going for it, eh?'

It was Kath Larkspur's voice. Luisa turned with a smile to see the woman standing in the doorway of the greenhouse. In the past three weeks since that Easter bank holiday, Mrs Larkspur had become a daily visitor to the garden site. She rarely stayed long, but popped in and out several times a day as and when she could, helping here and there.

'Morning,' Luisa said. 'Have you got time for coffee? I was going to go in and make one for myself before I got started on watering.'

'Better not.' Kath said. 'I'll just give you a quick hand in here and then I'll have to get back. Sorry.'

Luisa smiled. 'It was good of you to come.'

'Aye, well, it's good to have the break, to tell you the truth. I'll get those cans filled, shall I?'

Kath picked up the two watering cans by the door and ducked around the side of the greenhouse to fill them from the tanks. For the past fortnight Luisa had been trying to get Kath to bring her husband Arthur with her on her visits, too, but she'd said there was no way he'd agree. Arthur hated using the wheelchair that was now a necessary part of his life, she'd explained. He dreaded seeing their friends while he was in it, who had known him as such an active man.

'None of them care, of course,' Kath had confided, with a sigh. 'They'd be pleased as punch if he started going out with them again. But no. It's pride, I suppose.'

'Has he seen a therapist?' Luisa had asked, a suggestion that had been met with a loud snort.

'Has he heck,' was Kath's answer. 'It's hard enough to get him to the doctor for a check-up. Since he was discharged from hospital he swore he'd only go back if he was unconscious and couldn't refuse to get in the ambulance. It's ridiculous, but there it is.'

Luisa understood. She now knew that Arthur's leg injuries were as a result of a car accident. She could still remember her own sojourn in a blank white hospital room in the wake of the accident she herself had survived and Reuben had not. How long she'd spent staring at a ceiling, her body healing while her mind just kept taking her back to that mountain, to the memory of Reuben's last hours—

Anyway. Luisa understood Arthur wanting to steer clear of anywhere that would bring back similar memories. Besides, perhaps it was enough that Kath's frequent visits to the garden were providing a respite for the woman herself.

'Here we are then,' Kath said now, returning with the two watering cans full to the brim and handing one to Luisa. 'Thirsty beasts, these little plants, aren't they?'

They started on their rounds, making sure each of the growing seedlings got a good watering. Luisa thought about the water reclamation unit Harper had discovered. Wouldn't it be fantastic if such a thing could be rigged to a sprinkler inside a greenhouse like this? It would mean automatic watering.

'No Harper again this morning?' Kath asked, as if she'd read Luisa's mind.

'No. She's back at school this week, though. I guess she's got a lot on her plate.'

'Aye,' Kath sighed. 'That's true enough.'

Harper had been largely absent from the garden during the two weeks of the Easter holidays. Luisa wasn't sure why. She'd left a note for Cas – they had resumed this method of communication, a hurried and uncertain line she'd drawn between them – but he'd not seen her, either. It was a pity, because Luisa had thought there had been a breakthrough on the day of the Potato Planting Party, but apparently not.

In other regards, a lot really had changed in the three weeks since Easter.

'It's as if I found a key that unlocked the exact door I

needed to open,' is how she described it to Jo. 'Then, inside that room were all the keys I'd been missing to open the rest of the doors in the house.'

Encouraging people to plant their own seeds meant that they kept returning to see how what they had planted was getting on. The children were particularly excited but even the older residents had dropped in several times since. While they were there Luisa always asked them to do some little job or other – watering, or raking over a new bed. These were always small jobs and at first she couched it as a quick favour. It soon became habit. After a couple of visits those returning became active volunteers, looking for jobs that needed doing. Spending time in the garden – even though it wasn't really a garden yet – was as addictive as it was therapeutic.

Luisa shut her eyes and breathed in the loamy scent of water on earth and leaf. She completely understood the sentiment.

'This is where you keep disappearing off to, then, is it?'

The voice came from behind them. A man in a wheelchair was blocking the doorway of the greenhouse, an angry look on his face.

'Arthur!' Kath exclaimed, making her way to him. 'What are you doing here? How did you—'

'Came to see where my wife was sloping off to all day every day, didn't I?' Arthur said. 'Popping out every minute you get, leaving me on my own. Thought I couldn't follow, didn't you? Thought you could just leave me behind like a sack of coal.'

'I'm sorry,' Kath said. 'I was just helping out. I did tell you—'

'Helping! You've got plenty of helping to do already – with me, at home, where you're supposed to be. Or have you forgotten that? And anyway,' he said, with a disdainful glance around the site, 'you said this was a garden. This isn't much of a garden as far as I can see.'

'It isn't yet,' Luisa agreed, before Kath could answer her irate husband. 'But it can be, with help from people like Kath. And you too, perhaps, Mr Larkspur?' She went over and held out a hand. 'Luisa MacGregor.'

Arthur Larkspur ignored Luisa's offered hand and looked back out across the bare site. 'You'd be better off paving it over and turning it into a car park. Less hassle and you might at least make a bit of money from it instead of faffing about with flowers.'

Luisa tried for a smile. 'We'll work at it a bit longer first before we give up and do that. There are quite a few volunteers now, including Kath. She's been wonderful.'

Mr Larkspur snorted and Luisa struggled to see him as anything other than a deeply unpleasant man. Still, she knew first hand that pain could do terrible things to a person.

'Would you like to see the plans for what we're hoping the garden will look like?' she persisted. 'Kath's been a part of designing the memorial garden and pond that'll be going in the south-east corner. We'll be starting work on that next week. We're not just growing flowers, either – over there you can see where we've already started planting potatoes and,' she indicated the growth around them in the greenhouse, 'we've got various varieties of veg almost ready to go out. Here, I've got a flyer you can take with you . . .'

Luisa picked up one of the sheets she'd had printed – it had the site plan on one side and details about volunteering on the other. Larkspur snatched it out of her hand but didn't look at it.

'What I want,' he said sharply, 'is to go home.'

'All right, Arthur,' Kath said. 'I'll come with you now. I'll make us some coffee.' She shot Luisa an apologetic glance. Luisa smiled back, wanting to point out that Arthur had obviously made his way to the site on his own, so he could probably get back alone, too. She didn't. As she watched Kath walk with him back to the site gate she hoped this incident wouldn't put Kath off from coming back again. Mrs Larkspur had proven fun to spend time with and Luisa hadn't been lying when she'd said she was a great help.

The couple disappeared from view and Luisa continued preparing for the day. The students of Class 4 at Collaton Primary were coming in to plant sunflowers later. Luisa imagined the children's faces, as bright and happy as the blooms they would be encouraging to grow.

Chapter Twenty-eight

'You need to start dating again,' his friend Chris told him, as they sat together with a beer. 'Unless you're still hung up on Annika?'

'No,' Cas said. 'I'm just busy. Anyway, I need to focus on finding my own place, don't I? I can't clutter up your spare room forever.'

'Ach,' Chris said. 'That'll happen soon enough. Meantime, Becky loves having you here and the kids do, too. I'd get back on the bike asap, if I were you. Sure, the lasses still think you're hot right now, but you're not getting any younger, are you?'

'Thanks, Chris,' Cas said. 'You're all heart, really.'

Chris shrugged. 'It's life, mate. It'll pass you by quicker than you can blink if you're not careful.'

Chris was right. Cas wasn't quite sure how he'd ended up where he was at his age. He'd always intended to have a decent home, a family to raise in it. Instead he'd found himself with nothing to show for any of his efforts but a 'timeshare' on a dusty gym he couldn't afford rent on and a difficult tribe of teenagers who weren't his, despite sometimes feeling more like a parent than a teacher.

'I wouldn't know where to start,' he said.

It had been four years since Cas had last been on the singles scene. The speed life moved at these days probably meant he was now completely off-the-radar out of touch with how things were done. Tinder, that was the way people hooked up nowadays, wasn't it? Although in a place as small as Collaton that struck Cas as being fraught with nightmarish possibilities. The local dating pool was so limited that he'd likely end up being paired with colleagues, or the mothers of students, or, worst of all, *ex*-students, which filled him with a particular sense of horror. In fact, that thought was so terrible that it was enough to put Cas off the idea completely. Which left – what? How did people connect these days if not via the Internet?

'That salsa club in Carlisle's still there,' Chris suggested, when told of this quandary. 'Becky would be up for a night out if we can get a sitter. We can go together, it's been an age.'

'Right, so I can play the gooseberry while the two of you get your jiggle on?' Cas asked. 'Fat chance.'

'Oh, come on,' Chris scoffed. 'When have you ever gone without a partner? Show up and you'll have a queue in five minutes and you know it.'

Cas made a face. 'I don't know. I haven't danced in years. I'm probably too old and stiff now.'

'Nah,' said his friend. 'Float like a butterfly, sting like a bee, right? The boxing you do with the kids – that'll keep you nimble. Just practise a few steps before we go and you'll be right. It'll be like old times.'

Cas couldn't think of a better idea, which is how he found himself in the gym early on a Sunday morning, the only time he could be sure it would be free. There was more space there than in Chris and Becky's front room, and besides, he didn't want to embarrass himself in front of either of his friends. He'd tread the worn gym parquet instead as he discovered whether or not his muscles remembered how to move to music.

He flicked on the gym's sound system (a new addition courtesy of Luisa that had further endeared her to the club kids) and toggled his phone's Bluetooth through its speakers. The sound of salsa filled the air, a quick, complicated melody that immediately made him think of blue skies and tropical heat, of bright colours and sandy beaches. He started practising steps, trying to loosen up, to feel the music. It was ironic, Cas considered, that he thought nothing of explaining the off-side rule to a football pitch full of know–it–all kids, or launching a basketball through a net, or standing up in that boxing ring figuring examples of boxing stances for dismissive teenagers, but he now couldn't seem to move his feet in two dance steps together without feeling horribly self-conscious, even though there was no one there to see them. It had been a long time since he'd done this and he was old now. Too old for this, most likely. He felt ungainly and daft, like a lumbering bear in a tutu. It was probably because he was doing this without a partner, he told himself. Dancing was designed for two.

'Hi!'

Her voice took him by surprise. Cas turned to see Luisa in the doorway. Her cheeks were flushed pink, her hair loose and wind-blown around her shoulders. She was wearing a battered pair of blue jeans with a rip in one knee, her usual steel-toe-capped work boots and an old black sweater. She had a smear of dirt across one cheek like the one he'd only narrowly stopped himself from smoothing away a few weeks before and her smile was a 1,000-watt floodlight even from the other side of the room. Cas was dismayed to feel something illicit tighten in the pit of his belly.

'I haven't seen you for ages,' Luisa said, as she crossed the room. 'I thought you'd forgotten me!'

'Oh,' he said, utterly knocked askew and cursing himself for it. 'No, just . . . busy.'

She came to a stop in front of him, still smiling. 'Were you dancing?'

He put his hands on his hips, made a face. 'I used to dance a lot – at least, I thought I had. I'm beginning to wonder if my memory is playing tricks. Either that or someone's swapped my feet for lead.'

She laughed and Cas relaxed a little despite the tension he felt. It was good to see her. He couldn't pretend otherwise, even to himself. What did it matter, anyway, if he had a little crush?

'I'm a terrible dancer,' she said, oblivious.

'I can't believe that,' Cas said. 'Trust me, if a hulk like me can do it, anyone can.'

'What is this, anyway?' Luisa asked, waving a finger at the music, still undulating swiftly around them. 'It sounds complicated.'

'Salsa,' he told her and later Cas wouldn't be able to say what possessed him in that moment, but he reached out both his hands to her. 'Come on, I'll show you the basic steps. It's easy, I promise.'

Luisa slipped her hands into his, an arm's length between them. As soon as they touched they both fell quiet. Her hands were warm in his and she seemed to have trouble raising her chin to look up at him. Cas immediately regretted his impulse, a sudden tension rising with the beat of the music.

'Um,' she said after a second, clearing her throat. 'Sure you want to risk your toes?'

'I think I'll survive,' he said, feigning levity. 'Right, now, it's about flow and back-and-forth . . .'

He showed her the easiest steps he'd learned all those years ago as a student, him stepping into her, her stepping away and then back again, the movement mirrored and repeated by both of them.

'Okay,' Luisa admitted, her laugh returning, 'I think even I can do this!'

'Of course you can,' Cas said, ever the teacher. 'Now, if you wanted to add in a bit of fanciness, you could put in a turn . . .' He changed the position of his left hand where it held hers, palms up together, fingers laced. He lifted his arm and she rotated under it, their fingers still connected as Luisa spun. He'd thought they were going slowly enough, but she still stumbled as she turned and he pulled her closer to steady her, his hand leaving hers to catch her waist instead.

Luisa laughed, holding onto him, pressed against him but looking down at her booted feet. 'See? I told you. Terrible!'

'You're not,' Cas said. 'Why don't you come out with me next Friday night? Some friends and I are planning to go to a salsa club in Carlisle. It'll be fun.'

He felt her fingers flex against him, a little convulsion of surprise. Luisa looked up at him and Cas was suddenly aware of how close they were.

An unexpected voice made them both jump. 'Lu?' it called, from the hallway outside. 'Where are you?'

Luisa took a hurried step away from him as Cas turned to see a younger, fairer-haired version of the woman he'd just been dancing with appear in the gym's doorway.

'I'm here, Jo.' Luisa glanced up at Cas, her cheeks a little flushed. 'This is my sister, Joanna,' she said, as the newcomer made her way towards them. 'Jo, this is Cas.'

Cas flicked off the loud beat of the music as the new arrival came closer. She held out a hand for him to shake as soon as she was near enough, beaming a smile that was almost as bright as her sister's. 'Cas! Hi!'

'Hello,' he said, still a little off-balance but smiling all the same. 'It's nice to meet you.'

'And you,' Jo said, emphatically. 'I've heard so many good things about you.'

'Oh?' Cas was a little surprised by this statement. 'Have you come to visit the garden?'

'Yes, and to lend a hand,' Jo said. 'I've been too busy to find time before now, which I feel horribly guilty about. Although, judging by the crowd she's managed to gather out there on a Sunday morning, I shouldn't have worried!'

He smiled, enjoying Jo's enthusiasm. 'Well, your sister has a way about her. It's hard not to want to help. Although – have I missed something?' he asked, turning to Luisa. 'Is there some particular reason you're working on a Sunday morning?'

'No – I'm sorry, I know this is on your gym time and I'm not supposed to be here,' Luisa said. 'It's just that we've decided to put up a shed for storage. I didn't want to leave everyone else to do it without me and this is when the most people were free to help, so—'

'Luisa,' he said, interrupting. 'This is your space. You pay the bills, remember?'

She smiled a little, her gaze flicking away. 'You know I don't think of it that way.'

'Even if you didn't,' Cas added, 'you'd be welcome any time. I'm just sorry I can't stay and help in the garden – I've got to go and view a flat before the club session later.' He looked at his watch. 'In fact, I'd better get going. It really was good to meet you, Jo. Luisa—'

It was only as she finally looked up at him that it occurred to Cas that he'd just asked her out and she'd said ... absolutely nothing. He cursed himself, because right there in her eyes Cas could see the awkwardness he'd wanted to avoid.

'Cas—' she began, clearly uncomfortable.

He touched her arm lightly, gave a smile, dismissed it all with a shake of his head, moving on as if it were nothing. 'It's fine. It was just an idea. I've got to go.'

He smiled a final goodbye to Joanna and headed out of the gym, very aware of their eyes on his back. There was a conspicuous silence behind him even as he walked down the corridor to the main doors and out into the pale sun of a late April day.

Cas took a deep breath and started walking.

Well, you asked, he told himself. *And you got an answer. Get over it.*

But he could still feel the warmth of her skin through her top as he had rested his hand at her waist, her eyes as she'd looked up at him from what was very nearly an embrace.

Chapter Twenty-nine

Luisa watched Cas go with a horrible feeling of trepidation. Beside her, she could feel Jo gearing up to speak, just waiting until he was out of earshot. It didn't help to settle her heartbeat, still uneven from that moment when she'd looked up at him, one hand in his and his arm around her waist. She knew her sister and could imagine exactly what Jo—

'All right,' Jo said, finally breaking the silence left in the wake of Cas's faded footsteps. 'You told me he was a good guy. You didn't tell me he also happens to be *hotter than the sun!*'

Luisa turned away, hating the flush she could feel creeping into her cheeks at her sister's words, not wanting to address any of this and certainly not with her sister. 'Jo, don't.'

'Don't what?' Jo demanded. 'You can't tell me you haven't noticed.'

'We're colleagues,' Luisa said, adding lamely, 'sort of, anyway.'

'What's that got to do with anything?'

Luisa headed down the corridor, confident that the man in question would be long gone from the square by now. Outside, the morning air was cool but the sun was bright. Voices and laughter already echoed from the garden site. She breathed in, settling herself as she waited for Jo to follow her out so that she could lock the door. Her heartbeat was finally returning to normal. *Everything's fine*, she told herself. *He was just being kind, as he always is. That's all he meant when—*

'Hello?' Jo said. 'Earth to Luisa?'

'What?'

Joanna narrowed her eyes. 'Did you hear anything I just said?'

'Probably not. I'd learned to tune you out by the time you turned one.'

Her sister made a face. 'Very funny. I was asking what Cas was talking about when he said "It was just an idea".'

Luisa, having locked the door, headed for the garden. 'Oh, nothing.'

'"It's fine. It was just an idea",' her sister repeated verbatim. 'That doesn't sound like nothing. Especially not when the two of you were – I don't know what you were doing, actually.'

'Dancing,' Luisa said, shortly. 'I walked in on him mid-practice and he was showing me some dance steps because I said I was a terrible dancer. He's a teacher, he can't help it, it's what he does.'

'Practising?' Jo asked. 'What for?'

Luisa did not want to open that can of worms, not when

she still had to process it herself. She knew exactly what her sister would say and it would not involve Luisa staying as far away from Cas and a salsa club as possible. 'Does it matter?'

'I suppose not,' Jo said, as they reached the garden gate. 'Except . . .'

Luisa looked up to see Jo biting her lip and was surprised. It wasn't like her sister to meter her words. 'Except what?'

Jo shrugged, looking around. 'You looked good together. Hey – this is great!'

Luisa smiled as she saw the garden through her sister's eyes, letting everything else slip away as she contemplated the site. It was easy to forget the progress that had been made when she experienced it every day, but it was true, the garden was really beginning to take shape. Most of the potatoes had sprouted, the bowls of their thick green leaves exploding from the earth with leafy enthusiasm. The brassicas had grown large enough to transplant and were now under hoops covered with fine mesh netting. They'd been set beside the potatoes and just this week the peas had gone out, too, set to climb the high wire mesh that staked alongside them. It gave the vegetable side of the site a real market-garden feel. The flower seedlings would be going out this week into beds that had been linked by smaller pathways that marked them out like the lead in a stained-glass window, ready for colour to fill in the voids. The 'memorial garden' was coming along well and the small pond had been dug out and lined, the next step an edging made from the remainder of the old factory wall.

The place no longer looked abandoned. It looked like somewhere that was ... *becoming*.

'It does, doesn't it?' Luisa agreed, forgetting her irritation with her sister. 'And we're still just getting started.'

'There you are,' said a strident voice. 'Can I have a word?'

Luisa looked over to see Arthur Larkspur wheeling swiftly towards them across the tarmac from the greenhouse, a determined look on his face. *Oh no*, Luisa thought. *What now?* She hadn't seen Arthur since he'd come to retrieve Kath a couple of weeks before. His wife had continued to visit, seemingly uncowed by her husband's annoyance, but Arthur hadn't shown his face again. Luisa could see Kath inside the greenhouse, probably busy watering seedlings – the first week of June was turning out to be another dry week.

'Mr Larkspur,' Luisa said, aiming for cheerfulness. 'It's great to see you again. This is—'

'Benches,' he said, interrupting her introduction of Jo. 'That's what you're going to need. You've got nowt for folk to sit on, have you?'

'Oh,' Luisa said, taken aback. 'Well, that's something we've been discussing, actually. I'm sure we can find the budget for—'

Arthur Larkspur made an impatient sound in his throat. 'You'll be thinking about cheap tat from some crappy enormo-dealer somewhere, no doubt. I'm talking about good stuff, stuff that's built to last by proper hands, not by a machine punching 'em out on the other side of the world. Wood, lass! That's what you need. Wood!'

Luisa heard Jo stifle a snort of laughter.

'Do you know what, Mr Larkspur, I completely agree,' Jo said. 'Luisa definitely needs some wood. I've been saying it for a while.'

'Jo,' Luisa hissed.

'Oak,' Arthur Larkspur stated, stoutly, completely oblivious to Jo's childish double-entendre. 'Find me some decent green oak. That way it'll weather with the place, bed in with the rest of what you've got going on.'

Luisa backtracked for a second, unsure what was happening. 'Wait,' she said. 'Mr Larkspur, are you volunteering to make benches for the garden?'

He shot her a withering look. 'That's what I just said, isn't it?' He waved at the perimeter fence. 'I'll make a few to curve around those saplings you've got, for a start. Leave enough space so that as the trees grow, it'll give folk somewhere nice and shady to sit.'

This was so out of left field that Luisa didn't know what to say.

'I'll need a hand or two here and there, obviously,' Arthur said, not noticing her silence. 'And you'll have to sort me out in this new shed of yours – I can't stand for long so I'll need to work sitting down. But I've still got my kit. Not been used for a while, but I've kept it in fettle at home.'

'You're a joiner?' Luisa asked, still trying to fathom what was going on.

'Keep up, lass,' Arthur said, still impatient. 'Of course

I am. What, you thought I was going to learn how just to help you out?'

'Yeah, Lu,' Jo echoed, a trace of a teasing laugh in her eyes as she looked at Luisa. 'Keep up.'

'Right, then. You,' Arthur said, thrusting a notebook and pencil at Joanna. 'You can give me a hand. I need to measure. Might as well get on with it now, since I'm here, and seeing as they haven't got the pathways in yet you'll need to do the basics while I supervise. Come on.'

Jo opened her mouth to protest but he was already making his way past her.

'I haven't got all day!' he barked, over his shoulder.

Luisa smiled sweetly at her sister. 'You heard what the man said, Jo. Chop chop.'

Jo muttered something and stalked off after the old man. Luisa watched for a moment and then turned to see Kath standing in the greenhouse doorway, a faint smile on her face.

'Well,' Luisa said. 'That's a turn-up for the books.'

'I know,' Kath agreed. 'I'm as surprised as you are. I think that plan of the garden you gave him last time he was here must have given him something to think about. Who knows – maybe this is just what he needs. A project, you know, something to focus on that isn't just himself.'

'Well, in that case I'm all for it,' Luisa said, although from what she'd seen so far he wasn't going to be the easiest person to get on with. At that moment she could hear him yelling orders at Jo.

'His bark's worse than his bite,' Kath said, as if she could read Luisa's mind.

Luisa smiled. 'Don't worry. Jo's more than capable of giving as good as she gets. And besides, she could do with a bit of ordering about, in my opinion.'

There came the sound of footsteps scuffing across the tarmac behind them and Harper appeared.

'Harper!' Luisa said, as she approached. 'It's lovely to see you. How are you doing? I thought you might have given up on us completely.'

Harper forced her mouth into something that was probably supposed to be a smile. Her tired eyes were set deep in dark circles. 'Still got some hours to work out, haven't I?' she said. 'I'm sorry I haven't been here. Life is . . .' she hesitated, and then said, simply, 'busy.'

Luisa squeezed her arm. 'Not to worry. It's just good to see you. You remember Mrs Larkspur, don't you? From the open day at Easter?'

The shadow on Harper's face seemed to grow denser for a moment as she looked past Luisa at Kath. 'Yeah,' the girl said, quietly. 'Hi.'

Kath smiled, although it was a little reserved. 'Hello, Harper.'

Luisa wondered again if they had a history of which she was not aware. Collaton was the kind of place where connections ran old and deep.

'I can't stay long,' Harper said. 'Carl's opening the garage for me even though it's a Sunday so I can go in later. The

Mini's almost finished. We might be able to put it through its MOT next week.'

'That's great news,' Luisa said. 'Does Mr Pattanyús know? I bet he'll be delighted.'

At the mention of Cas, Harper's gaze slid away, a frown creasing her forehead. 'I haven't seen him for a while. I'm too busy for the club now. Haven't been for ages.'

Luisa couldn't quite figure out Harper's mood. She seemed subdued, but surely finishing the car was something she would be excited about? With Kath there Luisa didn't feel right asking Harper about it. She hoped that during the course of the day she could find out what was wrong. 'Well, perhaps once the car's finished you'll have more time?'

'Yeah,' Harper said. 'Maybe.'

A phone beeped, a text arriving from the ether with a tinny fanfare. Harper's tired eyes widened slightly, her pale face further draining of colour. There was a second of silence and then she backed away.

'I've got to go,' she said.

'What?' Luisa asked, confused. 'You've only just got here.'

'I'm sorry,' Harper said, already heading for the gate. 'I'll try to come back later, okay? I'm sorry.'

'Harper—'

It was too late, she'd already vanished beyond the fence. A moment later there came the loud rev of an engine and the pounding of loud music as a car sped into the square. It roared past the open gate of the garden and Luisa thought she recognized it. Was it Darren Dixon again, planning to try the same intimidation technique as last time? The car turned another corner of the square. Then came the screech of brakes as it pulled to a halt. There was the slam of a door and then it took off again. Luisa tried to peer through the fence, but her view was obscured by the saplings, now in full leaf and growing with abandon. Luisa wondered for the first time just how well Harper knew Darren Dixon.

She turned back to see a troubled look on Kath's face. The older woman shook her head.

'Kath?' Luisa asked. 'What's the matter?'

Kath had no time to answer, because that was when the remaining members of their little volunteer troop arrived and the rest of the day was devoted to putting up the shed. Luisa kept hoping that Harper would come back to help, but she didn't.

Chapter Thirty

It was a Tuesday morning in mid-June and Luisa was on her way to Collaton when Owen Lawrence called her. This was unusual – they had kept up their weekly Friday updates, so Luisa couldn't imagine why he needed to speak to her again so soon.

'Owen, hi,' she said, as she answered. 'Is everything okay?'

'Morning, Luisa,' Owen said. 'And the answer to that is maybe, but maybe not.'

'Oh?' Luisa said, frowning a little. She had a sudden irrational fear that he was going to say he wanted the Collaton land for himself after all. He wouldn't do that, surely?

'We've just had the speaker for the summer gala cancel on us out of the blue,' he said. 'It's pretty inconvenient, to tell you the truth. It's extremely short notice to round up a suitable replacement.'

'I see,' Luisa said. 'Sorry to hear that.'

She hadn't been to one of Owen's summer galas for years. They were huge, ostentatious affairs held on his estate, hosted by Owen for the great and the good of the business world. Ostensibly a charity event, in truth, Luisa had always felt rather cynical about them. Yes, each plate of food commanded an insane price tag, and yes, the difference went to whatever cause Owen had chosen to support that year. But it hadn't taken her many such events at Reuben's side to realize the main purpose of the evening was networking at a level she couldn't even imagine. The worth of the deals that were done over Owen Lawrence's champagne flutes – or sometimes the next morning, over an equally opulent and only slightly less boozy brunch – was phenomenal. The fact that they happened in Owen's sphere helped him keep his fingers in a lot of different pies. Against this backdrop the charity element had seemed little more than a useful fig leaf.

'Anyway,' he said, 'I thought of you.'

Luisa blinked. 'Me?'

'I wondered how you'd feel about giving one of the after-dinner speeches to help fill the gap?'

'Wait,' Luisa said. 'What? But they're usually big tech pitches, aren't they?'

'Usually,' Owen agreed. 'The speaker who should have been coming has a nascent design for a new type of bird-friendly wind turbine. Eco tech is on the up right now, I think it would have gone down a storm. But that can't be helped and I was thinking that it's actually a perfect opportunity to promote the garden charity, isn't it? Might help refill the coffers a bit?'

'But—' Owen's mention of money made Luisa pause. Her automatic reaction was to say no, she couldn't do it, but he was right. She'd been looking at the charity funds just the night before and wondering what to do about fund-raising. The money she'd started with was disappearing fast. 'What would I need to do?'

'You'd have about fifteen minutes straight after dinner,' Owen told her. 'You'd need some sort of presentation detailing what the project's about, what you've achieved so far and what the next steps are. I'd suggest a visual element if you can pull it together, some video footage, that kind of thing. Anything that can catch the attention of people who spend their entire lives having people try to catch their attention. You know how it is.'

'Right,' Luisa said, faintly. 'Owen, I . . . I'm really not sure I can do that.'

Reuben was the one who had always done the pitching back in the day. He was the one who knew how to get through to an audience. Look what had happened the last time Luisa herself had tried to do that. She hadn't been able to get through to Darren Dixon. It had been a disaster.

'I believe in you, Luisa,' Owen said. 'You can do it, I know you can. The gala's at the end of July, so you've got about six weeks to prepare. Think about it, at least?'

Luisa pulled to a halt outside the garden and squeezed her eyes shut. Fund-raising was even less of a forte of hers than pitching, and here was Owen offering her the perfect chance to talk to a captive – and very rich – audience. Collaton was on the verge of being a success, it would be devastating for it to fail for lack of funds.

'Okay,' she said. 'I'll do it, Owen. I will.'

'Well,' said Kath Larkspur a little later, as she and Luisa tended to the plants in the greenhouse. 'I can understand you being nervous, but it does sound like a good opportunity, doesn't it?'

'Yes,' Luisa admitted. 'But the idea of getting up in front of a room full of people of the sort I know will be there fills me with dread.'

'Ah, you'll be all right, lass,' Kath said, patting her shoulder. 'You need a presentation, you say? Why don't you hit up young Mo for some help? He's always wandering about here with his camera out. Says he's filming stuff for TikTok or some such. I bet he'd jump at the chance.'

'That's a really good idea,' Luisa said. 'In fact, it'd be great to involve the regulars, wouldn't it? If we film little segments with lots of different people all doing different things in the garden, we can cut them together.'

Kath smiled and pulled on her gardening gloves. 'There you go, you see? Nothing to worry about.'

'You, Kath, are a godsend,' Luisa said. 'What other great ideas are in that head of yours?'

Kath paused, brushed off her hands and picked up her coffee. 'You said there'll be a big dinner before you have to do this?'

'Yes. It's the main event, usually goes on forever.'

Kath nodded and looked out of the greenhouse at the neat rows of plants that were really beginning to flourish in the vegetable patch. 'And this shindig's happening at the end of July?'

'That's right,' Luisa said, following her gaze.

Kath shrugged. 'I bet the sugar snap peas will be really going for it by then,' she said. 'The courgettes, too. There'll be first earlies ready to lift as well.'

Luisa tilted her head, catching on. 'You think we could get them to use some of our produce in the banquet?'

Kath nodded. 'You said you needed to catch their attention. Might be a good way to do it.'

Luisa held out her half-full mug and clunked it gently against Kath's in a makeshift toast. 'Another brilliant idea. I'll get Owen to put me in touch with the caterer. What would I do without you? You don't fancy doing the presentation for me too, do you? I bet you'd be great.'

Kath snorted. 'You don't want me getting up in front of a bunch of that sort,' she said. 'I'm a born socialist, me. I might tell them what I *really* think.'

They laughed together and went back to work, but Luisa's mind kept returning to that phone call with Owen. He was right, it was a huge opportunity to talk to a room full of business folk to whom the average person would never have access. She couldn't throw that away for the sake of her nerves. It was too good a chance to pass up.

Sometimes I wish I could wave a magic wand to give them all a chance, even if it's just one.

The potent memory of Cas's voice took Luisa by surprise as it echoed in her mind. She remembered how he'd looked as he'd spoken of what he wished he could do for his students: how serious his voice had been, how it had felt to listen to him as they ate fish and chips looking out over the grey, turbulent sea.

How often did good chances come along?

'Penny for them?' Kath asked, pulling Luisa back to the present. 'You look as if you're miles away. Or are you just having a few good ideas of your own?'

'Maybe,' Luisa said, thoughtfully.

'Harper?'

Luisa hadn't known how to track Harper Dixon down apart from making sure she was outside Collaton School when it let out for the day, so that's exactly what she'd done. Once there she'd hung back, scanning the groups of kids that began to pour out as soon as the clock had declared the end of the school day. Harper left alone, the collar of her usual black jacket pulled up around her ears, her head dipped as if not wanting to be noticed. The girl wove through the throng, striding quickly as if being pursued.

'Harper!'

This time Harper heard her and turned, glowering at her with the sort of annoyed, insolent expression that she'd not levelled at Luisa for weeks now. 'What are you doing here?'

'I just needed to talk to you about something. Can I give you a lift home?'

If possible, Harper looked even more tired than the last time Luisa had seen her. She looked away, clearly unhappy. 'I haven't got time to help in the garden tonight,' she said. 'I've got to work.'

'That's fine,' Luisa said. 'I wasn't expecting you to. Come on – tell me where you want to go and I'll drop you there.'

Harper looked undecided for a moment, then shrugged. Luisa took that as a yes and led her to the Land Rover.

'Where to?' she asked, starting the engine.

Harper frowned a little. 'The garage.'

Luisa pulled away, navigating the school-run traffic. 'I know you're busy,' she said. 'The last thing I want to do is interfere with your school work. But I've been thinking about your water reclamation unit.'

Luisa felt Harper staring at her, hard. '*What* water reclamation unit? It's just an idea. It's not a real thing.'

'It could be, though,' Luisa told her. 'If you worked out how to do it. And here's the thing. A friend of mine hosts this big event every year. He's invited me to talk about the project. It would be fantastic if you could present the unit there as well.'

Harper rubbed a hand over her face. 'There *isn't* a unit.'

'It doesn't have to be the finished thing. It doesn't even have to be a prototype. If we had a few diagrams and you talking about the basic idea, that would be enough.'

'There *isn't* a unit!' Harper said again, louder this time. 'What about that don't you understand?'

'Are you telling me that you haven't been thinking about

it?' Luisa said. 'Because as busy as you are, I can't believe that. I bet you've at least been turning it over in your head.'

Harper stared out of the window in silence. Luisa turned onto the street where the garage stood, knowing her time was up. She pulled the Defender to the kerb.

'Will you at least consider it?' Luisa asked, as Harper climbed out. 'This could be a really good opportunity for you, Harper.'

Harper paused, looking back at Luisa with a frown. 'How do you work that out?'

'There will be a lot of influential people there. Business people, the sort of folk who are always looking for the next thing worth their investment, whether that's people or technology. If you present something like the reclamation unit, I guarantee it will generate interest. At the very least, doing the work would look excellent on your college application.'

Harper climbed out of the Defender. 'Thanks for the lift.'

'Will you at least think about it?' Luisa asked. 'An innovation like this, coming out of the garden – it'd be huge in terms of generating financial support for the future.'

Harper gave a sardonic smile. 'Ah, right. *Now* I get it.'

'No, that's not—'

'I've got to go,' the girl said, and slammed the door shut hard enough for it to rattle.

Luisa watched her stalk away.

'Brilliant, Luisa,' she muttered to herself. 'Good job. Well done.'

Chapter Thirty-one

Harper didn't look back as Luisa drove away. She was beyond exhausted. For weeks Darren had kept summoning her at all hours of the day and night. It was a power thing, she guessed. He wanted her rattled, conditioned to always respond to his texts, whatever else she had going on. He had interrupted her so often at the garage that Carl had begun to lose patience.

'You're not doing yourself any favours, you know,' he'd said, the last time she'd had to leave in the middle of work. 'What's got into you? Do you actually want this apprenticeship, or are you just mucking me about?'

There was no way for Harper to explain. She'd lied, said that Max was ill. Carl had always been a sympathetic boss, but that could only last so long.

Harper had obviously been obedient enough to prove herself because things had finally begun to settle down. All that meant, though, was that she now had a regular 'shift'. It put her on the street between 9pm and 2am every single night.

She was also still trying to keep up with school and her shifts at the garage. Harper was desperately stumbling towards that little light at the end of a tunnel that was beginning to seem endless, the promise of college and an apprenticeship, a proper job, a way out. She couldn't let that distant hope blink out. If it did, there would be only darkness.

Harper had thought that if she could just get the Mini through the MOT, she'd be able to take Max and go somewhere, anywhere, just *go*. Except that she had hardly any money because she'd missed out on so much work at the garage thanks to Darren, and anyway, she could no longer guarantee that Max would go anywhere with her willingly. She could see the *Daily Mail* headlines now: *Drug Dealer Sister Attempts Kidnap of Brother, Goes on Run.*

She scuffed across the oil-stained concrete floor of the garage and shucked her rucksack, dumping it beside the short line of lockers to dig the key out of her pocket. The clock said she was five minutes early, a rare occurrence these days. It gave her time to make a quick coffee before getting on with the tyre change on a Kia that Harper saw was on her slate for the afternoon.

'Harper.' She looked around to see Carl standing outside his office. His dark eyebrows were drawn together in an expression that instantly made her stomach plummet. Her boss jerked his chin towards his open door. 'I need to talk to you.'

She knew the minute she sat down at his desk. Harper could see it in Carl's face, the disappointment now mixed with anger, both directed straight at her. She swallowed, feeling sick, not meeting his eye.

'I saw you,' he said, his voice steady and quiet. 'Last night.'

Harper cleared her throat, her heart racing. 'Last night? What do you mean? Where?'

Carl crossed his arms. If she looked at him his eyes would be like two drills boring holes into her, she knew that for a fact. 'Don't play dumb with me, Harper. What did I tell you? Keep out of trouble. Keep your nose clean.'

'I am!'

He leaned forward, his voice dropping to a low hiss. 'Then why did I see you over by the old station, *dealing*?'

Harper's heart sank further. He really had seen her. Her mind went into overdrive, trying to think of a way out. 'You must have seen me with my cousin. I told you, Max is ill. But I didn't have enough cash to get him medicine so my cousin – he lives that way – said he'd help me out but I had to go and meet him to get it and—' She risked a glance at him. Her stomach plummeted further.

Carl was shaking his head, leaning back in his chair, his arms crossed and his jaw set. 'It's not the first time I've seen you there,' he said, with a quiet finality that stopped her heart. 'It's not the second, either.'

Game over, dude. Game over.

'At least it explains what's got into you over the last few weeks,' Carl said, into her silence. 'I think I knew ages ago, actually, I just didn't want to believe it, not of you. I like you, Harper. You know that.'

'You don't understand,' she said, in a whisper.

Carl spread his hands. 'Then explain so that I do. Why would you do this? After I warned you what would happen? After I've tried so hard to help you?'

Harper thought about laying it out there, telling him exactly what was going on. But where would that lead? Carl would urge her to go to the police, and when she refused, he'd go himself. Then it'd all come out, wouldn't it? Not just the dealing but everything else, from her shoplifting to the way Mr P had shielded her from those consequences. And that was before they even got to Max's own little thefts and problems.

'Please,' she said. 'I just want to work, Carl. I just want to get to college.'

Carl was already shaking his head again. 'I'm sorry,' he said. 'But this place is all I've got. I can't have it here. I just can't.'

'I've never brought anything here. I never would.'

'That's not enough, Harper. There's something bad gathering in this town. It's getting worse and I don't want it anywhere near me. I've got a family to think about. A business.' He opened his desk drawer, took out an envelope and slid it across the desk to her. 'The MOT on the Mini's done. It passed. The paperwork's in there, with the key and the pay you're owed up until today. You can leave it here until you sort out the tax and insurance. That's the best I can do.'

It was over. What else was there to say? Harper stood, took the envelope, scooped up her rucksack and left without another word. At the far end of that tunnel, that lonely little light blinked out.

Really, though, she wondered, what had she expected? She'd failed Max. She'd failed herself. She was never getting out of here. She should have known better than to ever think she could.

Harper walked home on autopilot, lost yet still tethered in place, her mind a fog of tiredness and misery. A movement caught her eye as she approached their street: it was Max, carrying a loaded plastic bag in each hand, scurrying along as if he had somewhere important to be. At first Harper assumed her brother was headed home, but he suddenly veered off, ducking into the narrow alley that led between their street and the old scrapyard.

She stopped opposite the alleyway entrance, watching. No one used that path. It was overgrown and strewn with rubbish. What was he doing? After a moment Harper followed. She had no idea where Max was going, but if she found out that it had anything at all to do with Darren Dixon, Harper would make sure their cousin paid for it from here until doomsday, whatever it cost her.

She tried not to make any sound that would alert Max to her presence. It was tricky, what with the amount of junk that littered the overgrown path. She looked down at her feet for a moment to negotiate an old Belfast sink. When she looked up again, her brother had vanished.

Harper stopped, listening. There was no noise apart from the rustle of the weeds as the wind whistled past her.

She realized that she was standing behind her own house and looked up at the window of Max's room, wondering whether he'd found a way to sneak in and out of it, but there was no sign of him. Harper continued on, picking her way through the undergrowth.

'Max?' she called, quietly.

There was no answer, no flurry of hurried feet. Harper fought her way onwards. Where could he have gone?

She got her answer in the form of a hole in the wooden fence, leading into the scrapyard. It was partially hidden by a mass of weeds and what Harper thought might be a deliberately positioned rubbish bag. She glanced up and down the alley, but it was empty. She looked up at the windows of the overlooking houses, too, but there was no sign that anyone was watching. She dragged her backpack from her shoulder, dropped to her knees and crawled through the gap.

Someone had cleared a little passageway through the junk on the other side of the fence, as if a lesser Moses had commanded a parting of metal debris. Harper got to her feet, surrounded on both sides by walls of scrap.

After a few steps she reached a wider pathway that bisected the yard. She still couldn't see Max. She stood still for a moment, getting her bearings. Half way down the wall of wreckage to her right she could see another passageway. This was different to the one she'd just made her way through – it was lower to the ground, as if something had burrowed beneath the piles of junk. Harper crouched down in front of it, peering inside. To her surprise she could see a gleam of sunlight, as if the metal tunnel opened up further on. She sat back on her haunches and looked around again, but there was still no sign of Max. Could this be where he'd gone? There was only one way to find out.

Mercifully the crawl space wasn't long. The tunnel ended suddenly and she found herself no longer on rough concrete but on a slope of metal coated in old, sun-puckered black rubber. The space above her head opened out into a burst of dappled sunlight. She looked up to find herself kneeling in the central, open doorway of a double-decker bus.

'Oh my *God*,' she said aloud, in shock.

There came a clanging sound from above her and then the sound of footfall on the spiral of steps that led down from the upper deck. Harper got to her feet as Max appeared. He froze on the stairwell, clearly horrified to see her.

'Go away!' he said, his voice plaintive. 'You can't be here!'

'Max,' Harper said.

'No,' he said. 'This is mine! You can't have this as well!'

'Is this where you've been coming to?' Harper asked, looking around. 'All this time you've not been at home, you've been here?'

'Go *away*,' Max said again and then stomped back up the stairs.

Harper followed. The bus seemed remarkably intact – none of the windows were broken despite the piles of scrap pressed up against them from the outside. The tide of detritus, which had washed like a wave right up the rear end of the vehicle, was lower towards the front, allowing light to filter in. The seats were still there, too, although their covers had mostly rotted or been stripped away, exposing the blank benches beneath. They were piled with containers of all sorts. Harper was perplexed to see two of the bags of compost she'd last seen in their front yard, as well. Had Max dragged them here? Why?

Harper could hear her brother moving around upstairs. She went up the steps and emerged onto the upper deck as a flare of bright sunlight burst through the unencumbered windows. Harper stopped, one hand still on the railing, her mouth dropping open.

It was a greenhouse.

She was standing in a greenhouse!

As on the lower deck, the seats had been stripped back to their bare benches. Up here, though, each bench was crammed full with plants growing out of a plethora of scavenged vessels. There were yoghurt pots, tin cans, plastic water bottles, even old rubber tyres – anything that could have drainage holes poked in it and that would hold soil. Many of the makeshift planters had greenery sprouting from them – some of the plants were no more than tiny seedlings, but others looked as if they already needed more room. It wasn't just the benches that were covered, either – the bar that would once have rung the bell for the driver to stop had been repurposed into a hanging garden. Buckets and tubs with holes cut in their bottoms sprouted what Harper recognized as small tomato plants, growing upside down to maximize the space. Nothing was in flower yet, but even

Harper, as clueless as she was about cultivating any sort of plant, could see that everything was thriving. Besides, the bees seemed to think there was something to find up here – there were several buzzing industriously in the background, tottering hopefully from bench to bench.

Max himself was still studiously ignoring her. He was busy filling a watering can from a dented galvanized tank set on the front bench. There was a hosepipe leading up and out through one of the windows, dropping down past the window towards the ground.

'Max,' Harper said, when she finally found her voice. 'Did you do this?'

Max moved slowly along the bus's main aisle, carefully watering his secret garden.

'My plants weren't safe in the house,' he said eventually, 'so I brought them here.'

Harper looked around again. 'How did you know there was a bus in the scrapyard?'

'I could see the roof from my window,' Max said. He emptied his watering can and stalked back towards her to refill it, eyes lowered but jaw jutting defiantly. 'It's mine.'

He went to push past her but Harper caught him in a brief but fierce hug. 'I can't believe you did this all by yourself,' she said. 'It's amazing, Max. You're amazing.'

Max pushed her away. 'I'm not a baby.'

'I know you're not! I couldn't have done this. Not on my own. I don't know anyone who could.'

There was a silence. He moved past her and refilled the

watering can. Then Max handed it to her and pointed to the hanging tomatoes. 'You do those,' he said.

Harper did as she was told, revelling in the fresh smell of water on earth, of plants in the soil. She slowly worked her way along the line of hanging 'baskets'. Quiet reigned, a well of calm that made her draw in a long, deep breath. For a moment, just a moment, there was nothing outside of this place. She was cocooned, safe, a million miles away from the reality that lurked in the streets outside. She never wanted to leave.

'Harper,' Max said, into the silence. 'I'm sorry.'

She lowered her arm and looked back towards him. He looked small between the benches, unhappy as he twisted his fingers together. Her heart clenched.

'I'm sorry, too,' she said. 'I didn't want to take away a friend from you, or a job. Really, Max, I didn't. I want you to have both of those things. I want you to do whatever makes you happy. I'm just trying to keep you safe. Darren – he's not a good person.'

Max looked at his feet. 'Is he horrible to you?' he asked, his voice shrinking even further. 'Does he hurt you?'

She made her way back towards him. 'No. You don't have to worry about me.'

'But you're never home,' her brother pointed out 'And you're always out late at night.'

'None of that matters,' Harper said. 'That's not for you to think about. It's not your problem, Max. Okay?'

Max's expression was still anxious. 'This is my place, Harper,' he pleaded. 'This is my garden. Don't make me stop.'

Harper smiled again, a more genuine one this time. 'I don't want to stop you coming here,' she said. 'I think this is the most wonderful place I've ever been. Really, Max, it's amazing. But I'm worried it's not safe. The way you have to crawl in—'

'It has to stay that way,' Max said, quickly. 'Or other people will find it.'

Harper watched her brother for a minute. 'You know that they're making a garden near the boxing gym, don't you?' she said, carefully. 'Wouldn't you like to do some gardening with other people? You might make some real friends. Some good ones.'

Max shook his head, a vehement gesture, his face twisted in a grimace of distress.

'All right,' Harper said, holding up both hands. 'You don't have to.'

He looked suspicious for another minute. Having made so much progress from where they'd been for too long, she didn't want to lose him again.

'I promise,' Harper repeated, softly and meaning it.

He relaxed a little then, busying himself with his bags. Inside were more salvaged pots. 'It's only just started,' he said, modestly, of the garden. 'But everything wants to grow.'

Harper looked at the hose coming through the window. 'Where does that pipe go?'

Max leaned over to look out of the window and pointed to the ground. 'There's a tap,' he said. 'The hose doesn't work very well.'

Harper looked along the length of the bus. 'What you need is a sprinkler system,' she said. 'I bet we can build one.'

'Really?'

'Sure. Why not? We'll have to do it together, though,' she warned him. 'There'll be no just leaving me to do it on my own.'

Max nodded with solemn concentration. 'I know where loads of things are in the scrapyard. To build it.'

'That,' she said, 'would be perfect. But right now I think we should go and have some tea.'

Max led the way down the stairs. Harper paused, looking around one more time. She might have failed in everything else, she thought, but this – this she could make work.

Chapter Thirty-two

The community garden came on in leaps and bounds until, by the end of June, everything looked as if it had always been exactly where it was now growing. It was amazing what a difference having so many more volunteers in and out during the week made. A list of daily chores had been drawn up: *Hoe between one row of potatoes (x4)*, a task might read. *Pinch out four of the tomato plants (x3)*; *Thin out a stitch of carrot seedlings (x4)*; *Dead head the roses.*

These tasks were parcelled out diminutively enough that it didn't feel like too much of a burden to take one on, each designed to only fill half an hour if that's what a visitor could spare. The list was on a whiteboard in the greenhouse, with a legend that declared anyone could do any task they wanted, it just needed crossing off once done. Rare were the days when there were tasks carried over into the next day. Two care homes had begun to bring residents over several times a week. Luisa always made sure they went back with bouquets of sweet peas for their rooms and any neighbours not well enough to come themselves, as well as bunches of aromatic herbs for the kitchen. Collaton Primary was another regular visitor, the classes of children adding as much colour and vibrancy as the flowers that were beginning to throw open their blooms to the sun. Throughout it all, the boxing club kids had continued to help out, even if Cas himself only appeared now and then.

It had been another dry year so far. The water tanks were so often in demand that Luisa had been forced to buy more.

'You see?' Luisa said to Harper, when the girl appeared in the garden one windy Saturday afternoon. 'And we haven't reached July yet! We need you, Harper. Everyone needs you and your brilliant ideas and clever ways to implement them.'

Luisa watched as Harper glanced around the flourishing garden site, wondering why the young woman seemed somehow different, even beyond the fatigue that lurked under her dark eyes. It took her a few minutes to realize that Harper's stark defiance had been subsumed by something else, something heavy and defeated that weighed her shoulders into a slump and lingered at the corners of her downturned mouth.

'Harper, is everything all right? Is there something you need help with?' Luisa asked, as they walked along the path they had both helped to lay so many weeks before.

The girl frowned. 'I need some hosepipe. Can you spare any?'

Luisa glanced at Harper. That hadn't been what she'd meant, but it was a start. 'How much do you need? Is it to water a garden?'

Harper looked uncomfortable. 'I can't say.'

'Why not?' Luisa had a sudden memory of that black car, appearing just after Harper had left the garden the minute her phone had pinged.

'What do you care?' Harper asked, with an attitude that reminded Luisa of the first few times she'd come to help in the garden. The girl stopped suddenly, as if realizing her tone wasn't going to help her cause. She chewed her lip. 'Sorry. I just — I said I wouldn't say. I'm helping someone out. I promised. But I can't afford to buy it and I don't want to break *another* promise.' She looked unhappy. 'I'm doing that too much at the moment.'

'Sure,' Luisa said, worried but aware that showing it wasn't going to get her anywhere. Harper had defences like a nuclear facility's blast doors. 'Let's go and find some for you.'

'Thanks,' Harper muttered. 'I owe you one.'

'Well,' Luisa said, jumping on the opportunity, 'I can think of one way you can pay me back . . .'

Harper sighed. 'Let me guess. The gala thing, right?'

'The gala,' Luisa agreed.

Harper shook her head. 'You don't want me there, trust me.'

Luisa stopped again. 'I do,' she said. 'Harper, I really think it would be as good for you as it would be for this place. I know you'll have the apprenticeship, but anything that—'

'I won't.' Harper stopped, turning her face away.

'What do you mean, you won't?'

'The apprenticeship isn't happening. Carl . . . changed his

mind.' She shrugged. 'You can stop going on about how good the gala would be for me now. Because there's no point. There's no point to any of it. Okay? Not for me, so just . . . leave me alone about it, yeah?'

'Harper,' Luisa said. 'I—'

'Look,' the girl said, the insolence back, showing in the defiant set of her jaw. 'I don't need the third degree. Forget the hose. I'll get it from somewhere else.'

Luisa caught her arm before she could stalk away. 'Wait. Harper, please, just stop for a moment. Listen to me.'

Harper turned back, wrenching her arm away and crossing her arms, setting her jaw, all spike and attitude.

'I'm so sorry about the apprenticeship,' Luisa said. 'But this makes the gala especially important for you.'

Harper made an incredulous sound. 'How do you work that one out?'

'I told you,' Luisa said, 'there will be a lot of business people there, looking for the next big thing worth investing in. That includes people, Harper.'

'I don't know what you're talking about,' Harper said. 'But I've got to go. Max is waiting for me.'

'I'm talking about a bursary or a scholarship – something like that,' Luisa said. 'Plenty of tech companies have them.'

Harper stopped at that, turned back slightly. 'A scholarship? You mean – money?'

'Yes. Something that could help with your studies, even without an apprenticeship.'

The girl stared at her. 'Yeah,' she said, 'because I'm

definitely the sort of person that gets handed money just for being herself.'

Luisa smiled a little at that. 'I think you could be. Especially if you present a brilliant idea like the water reclamation unit.'

Harper blew out a breath and shook her head, her face grim. 'You just don't give up, do you?'

Luisa looked away, across the Collaton site, which now looked like a real garden coming into full and vibrant life. 'That's not true, actually,' she said. 'I did give up once. But this place has reminded me why I should have kept going and why I won't give up again. And I don't think you should, either.'

Harper sent her a look. 'You and Mr P,' she said, 'are like peas in a bloody pod.'

Luisa ignored that. 'If I can guarantee that presenting at the gala would give you a shot at a scholarship or at least some kind of bursary,' she asked instead, 'if I get you that chance, Harper, will you take it?'

Harper looked at her hard for another moment, then gave a shrug. 'I'll think about it.'

Luisa was left with a bit of a quandary after this conversation. She was sure there *were* tech companies that gave out scholarships to students with promising futures. She just had no idea whether any of those companies would have representatives at the gala or if they would even have opportunities open that would fit Harper's needs. If there weren't . . .

'Trust me, Owen,' she said, when she called her benefactor

again to explain the situation and beg him for help. 'I really believe that Harper could make something out of this water unit idea. She's got the kernel already. She just needs some motivation, a reason to want to work on it. I'm pretty sure that knowing she's in with a chance of some monetary benefit if one of your attendees is impressed enough would do the trick. And a presentation like the one I've outlined would be perfect for the gala, wouldn't it?'

'It would,' he agreed. 'But can you guarantee that she's up to this, Luisa? How old did you say she was? Seventeen? Can you promise she's not going to flake out at the last moment? I'll pull in as many favours as necessary to make sure the right people are there. But if I do that and she doesn't come through . . .'

'I guarantee it, Owen,' Luisa said, with more confidence than she felt. 'She'll be there and she'll knock their socks off. You make sure the right people are there to listen and I'll make sure there's something they'll want to listen to.'

There was a brief silence. 'You really have a lot of faith in this girl, don't you?'

'Yes,' Luisa said, 'I do. She just needs a chance, Owen. I think if she got that, she'd go far.'

'All right, then,' he said, after another pause. 'Leave it with me.'

By the time Luisa was calling Harper's number later that day, she was beginning to feel as if she was in some complicated game of tennis.

'I can vouch for Owen Lawrence personally. He's the

person who gave me the land for the garden site,' she said. 'If he says he's going to do something, he does it.'

There was a silence at the other end of the line.

'Harper?' Luisa prompted. 'Come on. Please tell me you'll do this now?'

'I can't.'

'You *can*. Trust me – and yourself, just a little. Please.'

'No, I mean—' The voice on the other end of the line broke off for a moment before trying again. 'You don't understand. I didn't tell you before, but I have tried to figure out how to make the unit work. And I can't. I can't work out how to make it do anything more than the ones that are already out there. That's why I can't do this thing you want me to do. I've tried and I *can't*. I just don't know enough.'

'It doesn't have to be the whole thing,' Luisa said. 'I told you that. Even if you had the framework, or an idea of—'

'Look,' Harper said, cutting her off impatiently. 'The problem is the filtration. Turning the effluent from the compaction process from grey water into clean drinking water. That's not a mechanical thing. It's not an engineering problem. It's *chemistry*. And that's not me. I don't want to use chemicals anyway and I sure as hell don't know the first thing about them.' She paused. 'I'm sorry. I did try. I just can't do it.'

Luisa refused to believe this idea was beyond saving. 'Talk me through it,' she suggested. 'Maybe I can find someone to work on it with you.'

'In five weeks?' Harper asked, her voice incredulous. 'If it were that easy, someone would have done it already!'

She had a point, but still. 'Humour me,' Luisa suggested.

Harper made an impatient sound. 'I've already told you. I can't work out how to make sure the water's clean enough without some sort of chemical – you know, like chlorine. I'm just not smart enough to work out what else I can use as a filter.'

'Maybe you don't need chemicals,' Luisa suggested. 'What about something physical, like really fine mesh netting? There's that stuff we used over the seedlings in the garden. Would that work?'

'No,' Harper said. 'We're talking needing something that works at – I don't know what you'd call it – the molecular level? – to really clean out any impurities. What if there's bacteria transferred from the breakdown process? That could be picked up by the crops it's used to water, or ingested if consumed. There's the issue of microplastic, too – you know, I read recently that they've now found that stuff inside internal organs? If plastic can do that, think of what else is there – heavy metals, pollutants like petrol ... It has to be able to remove anything like that. Anyway, I'm not just thinking about *our* garden – if I can make this work, then it could be used everywhere, couldn't it? It could help a lot of people, not just us. Imagine if every house had one built into their kitchen.'

Luisa drew in a sudden breath as a thought occurred to her. It came accompanied by a memory, almost powerful enough to stop her heart.

'Hey,' Harper said, her voice crackling a little on the line. 'Luisa? Are you okay?'

Luisa blinked. 'Sorry,' she said. 'What you just said reminded me of something.'

'Yeah?' Harper asked. 'Like what?'

Luisa took a breath. 'A long time ago, someone I was at university with was researching the restorative properties of fungi.'

'Fungi?' Harper repeated. 'You mean – like the fertilizer thing that we used on the trees and the roses?'

'Yes. It's related. There had been some work in the States in the seventies by a mycologist called Paul Stamets who suggested that mycelium – that's the root structure of fungi, it's like a really dense web of roots that can stretch for miles underground – was capable of filtering out even the worst pollution. They'd tested their hypotheses on ground contaminated by diesel at a municipal car park, something like that. It showed astounding results. As in, within a month the fungi had ingested the contaminants and regenerated the soil. I can't remember the exact details, but I'm sure it's all online. Anyway, my friend was really excited by this idea. He thought there would be a way to incorporate this into everyday life. It was what his doctorate research was going to be in.'

'Mycelium,' Harper mused. 'Huh. Do you think I could talk to your friend? Did he ever make it work?'

'No,' Luisa said, quietly. 'He didn't. He died while he was doing his Master's degree. He never got to pursue his research further than that.'

'Oh,' Harper said, awkwardly. 'I'm sorry.'

'Other people did, though. I've still got his notes, as well. The research he did, before ...' Luisa took a deep breath, trying to loosen the grip of the past. 'I haven't thought about it for years, but I kept it all. I couldn't bear to throw it away. Who knows, Harper – maybe some of it will help. I'll look it out for you and bring it over.'

'Okay,' Harper said, warily. 'I guess it's worth a look.'

Chapter Thirty-three

'That's it,' Cas called, over the staccato thwack of leather on leather. 'Keep your elbow up, Tom, it'll give you more power on the follow-through. No, hang on, hang on. Time out.'

The two boys who had been sparring in the ring danced backwards as Cas parted the old ropes and clambered into the ring.

'Here,' he said, moving the smaller boy's arm into the right position, then demonstrating the move himself in slow motion. 'See?'

'Yeah,' Tom said, voice a little muffled by the helmet that hid half his face. He danced from side to side for a moment and then copied Cas's move. 'Got it.'

'Okay, that's good. Mo,' Cas said, to his sparring partner, 'you're doing a great job, just remember that weighting on your lead foot. Let's go again.'

He slipped back through the ropes to the floor, then lifted the whistle that was strung around his neck and blasted a brief note that echoed around the walls. The sparring pair started up again, Cas pleased to see Tom doing his best to follow his instruction.

'Evening,' said a familiar voice from behind him.

It was only because he hadn't been expecting to see her that his heart turned over, Cas told himself. He turned, already smiling, to see Luisa a couple of feet away. The salsa dancing plan didn't seem to be helping. If anything, now things were worse, because no matter who he partnered with on a Friday night, he just kept remembering that almost-dance he'd shared with her.

'Hello,' he said, as she came towards him. 'What are you doing here so late?'

'I had to go home to find something,' Luisa said. 'I came back to drop it off for Harper, she's going to collect it later this evening.'

'Really? That's a long round trip.'

'I thought it was worth it.'

She looked a little preoccupied, he thought. 'Everything okay?'

'I think so.' She smiled. 'But I wanted to talk to you about Harper.'

'Okay,' Cas said, keeping one eye on the kids sparring as they spoke. 'Although I've not seen her here for weeks. She's either doing school work or trying to get the Mini finished, as far as I can tell.'

'Oh, the Mini passed its MOT a couple of weeks ago,' Luisa said. 'Didn't she tell you?'

Cas was surprised. 'No, she didn't. But then if I see her it's only ever at school as she's passing on her way somewhere else. That's great news, though. I knew she could do it. That girl really is a wonder.'

'I know,' Luisa agreed, 'which is why I wanted to talk to you. I need to ask you another favour. There's this gala coming up. Owen, who gave me the land for the garden site, holds them every year. This year he's asked me to give a presentation about the garden and what we're trying to do here.'

'Okay,' Cas said, unable to see where this was going.

'I want Harper to present her water reclamation unit idea at the gala as well. If she can put together something short – a few words and a ten-minute PowerPoint, that's all it needs to be – I think she'll get huge interest. This could be a massive opportunity for her, Cas, it really could.'

'That sounds like a brilliant idea,' Cas said. 'You should definitely ask her.'

'That's the thing, I have. Several times. She's finally warming up to the idea,' Luisa said, holding up the files under her arm, 'and I'm hoping these will help. But I think what would really clinch it is if I could say you were going to be at the gala too. I know she'd find that reassuring.'

'When is it?'

'It's a Saturday night – the 30th of July.'

'Ah,' Cas said. 'Well, I'll certainly try, but that's the night before our exhibition day here. Where's the gala?'

'Over in Durham,' Luisa told him. 'Exhibition day? I hadn't heard about that.'

'We do it every summer,' Cas explained. 'We stage a few sparring bouts and open the place up to family, have refreshments and so on. It gives the club attendees a chance to show off what they've been learning. It's a bit of a fund-raiser, too – though on a much smaller scale than you're talking about, obviously.'

'Sounds great. I'd love to come myself.'

He grinned at her. 'Really? You think you'll be up to driving down here for ten on a Sunday morning after par-tying the night away at this gala of yours?'

She flashed him a smile, utterly artless and a mile wide, and he felt it like a sucker punch right in his gut. 'Cas,' she said, 'you've put yourself out enough for me over the past few months. The least I can do is show you the same level of support. I *want* to be here.'

After she'd gone the gym seemed less bright, quieter somehow, despite the customary cacophony that always accompanied a club night.

You're an idiot, he told himself. *What are you, a lovesick teenager? Get over yourself.*

The session was almost over when Harper appeared. She sauntered in with her hands in her pockets and her backpack over one shoulder, as if she'd never been away.

'All right, Mr P?' she greeted him, looking over at the darkened office. 'Luisa said she was going to leave something here for me.'

'Yeah, it's on her desk. Harper, wait,' Cas said, before she could walk past him. 'I haven't seen you for ages. How's things? Luisa says the Mini is on the road – that's great news. Have you driven it much?'

Harper gave him a black look that spoke volumes. 'I can't afford tax and insurance,' she said. 'Which doesn't matter because I can't afford petrol, either.'

Cas frowned. 'But I told you I'd help with those things,' he said. 'Why didn't you come to me?'

Harper's gaze slid past him to the office. 'It's not your problem,' she muttered.

'I know it isn't, but I offered, didn't I?'

She looked back at him and he saw how tired she was, how anxious. It set an alarm bell ringing at the back of Cas's mind but he couldn't quite work out why.

'You don't reckon people would think that was weird?' she asked. 'If you start paying for stuff for me as well as giving me a car?'

He put his hands on his hips, trying to figure her out. 'Has someone said something like that?'

Harper adjusted her backpack on her shoulder and looked over at the clock. It was well after eight by now, but the club always ran later as the exhibition drew closer. 'I've got to go.'

'Harper,' Cas said, following as she headed for the office. 'Hang on. Luisa asked me to talk to you about something.'

The girl picked up the stack of folders and turned back, rolling her eyes. 'It's not about this gala thing, is it?'

'Yes, actually.'

Harper bit her lip. 'She's convinced I'm going to have

something to say, but I won't. It's five weeks away. Even with this stuff,' she held up what Luisa had brought for her, 'I probably won't be able to understand it in that time, let alone work out how to use it.'

'What is that, anyway?' Cas asked, nodding at the folders. 'She didn't say when she dropped it off.'

'Research that someone she knew did years ago. She thinks it might help me work out how to make a water unit work,' Harper said. 'He died, but these are all his notes.'

Cas looked at the folders again, realizing the full significance of what Luisa had been willing to hand over on Harper's behalf.

'Mr P?' Harper asked, frowning. 'You okay?'

'Yeah,' he said. 'But look, Harper – I know how important those notes must be to Luisa. It tells me exactly how serious she is about wanting you at that gala. Please say you'll do it.'

Harper looked down at the folders. 'I guess he was a friend, but—'

'Not just a friend,' Cas said. 'They were married. To be honest I'm amazed she's given you the originals instead of scanning them in, but it's possible this is the first time she's looked at them since she lost him. Please make sure you take care of those papers.'

Harper gave him a speculative look. 'I will, Mr P,' she said, after a moment. 'I'll take care of them. Promise.'

'Good,' he said, making up his mind about something else. 'And look, she's invited me to the gala too, to cheer you on. We can go together, in the Mini. Yeah? I'll tax and insure it and you can drive us both.'

She smirked a little at that. 'Maybe.'

'Tell me you'll at least think about it? Seriously?'

Harper sighed. 'All right. I'll *think* about it. *Seriously.*'

He glanced up at the clock. 'Got time for a bit of sparring while you're here?'

Harper made an incredulous sound in her throat. 'Nope. Got somewhere to be.'

'Come on, Harper,' called Jake, one of the club kids who had missed Harper's presence the most. 'You've got to now you're here!'

There was a chorus of agreement from the rest of the room as Cas's charges gathered around them.

'Sounds like the masses have spoken,' Cas pointed out. 'Come on. You can spare half an hour, surely?'

The chorus of voices got louder. Harper laughed.

'Yeah, yeah,' she said. 'But only on one condition.'

Cas raised his eyebrows. 'Oh yeah? What's that?'

She jabbed a finger at him. 'You're the one who gets in the ring with me.'

'Me?' Cas said, over the volley of cheers that echoed around the gym walls at her demand. 'I don't think so. Get up there with Mo, he needs a decent workout.'

Loud boos accompanied his refusal, even from Mo. Harper crossed her arms.

'Here's the deal,' she said. 'I'll do the stupid gala presentation thing if you get in the ring with me.'

Cas shook his head, unable to hold in his grin. 'You come in here after weeks of no training and you think you can take *me*?'

There was a defiant glint in Harper's eye. 'I know I can, old man. Come on. I haven't got all night. Or are you too scared?'

The 'Oooohs' were almost as loud as the few shocked gasps. Cas shook his head, trying to rein in his amusement at her audacity. Despite the insolence it was good to see that Harper still had her spirit.

'Okay, okay,' he said. 'You and me. Let's go.'

Harper grinned and went out to change. It took her all of three minutes and then she was back again, slipping easily into the ring where Cas already waited, checking his gloves.

'Hope you're ready for this,' she said, dancing back and forth on her feet so easily that it was clear to Cas she hadn't forgotten a thing he'd taught her. 'Because I'm in a hurry and I've got a lot to prove.'

'Bring it,' Cas said, over the sound of the club kids whooping and hollering from the floor.

Harper waited until he was already out of breath to hit him hardest.

'Anyway, talking of Luisa,' she said. 'You made a move yet?'

The question blindsided Cas enough to let her get a shot in while he was off-balance. She darted in and clipped his jaw.

'What?' Cas asked, as he tried to recover.

'Oh, come on,' she said, ducking out of his way with

nimble ease. 'It's obvious you're crazy about her.'

'I don't know what you're talking about,' Cas said, puffing slightly. How was he this out of breath?

'What are you going to do about it?' Harper asked, as if he hadn't said a thing.

Cas gritted his teeth. '*Harper*—'

'Cos no offence,' she said, dancing deftly out of the way of his next poor excuse for an attack, 'but I think you might need to make a bit more of an effort.'

Cas tried to catch his breath. 'We're supposed to be boxing, here. Concentrate.'

She flashed him a grin. 'Fine. But I'm not the one puffing like a ten-ton ox, am I?'

Harper let him find his feet again for a moment. The cheering went on from the sidelines as Cas tried to get back into the bout.

'You know what I've noticed about Luisa?' Harper added, just as he threw another punch.

'*Harper*—'

'She always looks really happy around you. Or if she's talking about you. Or if someone even *mentions* you. It's . . . kind of sweet.'

'How would you know?' Cas countered, as he swung back towards her with a wrong-footed and clumsy upper-cut, of which she took full advantage. 'You're never here anymore.'

'Exactly,' Harper said, smashing his ribs with a smart left hook. 'If even *I've* clocked it, what does that tell you?'

'She's happy,' Cas managed through gritted teeth, parrying yet another blow but lurching backwards with the effort, 'because the garden's finally coming together.'

'Yeah?' Harper said, letting him swing and then plunging back again. 'Maybe. But what if that's not it?' she asked, with a pause before landing the killing blow. 'What if it *is* you making her happy? Cos she won't be here forever, will she? Once the garden's sorted she'll be off. There's nothing to keep her here. *Yet*, anyway. Maybe you should think about *that*.'

She slammed another fist into his ribs and Cas found himself pitching backwards, crashing against the too-slack ropes of the too-old ring with his too-old-for-any-of-this-crap back.

I have thought about it, he would have said, had Harper been anyone other than a student. *But I asked her out and she said no.*

'Sorry, Mr P,' Harper said, with absolutely no remorse and barely even out of breath. 'Looks as if you're on the ropes.' She turned to glance up at the clock to the tune of the club kids' roaring cheers. It was almost 9pm. 'I've got to go.'

Chapter Thirty-four

As summer waded into July, the garden entered a new phase. The flowers began to reach their zenith. Each morning they stretched towards the sun as it rose over Collaton, bringing with it a sustained warmth in which everything gratefully basked. One of the volunteers had suggested using the bare fence between the fruit trees for climbing plants. Now the rusting metal was festooned by intense explosions of colour – the large papery faces of summer-flowering clematis in multiple hues of purple and pink, the paint palette tangle of sweet peas that also gave out the most heavenly scent. The children who had been coming to the garden for the weekend's 'Little Growers' sessions had planted sunflowers in pots and now these were a line of happy-faced triffids, all trying to reach the sky.

The hollyhocks, which Luisa had planted as a dwarf variety but that had quickly reverted to type, were now almost as tall as her. The delphiniums had put out columns of delicate double-layered flowers that gleamed a blue as bright as the summer sky. They had shot up between the bushy phlox, which seemed to have a mind of its own and no regard for boundaries, much like the love-in-a-mist that strutted like a Hollywood starlet through the whole scene, trailing its feather boa of frond-like leaves. The earliest dahlias were beginning to flower too, one of the ladies having decided that the garden should have a full set of all the bishops. Oxford seemed to be the most vigorous, although Llandaff, the saucy scarlet devil, was close behind. Smaller bedding plants peeped between, finding their own place in the tangle of exuberant growth.

The vegetables were also in full rout – every day they picked bowlfuls of sugar snaps, which Kath complained appeared out of nowhere overnight or sometimes when her back was turned. The courgettes had gone into over-drive, the French beans were aiming for expansion, the beetroot were already the size of golf balls, and they had, with the judicious use of fine netting and the vigilance of Cas's army of diligent club volunteers, managed to wrest some cauliflowers from the very hungry caterpillars. Luisa had been in conversation with Owen's caterers about using some of this bounty for the gala banquet. Until then, though, the vegetables were divided between the volunteers who came to tend the site, the produce picked and eaten usually on the same day. One of the volunteers had suggested they hold a cook-out in August, at which the community could share in a meal grown, picked and prepared in the same spot.

The garden had become the 'happy place' for a lot of people – Luisa included. She found herself spending more and more time at the site, with Kath there every step of the way as the memorial garden and pond progressed from idea through build. Both were now finished and thriving, although they had yet to populate the pond with fish. Luisa had, on a few nights when she'd needed to work late on something and the club wasn't running, slept at the gym instead of making the hour's drive back to Carlisle. With her old sleeping bag and a pile of the exercise mats it was perfectly comfortable, especially with the added comfort of Cas's coffee machine.

There had been more than one Friday night when she'd looked up from whatever she was doing at home and found herself wondering about Cas. Was he dancing the night away at the salsa club he'd told her about? She felt a confusing pang of something approaching loneliness at the thought. He'd never asked her out again, never strayed close to it despite the warmth that continued between them whenever their paths crossed. Luisa was both appreciative of and disappointed by this – not that she ever let herself actually acknowledge the latter. *He was probably seeing someone new by now*, she told herself. *Why on earth wouldn't he be?*

Why are you thinking about this?

Such idle thoughts never crossed her mind when she was at the gym, perhaps because the shabby building held the warm atmosphere Cas had created for his students even in their absence. It was a soothing place to be, and now, when she looked up at the tatty walls, they were also festooned by Harper's hand-sketched designs for the water reclamation unit, alongside photocopied versions of Reuben's old notes. Harper had taken his early research and run with it, calling Luisa that very first evening she'd had them.

'It can't be this easy,' she'd said. 'It can't be. If it is, why isn't the whole world using mycofiltration already?'

Luisa had the sense that Harper wasn't really talking to her, she'd just needed to talk aloud to someone who would listen. A flash had come to her then, a fictitious history where it was Reuben that Harper was speaking to, Reuben she was bouncing her rapid and fascinating ideas around with.

As the weeks went on Harper brought his ideas back to life, combining them with her own and the wealth of more modern information readily available via the Internet to forge ahead in a new direction. It made Luisa feel as if Reuben were still in the world, still contributing to it – as if he were in fact there in person, working in tandem with this difficult, troubled, brilliant teen. What Harper sketched they had both built, as surely as if Reuben had been there in person.

With Reuben's ideas so manifestly alive around her, Luisa at last found herself able to think not of the hideous trauma of his passing, not the terrible, crushing weight of her guilt and loss, but of what had come before his death. Of the golden moments, like that one in the photograph she now carried again with her in her wallet. This ease of thought about him she had found nowhere but in Collaton, at a project of which they had jointly dreamed.

On the nights that she stayed at the gym, Luisa stared up at those walls and wondered why it had taken her so long to realize that true recovery from the devastation of his death required not for her to run away from what they had both loved, but to embrace it even in his absence. To grow, in fact, in all senses of the word – to plant seeds in soil, to help them flourish and, in so doing, feel her own self renewed with each new, unfurling leaf.

'It's beautiful, Arthur.' Luisa regarded the oak bench top, which had been lovingly hand-sanded to bring out the grain. 'Really, you've done an amazing job.'

'Well,' said the bench's creator with uncharacteristic modesty as he wheeled himself down the ramp they had built to provide easier access to the shed, 'let's see what it looks like in situ before we get too excited, eh?'

'It's going to look fantastic,' Cas said, over his shoulder, as between them he and Luisa picked up the heavy piece of wood and began to make their way slowly along the path to the far end of the garden.

'Cas is right,' Luisa agreed. 'Especially when the trees have grown.'

The base of the bench had already been set in place, two sturdy chunks of green oak that would slot into the corresponding shape that Arthur had hewn out of the seat's base. These had been set into the ground in front of the apple tree right in the centre of the line of espaliered orchard.

The oak was heavy, but finally they had the seat in place. Even without the tree at its fully grown height, the bench looked inviting beneath its young branches, almost as if it had always been there. Luisa stepped back and laid a tentative hand on Arthur Larkspur's shoulder.

'It's perfect,' she said, with a smile. 'Thank you so much, Arthur. It's a wonderful contribution to the garden.'

'Well,' Arthur chuckled, clearly pleased with his accomplishment. 'One down, eight more to go. If you're lucky, I might have 'em done by the time I'm eighty!'

'Arthur?'

It was Kath, coming down the path towards them.

'Hello, Kath love,' said her husband. 'We've just put the first bench out. Looks pretty good, doesn't it?'

Kath looked over at the bench and smiled warmly. 'Of course it does. You made it.'

'Aw, tsk,' said Arthur, taking his wife's hand and raising it so that he could kiss her knuckle. 'You've always been a flatterer, you.'

'It's not flattery if it's true,' Luisa pointed out as she watched this exchange. She had the sense that she was witnessing a return to a relationship that hadn't flourished for a while. It was good to see.

'Ach, you'll give an old man a big head, will the likes of you,' Arthur said, with astonishing cheerfulness.

'Anyway, must be time for lunch. I think I could do with a chip butty.'

'In your dreams, Arthur Larkspur,' Kath said, laughing. 'We'll both be having no-added-sugar tomato soup.'

Chapter Thirty-five

'Right,' Harper said, finishing her task. 'Is it secure at your end?'

'Yes,' Max told her. 'You can let go now.'

'You're sure? I don't want it to fall on your plants.'

'Yes!' Max insisted, impatient.

'Right then, here we go. Fingers crossed . . .' Harper let go of her end of the hosepipe they had lashed at intervals to one of the chrome handrails that ran the length of the bus's ceiling. She hesitated for a second, watching to see if the weight would pull the whole thing down, but it didn't. 'So far so good this end! Now you go!'

Max was standing on one of the seat benches at the back of the bus, where he'd climbed to fasten the last of the cable ties around the furthest end of the pipe. He let go and jumped down. His end of the pipe stayed put.

'Yes!' Max exclaimed, punching the air.

Harper grinned. 'Well,' she said. 'That's phase one complete. Do you want to do the honours with phase two?'

Her brother ran back towards her and she stood aside so that he could reach the metal tank that stood at the front of the bus.

'If this works and we put a pipe up on the other side, you'll have to make sure you change the end over depending on which side of the bus you want to water,' she told him, which earned her an eyeroll.

'I *know*,' Max said, almost bursting in his eagerness to put their plan into action.

They had spent hours on this idea, working on it together, talking about it over breakfast, scribbling down diagrams over dinner. Harper had sunk herself into it almost as much as she had the water filter, distracting herself from the realities that lurked outside the garden bus. It had been Max who had come up with a way to use the double-decker's internal architecture; Harper who had worked out the mechanics.

Max was at the most complicated part of the whole set-up now – a foot-operated pump that Harper had adapted from a piece of rusty kit she found out in the scrapyard. Her brother reached for the end of the dangling hosepipe that they had fixed overhead and tugged it towards him. They'd put a screw valve onto the end of it, but instead of using it to fix it onto a tap, this one attached to the end of the pump assembly inside the tank. Along the suspended length of the hose they had carefully inserted a series of sprinkler nozzles that were directed towards the rows of plants. Once the pump was attached, Max shook his hands dry, took a deep breath and stepped on the footplate.

'It's not working,' he said, after a few seconds of frantic stamping.

'It'll take a while! It needs some welly. Keep going – or do you want me to take over?'

Max shook his head furiously and kept pumping his foot.

Harper was just beginning to have misgivings about this whole set-up working when there was a faint gurgle and a trickle of water dribbled out of the first sprinkler nozzle. Max and Harper both looked at it doubtfully – was that as good as it was going to get? Then in the next second, the dribble became a full shower that bathed the seat below in a rain of water.

'It's working!' Max shouted, breathless as he redoubled his stamping.

One by one the nozzles sprung to life, until the whole left side of the bus was a mist of rain.

'Yes!'

'We did it!' Harper yelled, both of them elated. 'We did it, Max, we did it!'

Max kept planting his foot on the pump plate but Harper could see he was tiring.

'Come on,' she said. 'Let me have a go.'

Max stepped off the pump and the water flow faltered until Harper took his place, stamping and stamping on the footplate to drive the water along the hosepipe. Max laughed, running down the length of the bus, one hand held out beneath the streams. Harper laughed too, happy to see him happy. It was as if Max was a different boy inside the bus – as if here, in this tiny wonderland he'd created for himself, he had found a different world, one he understood and could navigate without hesitation.

'Thank you, Harper,' he called, running back towards her. 'Thank you for making this with me.'

Harper smiled. 'Thank you for letting me help with your garden.'

Max looked around. Everything seemed to have gone crazy in the weeks since they'd started work on the hosepipe project. Tendrils of green reached for the windows. Plants that had been seedlings smaller than Harper's little finger had begun to put out more and bigger leaves, vying for space in their pots.

'It'll be a jungle in here soon,' Harper joked, and then frowned as she saw a shadow dim Max's smile for a moment. 'Max? What's the matter?'

Her brother sighed. 'There are too many. I planted too many.'

Harper considered this for a moment. 'Well,' she said, carefully. 'Maybe you should give some away? What about—'

'No,' Max said, stubbornly. 'They belong *here*.'

'Okay,' Harper said, not wanting a fight when things had been going so well. 'We'll have to work out some solution, though.'

Max looked up at her. 'You can do that, Harper. You can fix this, too.'

Harper smiled, not wanting to cast doubt on his faith in her. 'I'll try. Come on, it's time for dinner. I've got to go out later.'

Back at home, she cooked for them and they sat at the

table together to eat. Max was quiet again and she wondered whether he was worrying about his plants. It would be such a pity to lose them now.

'Harper,' Max said, solemnly, as they finished eating. 'Will you help me with my homework?'

For a moment she was so taken aback that she thought she hadn't heard him correctly. Max had never asked for help with his homework before.

'It's all right if you don't want to,' Max mumbled, looking down into his plate.

'No,' Harper said, glancing at the clock on the kitchen wall. She had to be on her corner by nine o'clock and it was already nearly eight. But she couldn't say no to Max, not when he'd asked her something so momentous. Not when the horrible rift that had split them seemed to be closing again. 'Of course I'll help. We'll have to do it right now, though. Go and get it while I wash up, yeah?'

Harper tried not to look at the clock as they worked through the maths problems Max had been set. She wasn't actually convinced that Max needed any help, but either way it didn't matter. He'd asked her to be there with him and that was what was important. Except as the time slipped away her anxiety grew. She'd never disobeyed a text before, or been late for a 'shift'. With each passing minute Harper dreaded what might happen as a consequence, but she couldn't just walk out on Max, not now. Except that she had to, didn't she? For his sake, even if he didn't understand it.

'Okay,' she said, eventually, when the clock read 9.10. 'Do

you think you've got it now? I'm really sorry, but I've got to go. I wouldn't if I didn't have to.'

Max looked glum. 'It's my fault, isn't it?'

'What's your fault?'

Max lifted his chin at her backpack, standing on the floor by the kitchen door, ready for her to take with her.

Harper did reach out to him then, resting a hand on her brother's arm. 'No,' she said. 'It's nothing to do with you. Do you hear me? It isn't. But listen, I want you to do something for me tonight. I want you to stay in your room and pull your desk across your door so no one can get in. You do that sometimes, don't you? Can you do it tonight? For me?'

He looked worried.

Harper forced a smile and shook her head. 'Nothing's going to happen,' she said, hoping that she was right. 'I'm just . . . worried about Dad if I'm not here.'

Max hesitated for a second more and then nodded.

'Good.' Harper got up. The clock now read 9.15 and she wanted to run for the door, to run all the way to her pitch, but she forced herself to stay calm. 'I'm going to go now, okay? Make sure you brush your teeth. I'll see you in the morning.'

'Bye, Harper.'

Harper scooped up her pack and jacket and made her way to the front door. Outside, she made herself walk to the corner of the road, just in case her brother was watching. Once there, she ran as fast as she could to her spot. She expected to find one of Darren's lackeys already there, waiting for her, ready to rip into her for being late. There was no one, though. In fact, she didn't see any minders, just the usual stream of buyers. There were no angry texts on her phone, no drive-by check-ups. Harper fretted away the long hours, worrying about what was happening at home while she was stuck here, breaking the law to keep her brother safe. As soon as her stash was sold she sent the usual text to summon the pick-up crew to collect her take. Then she fled for home, terrified of what she might find when she got back there.

The answer was – nothing out of the ordinary at all. The house was still standing. There was no smoke coming through broken windows, no threatening figure lurking in the shadowy doorway. Harper looked up and down the street as she unlocked the door, but there was no sign of anyone aside from her. Inside, everything was quiet. She could hear her dad snoring loudly from the front room. She went upstairs and listened at Max's closed door. Beyond, she could hear movement.

'Max?' Harper asked, quietly.

'Harper?'

Harper gave a sigh of relief. 'You should be asleep!'

'I wanted to make sure you got home.'

'Well,' she said, through a smile, 'I'm home. Now go to sleep.'

'Okay.'

She listened for another moment, hearing the creak as her brother dutifully climbed into bed. Then Harper went to her room, dumping her pack on the floor by the bed. She had planned to do at least an hour of work on the water unit, but exhaustion overtook her. The adrenalin that had flooded her all evening drained away. No one seemed to have even noticed that she hadn't been where she should have been. Now what she felt was blank relief.

Harper fell into bed and slept.

Chapter Thirty-six

'Will you come with me? Please?'

'Is this a *quid pro quo* thing?' Jo asked, as she stood motion-less on a low stool, firmly bound into her chosen wedding dress. 'You know, I drag you to another of these fittings – no offence,' she said, with a quick and judicious smile at the shop's owner, who was busy pinning up her seemingly endless hem, before turning back to Luisa, 'and you blackmail me into coming to one of Owen's interminable gala nights with you?'

'It's not blackmail, it's moral support,' Luisa said. 'Please, Jo. I'm dreading it but I've got to make it look easy for Harper's sake and I'll feel so much better if you're there. Anyway, how do you know they're "interminable"? You've never been to one.'

'No, but I remember how you moaned whenever you had to go with Reuben,' her sister said dryly. 'I don't want to be Billy-no-mates at this thing. I bet I'll get there and you won't need me. You'll be spending all your time chaperon-ing Harper, won't you?'

'Cas will be doing that,' Luisa said. 'She won't need me.'

Jo, who had been rotated like a mannequin as they were speaking, stared at her from the mirror she now faced. '*Cas* is coming?'

'Yes. He's car-pooling with Harper. It's a way of making sure she doesn't go AWOL at the last minute.'

'Cas is coming,' Jo repeated, thoughtfully.

'Yes – *despite* the fact that there's an event at the gym the following day that he has to be there to set up for,' Luisa added pointedly. 'Come on, Jo. I need your support the way Harper needs his. Please?'

The seamstress stepped away and Jo turned to face Luisa, beaming a brilliant smile. 'All right,' she said. 'I'll come, on one condition. You let me choose what you wear.'

'What?' Luisa asked. 'Why?'

Jo shrugged. 'Because I know you. You'll leave it until the last minute and then haul out some old thing you've found at the back of your wardrobe, when we both know every other woman there will have put in the sort of effort most reserve for the Oscars red carpet.'

Luisa was bemused. 'I'm just going to wear a work suit,' she said. 'I'm not really there as a guest – I'm giving one of the after-dinner presentations.'

Jo spread both hands with a shrug. 'That's the deal. You wear what I pick or I don't come. Look at it this way, we can get this all sorted right now.' She waved at the half of the shop devoted to a colourful array of bridesmaid's gowns. 'I'll even pay for it. You can wear it at the gala and then at the wedding. I'm not precious about that sort of thing. It's not as if there'll be any guest crossover between the two, is it?' She turned to the shop owner. 'Can you help us find something for my sister? She's my maid of honour. Long, sleek, elegant and dark, I think. No ruffles, no lace, but a bit of diamante might work.'

The woman smiled. 'I can absolutely help with that. Give me a moment.' She retreated to the other side of the shop.

Luisa narrowed her eyes as she began to help Jo out of her dress. 'What are you up to?'

'I have no idea what you mean,' Jo told her. 'I just want my sister to look her best for the biggest presentation of her career. If it can do double duty in sorting out another aspect of my wedding arrangements, what's wrong with that?'

Luisa shook her head. 'I'm not sure I believe you, but I don't suppose I have much choice, do I?'

Jo, freed from the dress, stretched her arms over her head in relief. 'Nope.'

'In that case,' Luisa told her, admitting defeat, 'you can also help me find something for Harper to wear. That's another thing she's stressed about.'

Chapter Thirty-seven

Harper regarded the dress that Luisa MacGregor was holding up with narrow-eyed suspicion. It was black, knee length and looked like something a woman trained to recommend posh wine in a posh restaurant for posh people would wear under a posh jacket, which Harper definitely wasn't and did not have.

'You don't have to wear it,' Luisa said. 'You mentioned that you were worried about an outfit for the gala. I thought this might suit you. It's my sister's. But if you'd rather not . . .'

Harper shrugged. She'd seen worse. 'No, I'll wear it. Tell your sister thanks from me.'

'You can tell her yourself,' Luisa said. 'She'll be at the gala.'

'Right,' Harper said. She was still having trouble picturing exactly what this thing was going to be like. Part of her didn't want to, because when Harper tried to actually imagine herself getting up on a stage in front of a room full of people to give her presentation, she felt faintly sick. She focused on the practical instead. 'I've only got my boots to wear with it.'

Luisa smiled. 'That's fine. Whatever you're comfortable with.'

Harper wanted to say she'd be comfortable with not doing this at all, but didn't. 'Okay.'

There was a commotion in the corridor of the gym and Mo appeared with Arthur Larkspur, trailing a string of noisy kids behind them. Ever since finishing the rest of the benches for the garden Arthur had been finding himself other useful things to do around the place instead. This included helping Mo put together the video part of the gala presentation about the Collaton project. Mo had decided he wanted to film the little posse of mini-gardeners at work as a little insert for the presentation. Watching Arthur trying to wrangle them had been very funny. None of them cared about his grumpiness, or his tendency to perfectionism. There had been talk of him setting up a kids' woodworking class over summer, though, so Harper was pretty sure his complaints were just for show.

'Right,' Mo declared as he came towards Harper and Luisa. 'I think that's the last bit of footage we need. Arthur and me will cut it together later and then you can take a look, tell us what you think.'

'That's great, Mo, thanks. You too, Arthur, I'm so grateful for the help.' Luisa turned to Harper. 'The digital model is almost done too – the company working on it emailed this morning. It'll arrive on Tuesday, so we've got time to fold it into the presentation and make sure it's all in order. We can do a couple of complete run-throughs before the gala on Saturday.'

'Okay,' Harper said, her stomach backflipping uncomfortably. She couldn't believe it was less than a week away. Where had the time gone? The past few weeks had vanished in a whirlwind of preparation for the coming Saturday. She was still nervous about it, but she'd invested so much time into it that Harper couldn't back out now. She was relieved that Mr P would be there. Knowing that she would be able to look out from that stage and see him sitting there, Harper thought she might be able to convince herself that she was just in the gym's battered old boxing ring and he was down here on the floor, shouting at her to keep her elbows in, to make sure she followed through with her power. Maybe if she could convince herself that's all she was doing, she wouldn't make a massive mess of the whole thing?

Another lingering worry was Max. Sure, she was used to leaving him until the early hours of the morning, but usually she'd only be around the corner, close enough to ditch everything and run home if he really needed her. This time she was going to be on the other side of the country, with no quick way home. She talked to him about it later that same day as they watered the garden bus together – the sprinkler system was holding up well.

'I won't be back home until really late,' she said, as she helped him pinch out some new growth on the tomatoes, which had turned into triffids that reached almost to the floor from their hanging baskets, trusses of fruit already beginning to appear on their branches. 'I mean, I'm going to make sure I'm back in Collaton by ten at the latest but I'm going to have to go somewhere else first for a while.' She didn't have to spell out where that was – Max knew well enough already and Harper hated to speak aloud about it, as if not voicing the truth of her illicit night-time sojourns for their awful cousin somehow made it unreal, non-existent.

'I'll be fine,' Max insisted.

'I wish you could come with me to Durham.'

Max screwed up his nose. 'I don't.'

Harper laughed. 'Well, I'll have my phone with me. Now you've got your own you can call me any time, okay?'

'I'll bring my quilt and pillows and camp here,' he said.

It occurred to Harper that having Max do just that might not be such a terrible idea. She was going to be the latest she'd ever been to her pitch and although over the past several weeks she'd frequently pushed her 9pm 'shift start', it had usually only been by thirty minutes, or an hour at the very latest. She'd go straight there after the gala and she was fairly sure that no one would notice as long as she stayed until she got rid of her gear – they hadn't so far, after all – but still. She'd rather know that Max was out of harm's way. He was probably safer here with his plants than anywhere else in Collaton, including their actual home.

'You know what?' she said. 'That's a great idea.'

Max beamed, his excitement at the idea of an all-night campout in the garden bus evident. Harper smiled back, thinking again of plants changing the world. They certainly had changed Max's. His engagement with his 'greenhouse' was greater than any other of the short-lived obsessions she'd seen him pass through in the ten years of his fledgling life. Maybe, in a round-about way and if she didn't screw everything up at the last minute, plants could change Harper's life, too.

A few days later, Saturday afternoon. Harper was taking the Mini on its longest run yet as she and her passenger made their way across the Pennine ridge to County Durham.

'How are you doing there, Mr P?' Harper asked, as the Mini swung around another corner and the force pushed him against the window, neck at an awkward angle, the crown of his head crushed into the ceiling. 'It's a bit of a squash for you, eh?'

'I'm fine,' he said, though she could tell that he had his teeth gritted.

She tried not to laugh. 'Can't be that far away now,' she said, cheerfully. 'Hang in there.'

They took another corner and he grunted again. 'Are you doing this deliberately? Because I wouldn't let you turn around and go home?'

Harper glanced at him, forcing her eyes wide and innocent. 'I don't know what you mean.'

He shook his head, reaching out to pat the dashboard lightly, although with his other hand he kept a firm hold on the overhead handle.

'I can't actually believe that this is the same bucket of bolts that stood on Mum and Dad's driveway for so long,' he said. 'You really have done a remarkable job.'

'I can't believe this was ever your car,' Harper said. 'What on earth made you get a Mini?'

'It was what I could afford,' he told her. 'Besides, the girls seemed to like it. Did quite well in this thing in my late teens and early twenties.'

'Ew,' Harper said, with an elaborate shudder. 'That's way more information than I ever needed to know, thanks.'

They navigated towards the address that Cas had copied into his phone's satnav from the silver-embossed invitation Luisa had given him. It was after five and the midsummer sun was still high in the sky, gleaming on the landscape. The invitation said that guests were welcome to begin arriving from five-thirty. Luisa had the equipment and files for Harper's presentation and said there was no need for them to arrive earlier than that.

Harper, who had finally begun to settle on the long drive over, was beginning to feel increasingly out of place again the closer they got to their destination. Somewhere at the back of her head she'd assumed the gala would be held in some soulless, corporate business centre, somewhere blocky and concrete, probably part of a travel inn with a motorway not far from its front door. But the route in which the invitation was leading them suggested something very different. The houses on both sides of the leafy road were huge, their matching grounds expertly manicured.

Harper jiggled in her seat and pulled the skirt of her dress down towards her knees.

'God, dresses,' she complained, nerves bubbling in her stomach. 'Why does anyone put themselves through the hassle? Give me a pair of jeans any day. I look like an idiot.'

'You don't,' said Mr P. 'You look very presentable.'

'I look like a poor cow who had to borrow a dress because she hasn't got anything of her own that won't make her look like a poor cow.'

'I'm surprised you bothered, to be honest,' he said. 'I was expecting you to just turn up in your usual togs.'

She shot him a look. '"Togs"?' Harper repeated. 'God, Mr P, you really are beginning to sound ancient. Anyway, do you really think I want to stick out like even more of a sore thumb than I will already?'

'I don't think Luisa would have cared what you wore.'

'She was the one who found me this dress,' Harper pointed out. 'Although she did say I should wear what I feel comfortable in.'

'There you go, then,' Mr P said. 'Stop worrying. No one's going to care what you look like.'

Harper snorted a laugh. 'Yeah, sure. You do know that most of the women there will be wearing something that cost more than this car, right?'

There was a moment of silence. 'To be fair,' said Mr P, 'that wouldn't actually be very hard, would it?'

Harper shook her head. 'Don't be dissing my car, Mr P.'

'Wouldn't dream of it. Anyway, the point is, you look

fine. Stop worrying. Be the Harper who doesn't care what anyone else thinks. I know she's still in there somewhere.'

Harper kept her concentration on the road ahead but pointedly raised her eyebrows.

'What?' he asked.

'Why do you even own a tux, anyway?'

He looked down at himself and tugged the now-rumpled jacket back down from where it had ridden up a little. 'My ex always had these posh work things she wanted to drag me to. Waste of a month's salary *that* was.'

Harper snorted a laugh. 'Well, it kind of suits you.'

'Yeah?'

'Yeah. You scrub up okay. For an old guy.'

'I think that might be the nicest thing you've ever said to me.'

'It's true. I feel like I should call Luisa and warn her.'

Cas smiled. 'I'm so glad that you two are getting on better,' he said. 'I can't think of a better role model and look at what—' He stopped then, as if finally registering what Harper had actually said. 'Wait, what do you mean, *warn* her?'

Harper glanced at him again as she obeyed the satnav's voice to take another turn just a little too fast. It crushed him against the window again.

'She's only seen you in crappy gym gear or your other rubbish old-man "togs" up until now,' Harper pointed out. 'We don't want her having a heart attack when you walk in looking like James Bond.'

'She's seen me in my teaching get-up, it's not that different.'

Harper rolled her eyes. 'Yeah, it really is.' Something occurred to her. 'Come to think of it – you are prepared *yourself*, right?'

'I have no idea what you mean,' he said. 'Can you stop talking in riddles?'

'Oh my God,' Harper said. 'Okay, now I'm worried that *you're* the one who's going to have a heart attack. You do get that she's going to look a bit different to how you've seen her in Collaton, don't you?'

'Sure,' he said, with a shrug. 'I'm guessing there won't be many steel-toe-capped boots at this shindig, for a start.'

Harper shook her head slowly. This had the makings of a total train wreck. She was about to say something to this effect when she was interrupted by the tinny voice of the blue dot.

'You have reached your destination. The destination is on your left.'

Harper screeched to a sudden halt, which rammed Mr P's knees up against the dash as he braced himself to avoid ending up squashed into the windshield.

They both stared open-mouthed at the huge wrought ironwork gates just beyond the Mini's nose. Through the fence itself could be seen a wide tarmacked driveway winding through opulent surrounds to an enormous house that stood on a slight rise, which was at least half a mile from where they sat. The house looked like something the BBC would use for an episode of *Antiques Roadshow.* Several large cars could be seen on the driveway ahead, purring their way slowly towards the building.

Harper tightened her hands on the steering wheel. 'I don't think I can do this. I'm just going to turn around. We can go back home, right now.'

'No,' said Mr P, firmly. 'What about your presentation?'

'Luisa's got everything,' she said, wrestling the Mini's gearstick into reverse and preparing to gun the clutch. 'She can do it instead. I'm just going to—'

Another car pulled up behind them, a sleek silver Mercedes with blacked-out windows and a guy wearing a chauffer's cap in the driver's seat. Harper swore, loudly.

There was a rap at the driver-side window. They both jumped.

'Miss? Can I help you?'

'We're here for the gala,' Mr P said, before she could reply. He leaned over, holding out the invitation. 'We're guests of Luisa MacGregor.'

The guard took the invitation, looked at it briefly and then smiled at both of them.

'Welcome, sir, ma'am.' In front of them, the gates began to swing open at some silent magic command. 'If you drive on up to the house, a valet will help you with your car. Have a good evening.'

He stepped aside. For a moment Harper was utterly frozen.

'Harper?' Mr P prompted, quietly.

'Yeah,' she said, faintly. 'Yeah, I'm on it.'

Chapter Thirty-eight

They stood together in the reception hall, Cas with a glass of champagne. He had thought he wouldn't want a drink tonight, but as it turned out he needed something to settle his nerves. Who *were* these people? The house was as opulent within as it had appeared from without. He looked up at the soaring arch of ceiling above them, the great marble staircase curving towards the upper floors, the massive pieces of art depicting people who were presumably personally connected to this place, the multiple flower arrangements that likely each cost more than his monthly salary. Around them swarmed a crowd of people dressed richly enough to match their surroundings. Harper, it turned out, had been right about that.

'We could make a run for it,' she suggested, in a whisper. 'No one will notice.'

'Luisa would,' he reminded her.

Harper rolled her eyes. 'Right. Can't let Luisa down. Where is she, anyway?'

Cas scanned the crowd again as he took a sip of his champagne. None of the assembled people looked even vaguely familiar.

'Harper!' one of the strangers called from the throng. 'Cas!'

It wasn't until she smiled that he recognized her, in a shattering flash that blindsided him so completely that his heart stopped for four full beats. *Luisa.* Cas had lifted his glass to his lips again but at this realization he inhaled sharply, breathed in bubbles, choked, coughed, then almost dropped his drink. He only succeeded in saving it from falling at his feet by sloshing champagne over his fingers and the marble floor.

'I *told* you, didn't I?' Harper hissed as the almost unrecognizable cause of his consternation scythed through the crowd towards them.

'There you both are!' Luisa said, oblivious. 'I was worried you might have trouble with the directions.'

'You're joking, right?' Harper asked. 'This place is probably visible from *space*.'

As Luisa laughed Cas tried to regain his equilibrium. He had thought her beautiful from the first time they had met, but this evening made her a superlative for which he had no words. It wasn't even as if the dress she was wearing was particularly elaborate. Black silk and perfectly fitted, it fell from spaghetti straps at her shoulders until the full skirt met the floor. Her hair was coiled up in a complicated style, dressed with pins that glittered beneath the house's huge illuminated chandeliers. He tried not to gawp at her, tried to remember how to breathe.

'We need to do a sound check,' Luisa was saying to Harper. 'Let's get it done now, then it's out of the way. Cas, do you want to come with us, or stay here? We won't be long.'

He opted to remain where he was: an elephant in a dinner suit, skulking in the corner as he tried to reassemble his wits. It was seeing her in such a different setting that had thrown him so completely, Cas supposed. This was the world Luisa inhabited, was it? It helped him to absorb that, somehow, to know how large the gulf was between their daily lives. All he had known about her was what he'd seen in Collaton. She hadn't ever seemed out of place.

'It's Cas, isn't it?' Luisa's sister Joanna said, as she appeared in front of him. 'I'm Jo, Lu's sister? Hi!'

'Hi,' he said, taking the hand she held out to him to shake. 'Good to see you again.'

'And you. I'm so glad you came.'

'You are?' He couldn't work this out, wondered why she remembered him given how brief their previous interaction had been.

'Yes – and Harper, too. I haven't met her yet but Luisa's told me about her and she sounds fantastic.'

Cas smiled a little. 'She is.'

'Anyway,' Jo said, with another beaming smile. 'Since I have you to myself, tell me about you. Tell me *everything*.'

Cas was trying to work out how to approach this request when Luisa and Harper reappeared.

'Joanna,' Luisa said, shooting Cas an apologetic look. 'Stop harassing Cas and meet Harper instead. Harper, this is my sister, Jo.'

'Oh, right,' Harper said. 'Thanks for the dress.'

'You're welcome. Come outside and talk to me, would you? I need a breath of fresh air.'

'Jo . . .' Luisa said, reprovingly.

'What?'

'I thought you quit?'

'What, fresh air?' Jo asked, with obviously feigned confusion. 'Honestly, Lu, you can be so weird sometimes.'

They left, Harper casting a glance back towards Cas with an expression that hovered somewhere between a cry for help and relief at her escape. He turned back to Luisa to find her looking at him with frank appraisal.

'You look great, Cas,' she said. 'Really great. I've never imagined you in a tux, but—' She broke off, a slight colour suddenly tinting her cheeks. She dropped her gaze to his throat for a moment before shocking him by reaching out and brushing her fingers over his hand. 'Come with me for a second.'

She looked around quickly and then led him through a door into a small drawing room, book-lined and leather chaired, gleaming dark wood and the smell of furniture polish. Cas had no idea what was going on but as the door shut behind them the sound of the hubbub outside dropped away. He could smell her perfume and was trying to centre himself when she reached for his collar. He jumped as her fingers brushed his neck. He grabbed her wrists, shocked, holding her still, their closeness reminding him suddenly, sharply, of that failed dance in the gym.

'What are you doing?'

'I – your tie,' Luisa said, flustered. He could feel her pulse beating in both wrists, a quick patter against his skin. 'Sorry. I was just going to straighten—'

'Oh.' He let her go and cleared his throat. 'Right. Sorry. I've always been hopeless at doing them.'

Luisa reached up again, undoing his bowtie so that she could refasten it, that tint in her cheeks back again now, more pronounced. Cas focused on the glint of the pins in her hair to stop him watching her face, trying not to feel the touch of her fingers against his neck, how intimate the whole situation was. He could see how quickly she was breathing.

'There,' she said, stepping backwards swiftly once she'd accomplished her task, not quite looking at him. 'Done.'

'Thanks,' he said and then, before he had to struggle to fill a silence growing more awkward by the second, the deep, booming sound of a gong rang through the door behind them.

'Dinner,' Luisa said, with obvious relief. 'That's them calling us to table.'

Chapter Thirty-nine

Harper looked at her watch. It was after 9.30pm and they'd only just been served dessert. She was so glad Max was hidden safely away in the bus, because she was beginning to think that she was going to miss her entire 'shift' for the first time. Even if she left now she'd be pushing it to get back to Collaton by midnight, and she hadn't done her presentation yet. No one seemed to be in any rush to speed proceedings up, either. The ballroom rang with chatter and laughter, which probably had a lot to do with the glasses of wine that the catering staff kept topped up.

Harper never drank. There was so much in her life she was unable to control that she found the idea of being drunk and incapable utterly repulsive. She kept glancing at the stage, not quite believing that sooner or later she was going to have to get up there and talk in front of these people. One of the people on their table was wearing an actual Rolex, for God's sake.

Actually, though, everyone on their table had been

really nice. She was next to Joanna and opposite Cas and Luisa, who had been seated beside each other. Harper had a sneaking suspicion that might have been some sort of cock-up, because when Luisa came to take her place she'd done a double-take, as if she'd been expecting to sit somewhere else.

Besides the four of them were three total strangers, one old gent on his own and another couple who were husband and wife. The wife was wearing a dress that probably cost more than Harper's electricity bill for a year.

'I don't much bother with these things now, you know,' the old chap confided to her, as if they were old friends, 'but Owen called me himself to convince me to come. I hear you're a real talent to watch, Harper.'

'Yes,' piped up the woman in the designer gown. 'That's why we're here, too. We've got a stake in *The World* and I've been pushing them to find a more ecologically friendly way of dealing with food waste and water ever since it launched. I'm intrigued to see if you've got something we can adapt.'

Harper was mystified.

'*The World* is a ship,' Joanna leaned over to whisper, briefly. 'The biggest cruise liner on the planet. People lease an apartment on it, like they would an island in the Caribbean.'

'Perhaps you could join us for a trip, Harper,' the woman – who was apparently 'big in future tech' – suggested. 'We're always looking for new guest lecturers. We have all sorts, you know. Historians, mathematicians, theoretical physicists, archaeologists. Even an astronaut, once.'

'Oh,' Harper said, awkwardly, 'well, I'm still at school. I haven't even finished my A-levels. I can't teach anyone about anything.'

'Don't you believe her, Natalie,' Luisa said. 'Aside from designing the reclamation unit, Harper's just rebuilt herself a classic Mini Cooper. It's what she drove here in today.'

'Now that,' said the husband, 'is *my* kind of impressive.'

'Malcolm came up in cars,' Natalie supplied. 'Fascinated by them. That would be another great lecture series, come to think of it, wouldn't it, darling?'

'Definitely would.'

The woman put down her knife and fork and took out a business card from the pristine white leather clutch she'd rested on the table beside her instead. She held it out to Harper.

'Call or drop me an email,' she said. 'Let's talk.'

Harper took the card. 'But you haven't even heard my presentation yet.'

The woman eyed her shrewdly. 'You're still in school and you've already reconstructed a classic car and shown enough promise that Owen is willing to give you the floor here. My dear, I don't need to see your presentation to know you're someone I should have on my radar as early as possible.'

Harper mumbled a thanks and put the card into her pocket. Suddenly her nerves were overwhelming. She looked across the table just as Luisa leaned over to quietly say something to Cas. Cas smiled and glanced up at Harper, nodding, but that just made the knot of anxiety in her

305

stomach twist tighter. She looked down at her dessert, which remained virtually untouched. Everyone else, though, was finished. As she thought this a team of serving staff appeared to begin clearing. Harper could see that Luisa was preparing herself. A couple of minutes later one of the serving staff came over and bent down to whisper in Luisa's ear. She nodded and thanked him, standing up as he left.

'That's my cue. Excuse me, everyone. Harper,' she said, with a warm smile that did nothing to fill the sudden, yawning pit of dread that had opened up in Harper's stomach, 'just do exactly as you did in the sound check. You're going to be brilliant.'

The lights dimmed almost to darkness as Luisa stepped onto the stage, the chatter in the room dropping into silence.

'Ladies and gentlemen,' Luisa began, her strong, clear voice amplified perfectly by the microphone. 'Now that you've all had a delicious meal, it's time for the bit you really came for . . .'

Luisa went on, but there was a buzzing rising in Harper's ears, drowning out the words. She swallowed, her heart hammering in her ribcage, the dinner she had managed to consume churning in her gut.

'Does he always look at her like that?' whispered a voice in her ear, so quiet it was barely there.

Harper jumped a little. It was Joanna, leaning over in the darkness.

'What?' Harper whispered back.

In the thin gleam of available light Harper saw her indicate across the table. Mr P was sitting motionless, his gaze completely fixed on Luisa.

'Oh,' Harper whispered. 'That. Yeah. Pretty much.'

There came a sudden storm of clapping. Harper realized the video presentation had ended. She looked up at the stage to see Luisa looking back at her expectantly.

Jo nudged her and grinned. 'That's your cue,' she said. 'Knock 'em dead.'

Harper stood up with her heart pounding. Another round of clapping began, this time entirely for her. She glanced around the table at the smiling faces of Natalie, Malcolm, Mr P, all looking at her, urging her on. Harper briefly considered making a run for it, but she couldn't do that, could she?

She thought of the woman called Natalie, who had handed her a business card without even hearing this presentation, who had made Harper a suggestion as if she belonged there, as if it were the most natural thing in the world that Harper would have something to contribute.

This is it, she told herself as she walked onto the stage. *This is what might get you and Max out of Collaton. Get it done.*

'Of all the ecological challenges facing the world today,' Harper began, her voice rising over the room, 'we up here in the north don't often think about water, do we? Even during the summer heatwave down south last year, everywhere near us was still pretty green. The rain still fell, there were no hosepipe bans, no fields burned brown by weeks of sun.

It's easy to think it's always going to be that way. But that's why we should be thinking about conservation now – before we're forced to. The average person uses 150 litres of water a day. That figure doesn't even take into account the water needed to produce our food.'

Behind her, the screen burst into life right on time. Harper took a moment to centre herself by pouring a glass of water from the jug that had been set on the table beside her. She held it up to the light behind her, a rainbow refracting across the notes waiting there for her that she realized she didn't need. She looked out at the audience and smiled as the music from the sequence died away.

'Food waste, that's another pressing problem. We all know that we still throw away far too much. What if there was a way to address both of these issues with one simple, economical and ecologically sound piece of equipment?'

The screen behind her spun up again. Harper turned to see the digital model of her idea that had been produced specifically for this evening. It didn't look like much really, just a three-chambered metal box with a small chute that opened out at one end and a tap at the other, but that was the point. It was *so simple*.

'Most of us think of mushrooms as something delicious to chop into an omelette,' she went on. 'But as far back as the 1970s, mycologist Paul Stamets was experimenting with mycelium to create natural pesticides and clean up fuel spills. Today, among other things, it's being used to create building materials from construction waste, durable leather substitutes suitable for clothing and – most notably for us – as a way to purify waterways contaminated by chemicals.'

The murmurs continued. A few people seemed to be taking notes.

'Mycofiltration is the key to the Collaton Water Reclamation Unit.' Harper pointed to the on-screen model as it zoomed in on the slim middle chamber of her unit design, which then slid up to reveal its own framework of mesh-like mycelium. 'Building on the research of a young mycologist called Reuben MacGregor, I have developed the concept for this completely organic mycoremediation filter. Mushroom spores are encouraged to pack this chamber with mycelium. Once the chamber is full, we begin letting in the effluent from the main chamber. The mycelium will remove any contaminants as the water filters through the fungal roots and into the output chamber. The result is pure, clean water that can be used wherever it's needed. When a fresh network is required, the user slides out the chamber, removes the mycelium mesh and replaces it with fresh spores and growing medium. The old mycelium net is encouraged into spore production – mushrooms, which can be harvested for use as spore feeders in the next mycelium filters. Or,' Harper suggested, 'eaten in an omelette.'

A spatter of laughter echoes around the room.

'How we protect Earth's finite resources going forward is the most pressing issue we face today,' Harper said in conclusion, 'and that's why I believe that this fully organic water reclamation unit could be the key to the future of domestic recycling, not just here, but worldwide. This idea is at the very beginning of its journey, but it came about as a result of the Collaton Garden Project and is being developed there. I hope that at least some of you will consider helping us take this idea forward into the future and the next stage of its development. Our planet is in crisis. What are you waiting for? Thank you for listening. My name is Harper Dixon.'

Chapter Forty

'Luisa?'

It was Owen, coming towards her through the crowd. It was late, but the ballroom was still buzzing with the energy of a good evening.

'Owen,' Luisa greeted him as he reached her, glad to see that he was smiling. 'Well, I hope we lived up to your expectations?'

He gave a hearty laugh. 'She's a star, Luisa. In fact, that's what I wanted to talk to you about. Harper really should stay for the working brunch here tomorrow.'

'Ah,' she said. 'That might be a problem, I'm afraid. She brought Cas with her and I know he needs to get back to Collaton tonight. He has commitments there tomorrow morning.'

'That's a pity,' Owen said. 'There are so many people who want to talk to her further. She's really gone down a storm, you know. In fact, I'd like to find some time to talk to her properly myself.'

'Oh?'

'Yes. I can't help but feel that I need to get in on the ground floor. I've been thinking about what you said about a scholarship and it's something that Lawrence Homes should really be offering anyway. This seems like a perfect place to start. This water unit idea of hers, I think it has legs. The home-building business has got to adapt, far beyond making solar panels and heat pumps accessible. Talk to her, would you?'

Luisa nodded. Wasn't this the exact reason that she had wanted Harper to do this in the first place? Her gaze strayed to Cas, deep in conversation with someone Luisa recognized as one of the directors of BAE Systems' operation at Barrow-in-Furness. As she watched he glanced up, caught her eye and smiled. He was obviously so proud of Harper. He'd always been her biggest supporter, convinced that she had a bright future if only the opportunities could be channelled her way. Here was the biggest so far – who was Luisa to cut it short when there was an easy solution?

'I will,' Luisa said. 'If she's willing to stay, I'll take Cas home myself. That way she won't miss out.'

She was making her way over to Harper when she felt a hand brush her arm and turned to see Lady Caroline Percivant, a warm smile on her face.

'Lady Caroline! Hello. It's nice to see you again,' Luisa said, as the two women shook hands. 'I didn't know you would be attending.'

'Hello, Luisa. Well, to tell you the truth, I usually try

to avoid these things,' she confided. 'Between you and me, I find them interminable. I send a donation and make an excuse. But when Owen called to tell me you were going to be giving an after-dinner presentation, that changed everything.'

'Oh?'

Lady Caroline glanced around, as if to check who might be listening. 'I came in the hope that you might be able to rescue me. Or rather, Feldspar Hall and her gardens. Things haven't worked out with Marianne Boswell, I'm afraid. We've parted ways.'

Luisa was taken aback. Boswell Garden Architecture's contract papers were usually cast iron. There was no way that Marianne would have let a job like Feldspar Hall go easily.

'Anyway, to cut a long story short,' Lady Caroline went on, 'I need a new landscape architect and I'm hoping I can persuade you to take the job.'

'I – I'm sorry, what?' Luisa blinked. The room was noisy. Perhaps she hadn't heard correctly.

Lady Caroline smiled, reaching out to touch Luisa lightly on the arm. 'I know this is out of the blue. But I've been keeping vaguely in touch with how the Collaton project has been going through Owen. You've done a remarkable job. The garden's really established now, isn't it?' She glanced over at the stage where Luisa had talked about the progress in Collaton. 'That wonderful video demonstrated how the local community has taken it on. It must be time you thought about what comes next for you? I'm hoping I can persuade you to come my way. Feldspar Hall needs you, Luisa. *I* need you!'

Luisa wasn't sure what to say. 'Thank you for thinking of me,' she said. 'Really, it's very kind of you, Lady Caroline . . .'

'It's just Caroline,' Lady Caroline reminded her. 'And it's not kind, it's entirely pragmatic. I know we'd work well together and we both know how important that is on a long-term project like this.'

'I don't feel as if I'm ready to leave the Collaton garden yet,' Luisa said, her head spinning. 'There's still so much to be done.'

'Well,' Caroline said, taking a business card from the sleek clutch bag she carried and handing it over. 'Have a think, at least, won't you? If there's something that might sweeten the deal for you, let me know. You're the one I want, Luisa. It should have been you from the beginning, I see that now. Drop me a line whenever you want to chat.'

When the slightly stunned Luisa finally made her way to Harper, it was to find her with Cas and Joanna, flush-faced and happier than Luisa had ever seen her before.

'Say it quietly,' Cas said, 'but I think Harper here is having fun.'

Harper laughed. 'I'm not sure about fun, exactly . . . This is mental! People keep asking me questions and if I have any other ideas.' She held up a handful of business cards. 'I've asked them about scholarships for college and loads have given me these and told me to call them next week.'

'About that,' Luisa added. 'Owen says you're welcome to stay overnight, Harper. Brunch is always a bit of a work event here and he's got something he wants to talk to you about.'

'What? I can't do that,' Harper said. She glanced at her watch and froze. For a second she looked panicked. 'Wait – that's not really the time, is it?'

'Yeah, it's after midnight already,' Jo said. 'Time flies when you're having fun.'

'But I should be . . . My brother,' Harper stuttered, still anxious. 'I need to – I need to get back to him.'

'I thought he was staying with a friend tonight?' Luisa asked. 'He'll already be in bed by now. And don't worry about Mr Pattanyús, I can take him home.'

'But don't you want to stay too?' Cas asked her.

'Not if it means Harper can make the most of a good opportunity,' Luisa said. 'Harper? What do you say?'

'I can't stay here on my own,' Harper said. 'I don't know anyone!'

'I'll be here,' Jo said, quickly. 'I was going to stay over here with Lu anyway. Let her take Cas home.'

Luisa eyed her sister, sensing an ulterior motive. Jo looked back at her with a shrug and a face full of studied innocence that Luisa didn't believe for a second.

'I need to message my brother, make sure he's all right,' Harper said. 'Can you give me a minute? He'll still be awake – he'll be waiting to hear from me.'

She went to their table and grabbed her phone. Luisa saw

315

that the waiters were serving coffee and went to get one, aware that though right now the adrenalin of the evening had her wide awake, she was about to embark on a protracted drive after a very long day.

'You really don't have to do this,' Cas said, following her to the table. 'It's ridiculous. I'll get a cab. Or I'll stay and get Harper to drop me at the station first thing tomorrow morning.'

Luisa looked at him over the rim of her coffee cup. 'One of those options would be exorbitant and the other would take hours,' she said. 'Really, it's not a problem.'

Cas cast his eyes over her, his gaze lingering on her bare shoulders. 'Have you got a coat?' he asked.

'You'll just have to keep her warm, Cas,' Joanna said as she appeared at Luisa's side. Then, ignoring the venomous look Luisa sent her way, she added, 'You can spare your jacket for a damsel in distress, can't you?'

'I doubt that your sister's ever been that,' Cas said. 'But of course I can.'

Harper returned, some of the colour back in her cheeks. 'My brother's fine,' she said. 'Even if I left now it'd be after two in the morning before I got back, so ... yeah. I'll stay.'

Chapter Forty-one

It wasn't until Jo's sly, suggestive comment that the situation Luisa was putting herself in with Cas occurred to her. After weeks of carefully avoiding almost all one-on-one contact with Casimir Pattanyús, Luisa had now volunteered to put herself at close quarters with him, alone, for hours, late at night and after an emotional evening.

'Call me tomorrow,' Joanna prompted, as she waited with Luisa while Cas went to ask the valet for her car. 'Tell me how it went.'

'What are you talking about?' Luisa asked, feigning ignorance. 'I'm just going to drive him home.'

'Oh, come on,' her sister persisted. 'You can't tell me you haven't had one dirty thought about him. Even my ramrod straight big sister can't be *that* lacking in self-awareness.'

'Please stop it. Do you want him to hear you?'

Jo raised both eyebrows. 'I don't think that would be the worst thing in the world.'

'He's a friend,' Luisa added, striving for patience. 'That's all.'

'Sure,' Jo said. 'That's why he hasn't been able to take his eyes off you all evening. Just let yourself have fun for a change, Luisa. Please?'

'You don't know what you're talking about,' Luisa said, 'which is fine because I'm not listening to you anyway.'

By then, though, the damage was done, especially when Cas slipped off his jacket and held it up for her to put it on. Luisa tried not to be affected by the whisper of his fingers up the bare skin of her arms, tried not to wonder whether what Jo had said was true. She took a deep breath that was supposed to be steadying, but his aftershave lingered in the jacket now around her shoulders.

And really, a little voice whispered to her from somewhere inside her that she hadn't even known still existed, *where's the harm?*

'Well,' Cas said, as they began the long drive back to Collaton, 'that was a pretty amazing evening.'

His easy tone helped put a dent in the tension. Luisa smiled. 'Wasn't it? The best event of that sort that I think I've ever been to at Owen's, actually.'

She felt him look over at her. 'You go to a lot of these types of things, then?'

Luisa laughed. 'God, no. Owen was Reuben's godfather, so I used to attend them with him. I never found them easy, though. I mean, it's just a different world, isn't it?'

'Just a tad,' Cas said, with a slight laugh, tugging loose his bowtie.

'Although,' she added, 'seeing Harper come alive tonight makes up for every single one I've ever been to.'

'I know,' Cas said, a smile clear in his voice though she couldn't see it. 'I think tonight will prove to be a real turning point. I've always tried to tell her what she could be, but you're the one who's actually managed to show her.'

By the time they reached Collaton it was after 2am and Luisa was yawning heavily.

'I feel so bad that you've still got an hour's drive ahead of you,' Cas said. 'I can't even lend you a sofa to sleep on.'

'It's fine,' Luisa said. 'I think I'll just stay at the gym, though, rather than driving back to Carlisle.'

'What?' he asked, aghast. 'You can't sleep at the gym!'

'Why not?' she asked, laughing a little at his reaction. 'I've done it before. Besides, I was planning to be here for the exhibition anyway. This way I'll be early enough to help you set up.'

'Luisa—'

'I've got a sleeping bag, a wash kit and a change of clothes there already,' she said, cutting him off. 'I'll be absolutely fine.'

She could feel him watching her, his head turned in her direction as the night's shadows danced across his face. Luisa concentrated on the road ahead.

'I can't persuade you?'

'Nope. I'll be fine,' she said again. 'Really.'

He sighed. 'Well, if you're determined,' he said, 'drive there rather than dropping me off first. I'll see you inside and then walk, it's not far.'

A quiet sank into and around them as she pulled into the square and they got out of the Defender. Luisa thought of the first time she had driven Jo's car here, of her brief flash of fear as Cas's huge bulk had appeared out of the darkness. Now here she was, completely secure in his presence. Wasn't it strange, how drastically things could change and in such a relatively short space of time? Back then the garden had seemed an entirely impossible idea, a pipe dream, yet now here she was, standing in darkness, breathing in the scent of foliage drifting from it on a quiet breeze.

The early morning air was cool, the square deserted as they crossed it together. The sky was clear and cloudless, the moon vast overhead. It cast the broken houses in silver, the garden in a wash of uncanny light.

'Oh,' Luisa said as they reached the gym's old double doors. She looked at the clutch bag that was the only thing she'd brought with her. 'I don't have my key with me. I didn't think I'd need it. What an idiot.'

'It's all right,' Cas said, his voice a low rumble in the empty night. He reached into his pocket. 'I've always got mine.'

He unlocked the door and held it open so she could step inside. Cas stayed on the threshold, standing in moonlight as he wrestled the key from an overloaded chain before holding it out to her.

Luisa's fingers brushed his palm as she took it. 'Thank you.'

'It means you'll have to hang around tomorrow to let me in before you leave,' Cas said, with a note of apology. 'But I'll be here early.'

'I was planning to be here anyway, remember?'

He shook his head, face pensive as he looked past her into the dark corridor.

'Really,' she said. 'I'll be fine. Maybe you see me as this fine lady who can't deal with roughing it a bit, but—'

'That's not how I think of you, Luisa,' he said, his voice soft as he cut her off. 'Of course it isn't.'

'No?' Luisa found herself asking. 'Then how do you think of me?'

Cas shot her a look that turned her heart over. Her breath caught and she felt his gaze fixed on her as she looked away. There was a fraction of a pause.

'As a woman capable of building emergency shelters from scrap in the event of an apocalypse, obviously,' he said, into the silence.

'Oh,' Luisa said, because for a moment she'd thought he was going to say something else, something serious, something that would match the look in his eye at that moment, and she couldn't deal with her feeling of utter disappointment any more than she could pretend it wasn't there. 'Well, there are worse ways to be thought of, I suppose.'

'I should go,' he said. Cas took a step away from her, the shadows on his face sliding away as he moved.

'Wait,' Luisa said. 'Your jacket—'

Cas reached out to stop her before she could slip it from her shoulders. 'Don't,' he said. 'Really, keep it in case—'

They both stilled, suddenly aware of how close they had become. They stared at each other and Luisa felt as if she was going to lose her footing, as if she was going to spin right off her feet and fall towards him, as if towards a black hole. Cas dropped his hands but didn't step back, and then—

'Luisa,' he said, quietly, 'I keep trying *not* to think of you. But—'

'I know,' she said, on the whisper of an in-drawn breath. 'I *know*.'

The look he gave her was somewhere between lust and frustration. It ignited a charge between them and this time there was no wondering what it meant. It was all there, *right there*, and it stunned her, because it had been a long time since Luisa had felt anything that strongly or that clearly – more than a decade, in fact. More than the extent of one man's life.

Cas made a sound in his throat and reached for her, pulling her towards him. The second their lips met Luisa was lost. It was as if she'd been waiting for this for days, months, years, without ever once realizing what it was she wanted. For a second Cas was the most solid thing in her universe. It was inconceivable that half a year before neither had even known that the other existed. Time and space narrowed to them, here, now, and then—

Chaos.

From outside came the scream of a speeding motorbike. Then the high-pitched whistle of something being thrown, then an explosion: the sound of splintering glass; a huge and sudden bloom of bright yellow flame.

They staggered apart as the square outside erupted with

the whoops of raised, banshee voices, the screech of rubber on tarmac. More flames tainted the moonlight as the roar of fire took hold, then more explosions, more shouts and screams, the rattle of a metal fence being torn open.

'What is it?' Luisa asked, breathless, stunned. 'What—'

Cas was already heading into the flayed darkness. 'Stay here.'

'Cas!'

'Stay inside,' he shouted back to her, already half way to the garden fence. 'Lock the door, call the police!'

Luisa ran for the office, dialled 999, described the emergency as briefly as she could. From outside came more sounds of terror and Cas was out there, Cas was—

'Just send someone,' she screamed into the phone, before slamming it down and skittering back out into the corridor, cursing her stupid heels, the flowing dress that held her back.

Outside the gym the garden was burning, a conflagration scorching the night. The greenhouse had been smashed, its frame a ragged skeleton open to the sky, fractured slivers of glass still falling from the wrecked panes. The shed was on fire. Four motorcycles had forced their way inside the fence and were circling the site, spinning wheels churning up the earth and anything growing in it. She could see a figure on foot – Cas, silhouetted against the flames, heading for the maelstrom.

'Cas!' she screamed. 'Don't—'

Her words were lost beneath the roar of utter

pandemonium. The riders saw him coming and as Luisa watched in horror their attention turned to him instead. They circled him as he stood with his arms held up in a placatory gesture. She guessed he was trying to talk to them, but the only audible sound was of the engines, the flames, the falling glass. One of the bikes had a pillion rider and she saw the rider reach out, suddenly, as if throwing something for Cas to catch. He pitched backwards, falling against another of the bikes, its back wheel skidding furiously as he went down.

Luisa began to run, kicking off her shoes despite the rough tarmac, despite the glass, blind with panic as Cas was lost to the shadowy ground. In the distance came the wail of a siren, then another, drawing closer in tandem but still too far away. She lurched through the gate, feeling her dress snag against a wisp of metal, then tearing as she ran on. Suddenly the bikes were charging straight at her, riders clad head-to-toe in black, their helmets blank and impenetrable. She screamed, stopping dead as they roared past, close enough that she felt them brush against her, knocking her sideways. One of the bikes screeched to a stop beside her. The rider gunned the engine, spinning the back wheel on the spot as before, blasting past her in a shower of churned soil and crushed plants before speeding off again.

Cas lay with his eyes shut, gasping for breath. Luisa ran to him, dropped to her knees, touching his face, his arm, his chest.

'Cas,' she said, 'Cas . . .'

Her fingers slid against something warm and wet. She lifted them and saw by the light of the flames that her hand was covered in thick liquid. It was then she realized there was a wound in his chest, blood pouring from it in a river of scarlet turned black in the dark of the night.

'Oh God,' she said. 'Cas – oh *God*. Help! Someone *help* me! Cas, Cas—'

Luisa pressed both hands over the wound, but the blood kept coming, kept pumping between her fingers, covering her hands, her dress, her legs where she knelt beside him. There was nothing she could do except try to hold his chest together as the sirens drew closer, but they weren't moving fast enough, not fast enough by far.

Chapter Forty-two

Harper couldn't sleep. She'd finally been shown to where she'd be staying at around one o'clock, but despite how tired she was, she was far too wired. Besides, the room Harper found herself in was as ridiculous as the rest of the house, a vast expanse of pristine cream carpet and floor-to-ceiling windows draped in heavy matching velvet. It had its own bathroom and a bed so big she thought she might get lost in it. They'd even given her a pair of 'guest pyjamas' to sleep in. Who the hell had guest pyjamas just lying around? They were, perhaps unsurprisingly, cream-coloured. Still, Harper had put them on, standing in front of the full-length mirror in the bathroom, staring at someone she barely recognized. Then she'd got into the bed and sunk amid the pillows, her mind resolutely awake. There was so much to think about, so much to organize in her mind, but as always, it was Max who was uppermost in her thoughts. Now that she was alone, she felt guilty for leaving him all night. She'd never done it before and although she thought he was physically safe in his beloved bus, Harper worried that as the night drew on other nebulous fears would surround him, or that he would simply be cold. Her brother's enthusiastic reply when she'd asked if he minded her staying here had suggested he was still having fun on his campout, but that had been hours ago now. Was he still awake? She looked at her phone, which told her it was now closer to 2.30am. If she texted him now would it wake him up, do more harm than good?

She typed a text, hesitated over sending it, and then sent it anyway.

A reply came back almost instantly. No emojis this time.

There's a fire. Lots of sirens.

Harper pushed herself up in bed, her heart beginning to pound.

Where? In the scrapyard? In the bus?

No. Not here.

Harper shut her eyes, relieved, before another horrifying possibility occurred to her.

At our house?

No. I think in the square.

Harper stared at the words, turning cold. In an instant she knew, with a horrifying certainty, that yes, it was most definitely in the square. It was the gym. It had to be, didn't it? She'd missed her shift and Darren hadn't been able to find her. They hadn't been able to find Max either and so they had gone somewhere else they knew Harper cared about.

She struggled out of bed, throwing off the heavy duvet, her phone still in her hand.

I'm coming, she texted Max. *Stay in the bus. Promise?*

The reply came back quickly.

Promise! Smileyface.

Harper pulled on her clothes and then went out to knock on the door of the next room, where Jo had promised she would be.

'Harper?' Luisa's sister answered, sleepily. 'Are you all right?'

'Something's happening at home,' Harper said. 'I need my car.'

By the time Harper got to Collaton, dawn was breaking and the garden had gone.

It looked as if it had been bombed from orbit. The greenhouse was a wreck of broken glass. The remains of the shed still smouldered, burned right down to the shredded soil. Anything that had once been green was either mashed into the churned earth or had been reduced to blackened stumps. The smell of smoke was choking, strong even through the Mini's closed windows.

Harper drew to a halt, her hands gripping the steering wheel as she stared through the windscreen. There was a police car parked across the entrance gate. People were milling about in the smoke-clogged street.

A rap at her window made Harper jump. Kath leaned down to peer through it, her lips set in a grim line. Harper opened the door and stumbled out, nausea rolling thick in her stomach.

'Harper, are you okay?' Kath asked. 'I was going to call you. Wasn't sure if Luisa would have had time to let you know what's happened.'

'I haven't heard from her.'

Kath wiped a hand over her face. 'Aye, well. She's still at the hospital, I suppose.'

'Hospital?' Harper asked, mind blank. 'Why is she at the hospital?'

Kath looked at her steadily for a moment. 'It's Cas – your Mr P. They were here, you see, both of them. Don't ask me why but they were here when this happened.'

Harper felt a numbness creeping into her fingers, into her toes. It worked its way up her legs and arms, making for the thumping mess that was her heart.

'It was a bunch of thugs on motorbikes, it seems like,' Kath went on, into Harper's silence. 'Closest we can work out is that Cas tried to stop them.'

Of course he did, Harper thought, dully. *That's how much of an idiot he is. Can't leave anything well enough alone, he's always got to—*

'I got here after the ambulance arrived,' Kath added. 'There was a lot of blood. He'd been stabbed, I think.'

'Is he going to die?'

It was Harper's voice asking the words, though she barely recognized it.

'I don't know, lass. I'm sorry. But he's in the right place.

329

They wouldn't let Luisa go in the ambulance but she followed in the Land Rover. She's with him.'

Harper felt as if she'd disconnected from the world around her. Everything seemed unreal. Kath was speaking again, asking her something, but Harper couldn't hear what she was saying. She was going to be sick. And Max! She had to see Max, she had to make sure that at least Max was—

'I've got to go,' she said, stunned with shock. 'I can't – I've got to—'

'Harper?' Kath called after her as she stumbled away, but Harper didn't stop. She couldn't stand to see the state of the garden, to know that even at this moment Mr P could be dead and it was her fault.

'Harper!'

Harper started to run. She made it to the corner of her own street before she doubled over, retching into the last shadows of the night.

Chapter Forty-three

There was a child crying. The noise echoed over the rows of metal and plastic chairs that had been screwed into the cold vinyl-coated floor. The little girl was sitting on her daddy's knee in one corner of the room. He was trying to soothe her without jarring her arm, which was clearly bent at an odd angle. The sound went on and on. It wasn't piercing. The child wasn't screaming. She was just sobbing, quietly, helplessly. She hurt and she was too little to know that the future might be different and so to her everything about life was just pain: horrible, inescapable, unending pain.

There was tragedy in that sound.

Luisa couldn't tear her gaze away.

She had no idea what was happening with Cas. She'd followed the ambulance, her hands caked with his drying blood, but she wasn't a relative or his emergency contact, so the harried receptionist in the crowded A&E department wouldn't tell her anything.

'But I was with him,' she said, holding up her hands, still caked with his blood. 'I was— I was there.'

'Are you hurt?'

'No.'

'Are there relatives of his on their way?'

'I don't know.'

'You should go home,' the woman said.

'I don't—' She stopped, choked by the thought, had to start again, her voice breaking on the words. 'I don't even know if he's alive.'

The woman's face took on a sympathetic look. She tapped a couple of keys on her keyboard, glanced back up at Luisa with a tiny smile.

'They're looking after him now.'

Luisa nodded. 'I'll wait,' she said.

'I really think that you should—'

'I'll wait.'

Luisa found the bathroom and stood over the sink, turning on the tap, sinking her hands into the water as it ran. She watched Cas's blood dissolve and run from her fingers, flowing from her forearms like rivers of spilled watercolour. It swirled in chaotic red whorls for a moment, streaming across the white enamel and into the drain. Gone.

Back out in the waiting area, she took a seat again. Luisa looked over at the injured little girl, but she and her father had gone. The sound of her pain still lingered, somehow.

She remembered the abject grief of Reuben's parents, the sound of their wails as they realized their beloved son was dead, how it echoed around the walls long after they had left her alone in her own hospital bed.

Luisa looked down and saw that she was still wearing Cas's jacket. Beneath it the dress stuck to her, caked in his blood. There was so much of it, she thought. Could anyone survive losing that much?

She didn't know how long she sat there. The sun rose into a new day, glinting through the glass. Luisa watched the shadows on the floor, how they moved, shifted, shrank in the rising light until they were very nearly gone by the time she noticed that a voice was speaking to her.

'Excuse me? Are you Luisa?'

Luisa looked up to see a nurse standing a few feet away. 'Yes,' she said, standing up too suddenly, 'that's me. Is it Cas? Is there news? Is he—' *Is he alive? Is he dead?*

'He's conscious. He's asking for you,' the nurse told her. 'He seems convinced that you're hurt.'

'Oh,' Luisa said, barely comprehending anything beyond the fact that Cas was alive, was well enough to talk. The strength of her relief was a renewed shock. Blood rushed in her ears, deafening.

'His parents have been contacted and are on their way,' the nurse added. 'But we can't get him to settle. He's too concerned about you. We wouldn't usually allow visitors in at this point, but—'

'I'm here,' Luisa said. 'I'll come.'

Cas was in a small room on his own, lying on a high hospital bed surrounded by equipment. The nurse handed Luisa a mask and left her in the doorway. Luisa remained where she was, trying to equate the prone figure on the bed with the Cas she had come to know. He always seemed to her to be so full of life – so quick to smile and to laugh, so animated and driven. In this sterile room he was diminished, his broad chest swathed in bandages, his skin grey and creased with a frown that seemed so entirely at odds with the person she knew.

It was at that precise moment that Luisa understood how very sure she had been that she would never see him alive again. Moreover, she understood, in an epiphany that made her grip the lintel of the door to keep herself upright, how monumental that loss would have been. This knowledge scared her bone deep, made the shock she had been holding at bay since she'd seen him fall against the wheel of that motorbike all the more chilling. After all, she knew, with absolute clarity, what that kind of attachment meant: quiet, unmentioned and utterly indelible as it was. She'd been so careful never to put herself in that situation again, never to let herself feel anything so deeply that it could devastate just by its absence. She knew that kind of grief, the way the wounds never truly healed.

Experiencing that even once was too much, surely, for any human heart to bear. Luisa had already lost so many people in her life. She wasn't sure she'd survive losing—

'Luisa?' Cas was watching her with bleary eyes, blinking as if struggling to focus. 'Luisa – is that you?'

'Yes,' she told him. 'No – don't move.'

'Luisa,' Cas whispered, reaching for her as soon as she was

close enough, grasping one hand in his to pull her closer, the other reaching for her face, his fingers brushing her cheek. He was groggy, obviously confused, his fear abject and evident. 'Luisa. You were hurt, you were—'

'I'm fine.' Luisa put both hands on his shoulders, trying to make him stay still.

'But there was blood,' Cas said, running his hand down her neck, down her arm, as if trying to map her contours to make sure she was still whole. 'There was so much blood, you—

'It was yours,' she said, softly. 'It was yours, Cas. I'm fine. I'm here. See? I'm fine.'

She saw the moment his fear turned to relief.

'I thought you were hurt,' he whispered, both hands cupping her face.

'It's all right,' Luisa said, more aware than Cas seemed to be of his injured chest. 'Please take it easy. You're so lucky to be here. You probably don't remember, but—'

'I do,' he said, stroking both thumbs across her cheeks. 'I do remember, Luisa. I remember everything.'

His hands on her skin were warm and alive, the pulse in his wrist beating erratically against her cheek and she knew how very easily this could have been different. The distance of a millimetre, the space of a second. Life was too fragile, far too prone to breakages to be trusted. Luisa gripped both of his wrists, gently pulling his hands away from her face.

'Cas,' she said, quietly. 'Your parents are on their way. They might be here already. I'll go and meet them.'

'Don't go,' he said. 'Luisa, please don't go.'
'I have to,' she said.

A kind of numbness settled over Luisa as she drove home.
By then the wilderness of night had been beaten back by
the colours of full day. She drove in silence, skin growing
cold without the added layer of Cas's jacket, which she
had left with his mum and dad along with their painful
bewilderment.

Afterwards, Luisa could barely remember the drive. She
pulled to a stop outside the house and sat motionless behind
the wheel. Exhaustion and shock had hollowed her out. As she
unlocked the front door Luisa wondered whether Jo would
be up yet and then realized that no, of course not, her sister
was still at Owen's, in Durham. She was probably fast asleep
in a gigantic bed, with no knowledge of how the world had
crashed and burned on the other side of the country.

Luisa toed off her battered shoes, leaving them where they
fell. She dropped her bag beside them. She walked the length
of the hallway and climbed the stairs, slowly, one step at a
time, one hand on the banister. She did all this silently, in her
silent house. She went into her bedroom, bare toes pressing
into the thick carpet as she crossed to the en suite. She walked
straight into the shower and turned it on, cranked the heat
as high as it would go. The water struck Luisa hard in the
chest, soaking the gown she had not removed. Steam rose
around her, a thick vapour that flayed open all her pores as
if it was aiming to leave her raw. Luisa raised her hands to

the stream, but Cas's blood had already gone. Her cleansed skin remained pink in the water's wake. It must have been too hot, but she couldn't feel it. She couldn't feel anything.

She looked down at her toes, bare beneath the drenched carnage of her dress. Luisa reached behind her and tugged down the zip. She let the dress sag around her, the weight of water dragging it down over her stomach, over her thighs. It folded over her feet, a crumpled ruin of crushed silk. Luisa kicked it out of the way and then did the same with her underwear. Then she reached for the pins in her hair. One by one she pulled them out and dropped them. She heard each faint tinkle as they fell.

She stood beneath the stream and shut her eyes, but the terror was there, waiting for her. Flames and shouts, the smash of breaking glass, the roar of an engine. It rolled her into itself, spun her around, forced her down into an icy darkness that held another memory, her own screams mixed with the screams of a dying man that she couldn't help, couldn't reach, couldn't—

Luisa gasped, opened her eyes into the scalding water, had to lean against the shower tiles as the past receded again.

Enough, she told herself. *Enough. You can't go backwards. You can only go forwards.*

She left the dress crumpled in the corner of the shower. Much like the garden, there would be no saving it now. Coffee was what she needed. Coffee and a new job.

Chapter Forty-four

Luisa sat at the kitchen table. Over the hours since that scalding shower she'd consumed her own weight in coffee as she updated her CV. Luisa had no hopes that Marianne Boswell would give her a reference, but she was sure that Owen would be happy to fill that gap. It was, she thought to herself with a tiny tinge of bitterness, the least that he could do. Hadn't Luisa kept her end of the bargain? She'd given the Collaton project everything she had for six months, which is exactly what they'd agreed. It hadn't worked and now it was time for her to move on. The job market wasn't great, but Reuben's godfather had promised to help her in that regard, and however disappointed he might be, he was a man of his word. Besides, even if she had nothing physical to show for the months of effort she'd put into the Collaton site, Luisa could at least now add managerial skills to her catalogue of experience. No one could say she hadn't made something out of nothing. She'd built a workforce and together they had turned a wasteland into a flourishing garden. That had to be worth something in terms of transferable skills, didn't it?

She had begun the endless trawl through job sites when the front door opened and Joanna came in. Luisa heard her sister close the door and then a brief silence, as if her sister were listening, waiting for something. Luisa kept her eyes trained on her screen. She wished, suddenly, that she'd had the foresight to undertake this task in her bedroom, where she could have locked the door behind her and blocked out the world – especially her sister – completely.

'Luisa?' Joanna called. 'Are you here?'

Luisa didn't answer. She just kept scrolling, office job after office job. Office manager? Perhaps that would suit her now. Head receptionist at a busy doctor's surgery?

Jo appeared in the doorway, dishevelled and with a look of horror on her face.

'Luisa!' Jo crossed the room and dragged her into a hug. 'I've been trying to call you for hours! Where have you been?'

Luisa extricated herself from her sister's grip. 'What do you mean, where have I been? I've been here.'

Jo stared at her. 'But – the garden, Lu! Cas—'

At the mention of his name Luisa flinched, cursed herself for the reaction and pushed Jo away. She got up to make more coffee. She'd drunk too much over the past hours, she could feel the spent caffeine sluggish in her veins, but still she needed more.

'How do you know about the garden?' Luisa asked,

pouring more water into the machine. 'I assumed you'd still be at Owen's.'

There was a brief silence, in which Luisa could feel her sister's gaze boring holes in her back.

'I followed Harper to Collaton,' she said. 'The poor girl was in a state. Then when I saw what had happened and Kath said you'd been there, with Cas—'

'Do you want coffee?'

'Do I— *What?*'

Luisa turned around, feeling a flicker of annoyance. 'I said, do you want coffee?'

Jo stared at her. 'Luisa.'

'What?'

Her sister glanced down at the table, as if taking in for the first time the laptop and various printed versions of what Luisa had been working on since she got home.

'What are you doing?'

Luisa snapped shut the laptop and started gathering up her papers. She'd go upstairs, continue where she wouldn't be disturbed. 'Starting the job search.'

'The *what?*'

'Am I not speaking clearly enough this morning, or are you hungover?' Luisa asked, growing impatient now. Why did she need to explain the obvious? 'The garden's gone. I very obviously need an actual job, very quickly. Therefore: job search.'

Jo was still staring at her, but she'd grown pale now. 'Luisa, please—'

'Actually, I was even thinking that it might be a good idea to retrain,' Luisa said, cutting off whatever her sister might have been about to say. 'What about the legal secretarial job market? Would it be worth me taking that route, do you think?' It didn't seem as if her sister was going to answer, so Luisa started moving again. 'I'll look into it. Might be worth pursuing.'

'Luisa!' Jo moved before she could reach the kitchen door, reaching out to grasp her arm, pulling her around so that they were face to face. 'Stop. Just *stop*. Can't you hear yourself? After what you've just been through—'

Luisa pulled her arm out of her sister's grip, a sudden burst of anger flaring in her chest. 'For God's sake, Jo! I'm *fine*. I wasn't even the one hurt.'

'No,' Jo agreed. 'Cas was, and you were with him when that happened. Weren't you?'

'It doesn't matter,' Luisa said. 'Because Cas is . . . Cas is . . .'

'Cas is *what*?'

Luisa had been about to say that 'Cas is going to be fine', but the words stalled in her throat.

'Lu,' Jo said, reaching for her. 'Why don't you just—'

'No,' Luisa said. 'No, don't fuss, I—'

All she wanted was to leave, to get on with the task she'd set herself, to sink herself into it, to move on. But suddenly Luisa was back *there*, in darkness, with Cas lying on the ground, dying, her hands against his chest as she tried to keep him alive, his blood on her hands. She saw him looking at her from the hospital bed, eyes curiously fervent, felt his hands against her cheek. *Luisa— Luisa—*

'Luisa?' Joanna asked, into the silence. 'What is it?'

Luisa shook her head, unable to speak.

'Sit down,' Joanna said. 'Right now.'

Joanna didn't say anything as Luisa slowly began to describe what had happened. She just sat listening, one hand over Luisa's. It was when Jo heard about her lone wait at the hospital that those fingers flexed.

'Why didn't you call me?' Joanna asked quietly, once Luisa had finished. 'I would have come to be with you at the hospital, you know that.'

'I didn't think.'

'You were in shock.'

'I was fine,' Luisa said. 'Like I said, I wasn't hurt. I was just there. And then Cas's family arrived and I came home.'

'Luisa. Come *on*. That whole scenario would be a nightmare for anyone to cope with, but for you?'

Luisa stiffened. 'What are you talking about?'

Her sister raised her eyebrows. 'Look, I know you don't like talking about what happened with Reuben. I know it's still—'

'Jo, don't,' Luisa said, cutting her off. 'It was nothing like that. The ambulance was there quickly. Cas will recover. That's all there is to it.'

'That's not all there is to it,' Jo said, emphatically. 'I was there with you both at the gala. I saw how you were together, how much Cas made you smile and I mean *really* smile, Lu, in a way I've not seen from you for years. *Years*. Then he's stabbed in front of you and you have to hold his chest together to keep him alive and you're going to tell yourself that's nothing? It's not nothing, Lu. It can't be.'

Luisa got up, fractious, not wanting to listen to this. 'Joanna, stop it.'

'And what about the garden?' Jo went on. 'You put your heart and soul into that place. I saw you there, remember? You were so alive, Luisa, so *happy*.'

'*Stop it*,' Luisa said again. 'You're making this into more than it has to be. I'm upset that Cas is hurt, of course I am, but he's going to be fine. I'm upset that the garden has gone as well, but really – was it ever going to work? It was just an experiment, that's all, and it didn't work. I knew it probably wouldn't. Owen did, too. That's why we agreed on the six months in the first place, isn't it? To try it out and walk away if it didn't work. Well, I gave it a shot. It didn't work. Now I'm going to find a proper job.'

'"A proper job"?' Joanna asked, her voice as hollow as the look in her eyes. 'As a legal secretary?'

'Maybe,' Luisa said. 'What would be wrong with that?'

Joanna shook her head, her lips curling in a smile that was very far from happy. 'Nothing. It's a good profession. But it's not for you, Luisa. It'd be Marianne Boswell all over again and you can't do that. Not again.'

'What are you talking about?'

'Shutting yourself in an office again. Not doing what you really should be doing. You'd be running away in exactly the same way you did after Reuben's death. You can't do it again.'

'I'm not running away,' Luisa said, angry and indignant. 'I'm moving on. There's a difference. I've done it once, I can do it again.'

'No,' Joanna said.

'What do you mean, no?'

'I mean, no. You never moved on, Luisa. Not really. What you did was survive. You went through the motions. You know how I know that? Because when you really started to move on – when you started work in Collaton, when you were back where you belong, in a garden – *that*'s when you started coming back to life.'

'Oh, spare me your fairytales, Joanna,' Luisa said. 'Honestly, for someone who deals in the cold hard facts of the law every day of her working life you really do like whimsy a little too much.'

'At least take a break,' Jo advised her. 'Take a breather, Lu, let yourself process—'

'STOP!' Luisa shouted, the fury bubbling up on a tide of spent caffeine and emotional exhaustion. 'All I want from you right now is some support and encouragement. Is that too much to ask for?'

'Of course not, and I'm here for that,' Jo said, seriously. 'Of course I am. But I can't wrap you in cotton wool, Luisa. I've already tried that and it hasn't helped. Has it? It just helped you stay stuck in one place. I can't help you do that to yourself again.'

Luisa had heard enough. She stood again, gathering her computer and papers. 'You don't know what you're talking about.'

She left Jo at the table. She was in the hallway as she heard her sister's voice shouting after her.

'At least check your phone!'

There were a multitude of missed calls, mostly from Joanna but also some from Kath. The latter had obviously eventually given up calling and had sent a text, instead.

Let us know you're all right, love, Kath had written.

Luisa sank onto the edge of her bed and shut her eyes. She felt exhausted suddenly, drained of every emotion, every shred of feeling. There was nothing left but a spreading cold.

I'm okay, she typed back. It was all she could summon herself to say.

The reply came back almost immediately. *That's good. Take care of yourself. Don't worry about a thing here.*

Luisa stared at the message as though it might provide something more than the words themselves. What was there to worry about? The garden had gone.

She dumped her phone beside her laptop, fatigue dogging her every movement. Suddenly, what she wanted to do was absent herself from the world, to sleep like the dead, to never get up.

Luisa crawled beneath her quilt fully clothed and shut her eyes.

Chapter Forty-five

'Max?' Harper called, the loamy humidity of the garden bus enveloping her as she got to her feet in the doorway. 'Are you here?'

'Upstairs!'

She made her way up to the top deck, carrying the supplies she'd brought with her. It was four days after everything had finally come apart at the seams and both of them had been camping out here ever since. Max hadn't wanted to go home, a sentiment Harper shared. It was partly self-preservation, because she didn't think Darren was going to settle for destroying the garden when she was still out here walking around, and partly a desire to remove herself from reality. Here, in her brother's secret greenhouse, she could pretend she was in a fairytale bubble, outside which nothing mattered.

Harper couldn't bear to walk through the square and see what she had destroyed. The place was as dead as Mr P had almost been. She couldn't think about him either, even though word had come back to her via Kath that he was going to recover. He was still in hospital, and he was there because of her. Her guilt was all-consuming. The only saving grace was that Max had been safe here in the bus.

'I've brought breakfast,' she said, climbing the stairs to find her brother diligently pinching out his tomato plants, a job that seemed to be never-ending. The bus smelled of a recent watering. 'Yoghurt and banana. The banana's not mashed, but it is very ripe ...'

He took the yoghurt, but ignored the banana.

She made her way to the back of the bus and perched on the small space they had kept free on the back bench. Max paused in his task and came to sit beside her. They ate their little picnic surrounded by the manic growth of his plants. They all seemed to be throwing out more and more greenery in an attempt to carve out space for themselves. It was a jungle, truly, the thick foliage interspersed with sudden, bright splashes of colour where the flowers were in full bloom. Harper tried not to think about the blasted ruin of the community garden around the corner. The comparison was stark enough to be obscene.

Harper's phone rang in her pocket. She froze, still not free from the lurking fear of a sudden summons from Darren. Not that he had ever called her, and he'd never used this phone anyway. She'd thrown the last burner he'd given her into the Solway Firth on the morning after the gala, just as soon as she'd been able to stop throwing up. He'd catch up with her somehow, though, add that transgression to the list of her other debts. She knew that.

The screen told her it was Kath. Harper's stomach bubbled with more nausea as she stared at the name. They hadn't spoken since that night, only texted. What could Harper possibly say? Still, her guilt was such that she answered. It was the least she could do, after all.

'Hello?'

'Harper, it's Kath Larkspur. How are you? Are you okay?'

Harper stared at the banana skin in her hand. Was she okay? No, obviously not. How could anyone think she would be? Still, the question surprised her, though as far as she knew no one was aware of her involvement. Yet, anyway. It was only a matter of time. She expected nothing more than recrimination from all quarters, except perhaps from Max. Then Harper's heart froze – Oh God, what if Kath was calling because—

'What's happened?' she blurted. 'Is it Mr P? Is he – is h—'

'Oh!' Kath sounded harried. 'No. No! I'm so sorry. That's not— He's all right, Harper, at least since I last checked. I've not heard different. That's not why I'm calling.'

Harper shut her eyes. Her heart was banging so hard against her ribcage she thought it would be left with scars.

'It's the garden,' Kath said. 'Arthur and I need your help.'

Harper frowned.

'We've got to fix it,' Kath went on, into her silence. 'We've got to start again.'

What was she talking about? Kath had been there that

night, she'd seen how bad the damage was. Harper stared down the green tunnel of the garden bus. It was so full that she could barely see the water tank at the front. 'It's gone,' she said. 'There isn't a garden.'

'Not right now there isn't,' Kath said. 'But we can make it right. I know we can.'

Suddenly, Harper's guilt turned into fury. What was this woman talking about? If Luisa-bitch-MacGregor had never had this stupid idea in the first place, none of this would have happened, would it? Mr P would still be whole, would still be telling her to keep her elbow up, to stay in school, instead of—

'What about Luisa?' Harper demanded. 'This is her mess, isn't it? She was the one who started this. Why isn't *she* calling?'

Kath's sigh surfed the line. 'I think Luisa's really struggling with what happened,' she said. 'I haven't spoken to her, just exchanged a couple of texts. To tell you the truth I'm not sure if she's going to come back to Collaton. In which case, it's up to us, isn't it?'

'Do you not hear how insane you sound?' Harper asked, her voice carrying her sudden spike of anger like a knife blade. 'It was never going to work. *It is never going to work.*'

'It did work,' Kath argued. 'We can't let a handful of bad apples rot the whole barrel. We made something beautiful on that patch of land. We can do it again.'

'There's no point,' Harper said bluntly. 'Can't you see that? They'll just do it again. It's a total waste of time.'

'The only way it's a waste of time,' Kath said, staunchly, 'is if we let them win. And I'm not doing that, Harper. I'm not. I'll rebuild it on my own with my bare hands if I have to.'

'Fine,' Harper said. 'You do that, then.' She hung up, angry, guilty, hating the world.

Chapter Forty-six

The first time he'd woken, Cas had been convinced that the blood had been *hers*, probably because his jumbled recollections had been accompanied by the sound of Luisa's voice, screaming and desperate – *Someone HELP me!* Then there she had been, in the doorway, barely more than a shape in his blurred vision. The shape had resolved into her face, her arms, her hands trying to stop him from moving. Luisa had been alive, whole, unhurt. At that moment, for him, nothing else had mattered. Then the medication had taken over, dulling the edges of everything, keeping him numb for what had felt like months but had turned out to be only a week.

Now, when he woke, it was still to thoughts of her but accompanied by the certain knowledge that she would not be there. He hadn't been allowed visitors beyond his parents for the first two weeks of his hospital stay, but even once he was, Luisa hadn't been one of them. Cas understood.

More than anything, he wanted to know that she was

okay. Even barely knowing what was in her past, the fragmentary elements she had told him of her husband's death were enough for him to understand the renewed trauma she was likely now experiencing. In his dreams he still heard her screams as she struggled to hold his chest together – *Someone HELP me!* – and the terror in her voice never diminished. He hated the idea that, even unwittingly, he could have been part of something that caused her such distress. But she had not come to visit him and he did not want to cross the boundary she was so clearly establishing between them by reaching out to her himself.

As soon as the doctors had deemed Cas stable enough the police had come in to interview him about what he remembered and to take a statement about the events. They had already gathered forensic evidence from the crime scene. Cas winced to think of what the garden would look like now. He had walked into a hell of burning that night and had barely survived himself. This, again, made him think of Luisa. All her hard work, her hopes for that small patch of unwanted earth. Had it been for nothing?

'Did you recognize any of your attackers?' the police sergeant had asked him.

No, Cas hadn't, done up as they had been in dark clothes and dark helmets. He had his suspicions, obviously, and described the previous incidents of harassment – both the one in the gym and that absurd motorcade that had purposefully circled the garden. That wasn't proof of anything, though, was it? He thought it likely that Darren had not been present anyway. Men like that got others to do their dirty work for them.

Still, it was only a few days later that the police returned to say that they had arrested several people. They still couldn't find the knife with which Cas had been stabbed and without better identification it was impossible to know which of the five arrested men was responsible for the wounding, so for now that would have to do.

'Five arrests?' Cas asked. 'There were only four there that night.'

Darren Dixon had been arrested too, on conspiracy and drugs charges. Apparently, the police had been keeping an eye on him ever since he'd been released on parole. It was perhaps a pity, Cas thought but did not say, that that eye hadn't been a little sharper. But then, he was keeping his own counsel about a lot of things.

'Is there anything else you can remember?' the sergeant had asked, during her first visit.

'No,' he'd said. 'Sorry, there's nothing else.'

It was a blatant lie.

He did remember something else, very clearly indeed, but it was a memory that Cas thought would probably do more harm than good and so he decided to keep it to himself, at least for now.

The pillion rider who'd stabbed him hadn't done so out of the blue. He'd flipped up his visor and yelled something in Cas's face first.

'This is for Harper's debt,' his attacker had screamed, over the noise of the other bikes and the continuing destruction.

After that, he remembered little. Sinking into darkness, a coldness gathering in his extremities, creeping its way to his heart. Luisa above him, her beautiful face silhouetted against the smoke and the stars as she fought to keep him alive with her bare hands.

This is for Harper's debt.

Should he have kept this piece of information from the police? No, of course not. But the idea that Harper Dixon was caught up in something that had precipitated such violence seemed anathema to him. For all her innate fury, he couldn't imagine her a wilful thug. He had been the only human victim and he had his own issues with Darren. Cas couldn't give her up to the inevitable scrutiny that doing so would bring without at least understanding for himself what had happened. That Saturday night had been a turning point for her. He wanted it to be a good one, not a bad one. And he was fine, wasn't he? He was going to be fine.

He looked at his phone, failing to tamp down the hope that Luisa might have messaged him, but there was nothing. He sent Harper a text instead. This was something he'd never done before – he'd only recently acquired her number, after some of the club kids had come to visit him and Cas had asked Mo for it. Mo had seemed surprised that Cas didn't have it already. Then they had all tried to give him their numbers. He'd had to explain about appropriate boundaries outside of school and club. Sally had seemed oddly hurt and Cas wondered again at this curious community he had built. Had he ever got it right? Perhaps not, the pain in his chest as he shifted his bulk up the hospital bed a case in point.

Hey, Harper, Mr P here. I know you're busy but I'd love a visit from you if you get a chance. I want to know how the follow-up to the gala went!

He received no answer, though he could tell she had seen the message. Or at least, someone had. Mo wasn't the best with numbers, there was always the possibility he was texting someone else out of the blue.

The next day they moved him onto a ward, though Cas would far rather the hospital just discharge him. They obviously needed the bed and he was no longer on a drip.

'We still need to keep you a little longer, so that we can monitor you,' his consultant told him. 'It's not a good idea to rush. You've been incredibly lucky, you know.'

It hadn't been luck, though, had it? It had been Luisa MacGregor.

Chapter Forty-seven

Harper was reluctant to go to the hospital, but how could she not? Mr P was there because of her: she couldn't ignore a direct request from him to visit. The tone of his message had been light. Maybe he had amnesia regarding the attack? That happened sometimes, didn't it? Maybe no one had told him that the garden was gone, that everything they'd worked for had been destroyed, that Harper's hopes for the future had, in the space of one single night, reached their peak and then just as quickly had been frittered away by her own stupidity. Because that's how she felt, in the wake of it all. Stupid. Stupid that she had ever believed in herself and her future. Stupid that she'd thought she could change how the whole world worked.

He was on a ward with six beds. Harper stood by the door, watching him. It was weird to see Mr P so incapacitated. Ever since she'd met him he'd been the strongest man she knew. Now here he was in a hospital bed. At least he wasn't hooked up to machines and wearing one of those daft papery gowns. Someone had brought him normal clothes. He was wearing a T-shirt, one of the ones she'd seen him in at the gym before now. Harper didn't know why, but that little detail turned something in her chest, made her eyes well up. Harper Dixon never cried. What good did tears ever do? They were just a waste of energy. Might as well take it and stick it in your engine instead, rev up the rage machine, get things done. Better than sitting feeling sorry for yourself, waiting for the next bad thing to happen. This, though, here and now – she couldn't deal with this, knowing that after everything he had done for her, Mr P was in that hospital bed because of her. She turned to leave before he noticed her, but—

'Harper?'

Too late. She turned back again, slowly.

'You weren't going, were you?' he asked.

'Nope.' She made a show of using the wall-mounted dispenser to squirt more sanitizer onto her hands. 'Just don't want to risk getting the old man sicker than he already is.'

He grinned at her as she crossed the floor towards him. He looked pale, but not nearly as bad as she was expecting.

'Hi, Mr P.'

'Hi yourself,' he said. 'I wasn't sure you were going to turn up. You didn't reply to my text.'

She shrugged.

'How are you?' he asked.

Harper looked at him. 'You're asking me how I am?'

He glanced around. The six-berth ward was full, but two of the beds had their curtains drawn around them and the occupants of the other three were variously asleep or wearing headphones. When Mr P looked at her again his expression sent a skitter of unease into Harper's gut. *He knows*, she thought, with a sense of helplessness that turned her blood to ice.

'Come and talk to me,' he said, quietly.

She shook her head, numb. How had he found out so quickly?

'I haven't told anyone,' Mr P went on, calmly. 'And I don't intend to. But I need to know, from you, what happened, because I know you are involved somehow. I can't believe it was intentional. But the guy that did this said that you had a debt, and I don't want you to be in debt to anyone, Harper, especially not the kind of person that would do this. I think it's time you told me everything.'

She thought about running, but didn't. After all, where did she have to go?

'It's not what you think,' she said.

Mr P shook his head. 'I don't think anything at the moment. Sit down and start at the beginning.'

She did and actually, aside from the shame, what Harper mainly felt as she told the whole sorry story was relief. She couldn't look at Mr P at all as she spoke and she tried to keep her voice down, but she didn't leave anything out. Not even when she had to explain how she'd sold packets of filth to faces she recognized from school. Not even when she had to tell him that she'd got Max to hide on the night of the gala because she was worried about him, but she hadn't spared a single thought for what might happen to anyone else.

'It's my fault,' Harper said, ending with the only truth that she could see that really mattered. 'You being stabbed. The garden getting destroyed. It's my fault, Mr P. The garden's gone. It's just *gone*. There's nothing left. Kath thinks—' She stopped, another wave of guilt clogging her throat.

'Kath thinks – what?'

'She wants to rebuild,' Harper said. 'She called me a few days ago, asking me to help. Says the only way they win is if we don't. Daft cow.'

'Hey,' Mr P said. 'What have I said about that kind of language?'

Harper shrugged.

'You are going to help her, aren't you?'

'What's the point? They'll only do it again.'

Mr P looked at her, as if realizing something. 'Harper – you do know that Darren's back in jail again, don't you?'

Harper blinked. 'What?'

'He was arrested with four others of his crew. They're all being charged, but he was in breach of his parole so he's gone straight back inside. I don't think he'll be back for a long, long time. I don't think any of them will.'

Harper shook her head, stunned. 'I didn't ... I didn't know.'

Mr P smiled at her. 'Well, now you do. And there's no excuse not to help Kath with the garden, is there?'

Harper said nothing to that. She turned to concentrate on the little screen at the other end of the ward instead, trying to process this new information. Darren, *gone.*

'What does Luisa think?' Mr P asked, then, in a tone of voice that made Harper look at him again. He was concentrating on his hands. 'About rebuilding the garden, I mean?'

'I don't know. Haven't heard from her.' She narrowed her eyes. 'You have, though, right?'

Mr P smiled faintly. 'No. But that's okay.'

'Seriously?' Harper asked, incensed. 'She hasn't even bothered to visit you? Not once?'

'I didn't expect her to.'

'But—'

'Harper,' he said again, with a familiar tone of warning in his voice. 'She's dealing with a lot.'

'You're the one who nearly died!'

'Yes, but—' he started, and then stopped. 'Just go easy on her, please. You don't know the whole story.'

Harper shook her head. 'Kath says she doesn't know if Luisa will ever come back.'

She watched his face for a moment. He stared at his hands, then took a breath and nodded slightly. 'Well,' he said, quietly. 'As long as she's all right.'

Harper meant to tell him that they'd have been better if Luisa had never shown her face in Collaton, but instead what came out was, 'You love her, don't you?'

Mr P did look at her then, an expression of surprise on his face.

'I told you before, it's obvious,' Harper said. 'And at the gala—'

He looked away.

'At the gala, Joanna could see it too.'

Mr P smiled but it was a somewhat sad expression. 'I don't know her, Harper, not really,' he said. 'But . . . I think that perhaps, if our circumstances had been different, I would have liked the chance to.'

Harper swallowed, felt her eyes fill with tears that she tried in vain to blink back. 'I'm sorry,' she whispered.

Mr P sighed. 'Harper, none of this was your fault. None of it. I'm sorry that I didn't see what was going on. I'm sorry that you didn't feel you could come to me for help. Because that's what you needed most of all – help. I always said I'd try to give you that, and I failed, and I'm sorry.'

She looked at him with incredulity. 'Mr P, I'm the one who—'

'You didn't,' he said firmly, cutting her off. 'Stop thinking that way right now, before it poisons everything that comes next. It was Darren. It was all Darren. You were just trying to survive.'

Harper looked down at her hands. 'It doesn't make any difference anyway. Once the police find out they'll round me up with the rest of them. And I deserve it, don't I?'

'There's no reason for them to find out,' he said. 'I won't say anything.'

Harper shrugged. 'Then Darren will. He'll blame me. He'll want me to pay and he'll drag me into it with the police.'

'I don't think he'll do that. Dropping you in it would just incriminate him more. You're still a minor, remember, and he's already in deep enough without adding trouble for himself. I don't think there's any reason to think this goes further than between us. If it does ... then I'll be there to bat for you. You weren't there that night, and if it was recrimination against you for disobeying Darren's orders, that's surely a strike in your favour. I won't let this destroy you, Harper. It's not happening, not if I can help it.'

Harper's eyes filled with tears again. 'Look at what it cost everyone, though. You, stuck in here with a hole in your chest. The garden, destroyed.'

Just then the ward sister came over and told Harper that visiting hours were nearly over.

'You are going to help, aren't you?' he asked, as she got ready to leave. 'With the garden?'

She looked at him but bit off the words she'd been about to say. He was alive. He'd helped her out even from his hospital bed, though she'd been the one to put him in it. Harper would always believe that, no matter what he said.

'This isn't your fault, Harper, any of it,' he told her, as if he'd read her mind. 'But if you can help to start putting the garden to rights, that would be a good thing. A great thing. Wouldn't it?'

Chapter Forty-eight

Luisa seemed to be constantly exhausted. She couldn't make herself *do* anything. There was so much she should be helping with for Jo and Neil's wedding. The date was creeping closer. She still had to find somewhere to live. She needed a job now, too. Yet everything drained her, sent her crawling back beneath the covers. She slept for hours, removing herself from the world. She started therapy again, a counsellor who would speak to her via Zoom so that she could stay at home. It began to help, but progress was slow, which frustrated Luisa more than anyone.

'I wasn't the one hurt,' she said, continually. 'I'm fine. He's fine, too, or he's going to be. This is ridiculous. Why can't I get over it?'

The therapist encouraged her to be aware of the renewed trauma, to be patient with herself, but Luisa wasn't.

Kath had stopped sending her texts after the second week, apparently finally getting the message that Luisa was never going to answer. She didn't even look at them in the end, just deleted them unread. Owen tried, too. There had even been a message from someone who had identified herself as CP. It had taken Luisa a while to figure out that it was Lady Caroline, and that Owen must have given her Luisa's number.

Anything you need, Luisa, anything I can do, let me know.

Luisa didn't answer that one, either.

Jo continued to be endlessly supportive, despite her own busy schedule and the wedding growing closer by the day.

'I've got to find a new dress,' Luisa said. 'For the wedding. I know that. I'm sorry. I'll pay for it, obviously, because—'

Jo silenced her by pulling Luisa into a hug. 'Don't think about that now. It'll work itself out.'

There were so many things that Luisa tried not to think about in those days. Chief among them was Cas. Cas, who so desperately wanted to change just one thing for each of his students, to give them a chance. Cas, who had walked into the burning fray of that night with his hands held out, trying to talk, to appease and reason. Cas, who had looked at her first with heated silence and then later still in fear, not for himself but for her. *Luisa . . . Luisa . . .* Cas, who had so nearly died there on that hard tarmac, right under her touch. That broken ground on which he had lain, too, the garden that so many had tried so hard to make whole. Nightly she dreamed of what it must look like, of the burns and tatters, of the smashed glass and crushed plants. Only those who have never experienced the pain could say that it is better to have loved and lost than never to have loved at all, Luisa thought. Better by far not to risk the devastation in the first place. The world is a cruel place, but it cannot destroy what it cannot reach. How foolish she had been to let her knowledge of that slip.

'Luisa?' Jo's voice called up the stairs, three weeks after the night of the gala. 'There's something down here you need to see.'

'I'm in the middle of something,' she shouted back. Luisa was reading one of Giles Blunt's *Cardinal* novels. She had always found the detective's enduring grief over his wife's fate soothing in ways she couldn't articulate. 'Can it wait?'

'No,' Jo shouted. 'Quick, or you'll miss it!'

Her sister was in the living room, sitting on the sofa opposite the wall-mounted TV.

'Look,' she said, pointing at the screen as Luisa entered. 'It's the local news. It's *Harper*.'

Luisa blinked at the television. Jo was right – even if Luisa hadn't instantly recognized the short dark hair and defiant expression on the familiar young face that filled the screen, it was printed boldly on screen:

HARPER DIXON, local student and garden volunteer.

'There's been so much damage, though, hasn't there?' asked the journalist. 'The garden is devastated.'

'Yes,' Harper admitted, her dark eyes taking on a brief flash of anger. 'The attack destroyed everything. In some ways it's even worse than before we started.'

'Then ... and forgive me for being frank, but it seems

an obvious question,' the reporter went on. 'Do you really think you can start again? Is it worth it?'

Luisa watched as, on screen, Harper crossed her arms, jutted out one hip and squared her jaw. 'Yes,' she said, her voice clear and determined, 'it'll be worth it. Because if we walk away now the people who did this will have won. And that's not happening. We won't *let* it happen.'

There was a collective cheer at Harper's words. The camera pulled back to reveal a crowd behind her. Amid the gathered faces Luisa recognized many of the friends she'd made over the past months, among them Mo, Siddig and Sally. There were Kath and Arthur Larkspur, too, side by side, hand in hand.

'Well, there you have it,' said the journalist, turning to address the camera directly. 'Cumbrian spirit and determination out in force in the small coastal town of Collaton. Meanwhile, Casimir Pattanyús, a teacher at the local high school who was critically injured in the attack, continues to recover at Whitehaven hospital. Anyone with any information about the events of that night should contact the police.'

Jo muted the programme as Luisa stared at the screen, which had already moved on to another segment.

'Luisa?' Jo said. 'Are you all right?'

Luisa swallowed, aware of the suddenly painful thump of her heart. 'I'm fine,' she said.

'I didn't see the whole report,' Jo went on. 'I didn't see what state the garden's in. But it certainly seems as if they're working on bringing it back to life, doesn't it?'

'Well,' Luisa said. 'Good for them.'

She turned away.

'Luisa?' Jo said, quietly from the sofa. 'I think you should go over there.'

Luisa shook her head. 'They don't need me,' she said. 'They're doing just fine without me.'

'Maybe,' Jo said, gently. 'But I think you need them. Wouldn't it be good to see that there's hope that the garden can be revived, instead of remembering what it was like that night?'

Chapter Forty-nine

The high summer day was warm and fragrant as Luisa drove. The greens of the undulating fells and the low empty pastures before them were at their most vibrant. On her left a breeze bent the grasses one way and then another, brush strokes of gold sunlight glinting on the briefly flattened stems as if against the waves of a land-borne ocean. On her right was the sea, mirroring the motion with waves of its own, sun glinting on each watery swell. Luisa wound down the window and luxuriated in the flow of fresh air, trying to calm her nerves as the Defender ate up the miles between Carlisle and Collaton.

She leaned over to turn on the ancient CD player and the Land Rover was immediately filled with the raucous sound of Bon Jovi, who was still attempting to live on a prayer. Luisa's fingers remained outstretched for a moment, paused at the button. A rush of memory overcame her, of that day she and Cas had put up the greenhouse. How much fun it had been, how easy he'd been to spend time with. Of their fish and chip lunch, eaten beside the furious wash of the Irish Sea she drove alongside now. She could remember how relaxed he had been and how, every time she'd looked up at him, his attention had been entirely on her.

With a quick jerk of her finger Luisa ejected the CD and reached for something different instead. If only she could stop her memory there, or at the gala, or at that moment when they had stood in moonlight, staring at each other in a stark moment of realization. Instead, though, it always spiralled into the sounds of chaos, into the image of him lying bloodied on—

Luisa pressed play on whatever CD she'd blindly rammed into the player and Kate Bush started making a deal with God.

Been there, she thought. *Tried that.*

When she reached Collaton, she had to steel herself before pulling into the square. The notion of having to look at the destruction or worse at that patch of tarmac that must still be stained with Cas's lost blood filled Luisa with utter dread.

She pulled up and sat for a moment with her hands still resting on the steering wheel. Jo had offered to come with her but Luisa had wanted to do this alone. Now, though, she wished her sister were there beside her. From where she was Luisa could see the raw skeleton of the smashed greenhouse. The colours of the garden had changed, too. Gone was the leafy green of the young trees that had been growing so well against the old fences. There were no vibrant bursts of colour from the sweet peas that had once bloomed between them so beautifully, either. Everything was dull, a palette of ruin. Luisa's stomach churned. She didn't want to get out of the car. For a moment she contemplated turning the key in the ignition again, driving back the way she had come.

'Come on, MacGregor,' she murmured to herself. 'No slacking.'

She got out of the Defender and crossed the road to the gate, pulling her key out of her pocket. She went to fit it to the lock and stopped. She'd been expecting to see the tarmac beyond littered with debris: broken glass, the charred remains of the burned shed and whatever was inside it. Instead, there was nothing. The tarmac was bare, as if it had been swept clean. Luisa undid the gate and pushed it open. Beyond, the damage to the garden was obvious – the brutality of the attack inscribed in crushed foliage and the still-visible tracks of motorbike tyres. The old stone path still snaked its way down the centre, but it was leading nowhere. It seemed to Luisa that every single plant had been ripped up or trampled down, including the orchard saplings, which had been reduced to splintered sticks. There had been no rain since the night of the attack and the place looked like a desert. There was an acrid smell in the air, not just the residual smell of burning but something else too, possibly petrol.

That wasn't all, though. Yes, the garden was a mess, but there was evidence of fresh industry, too. Rakes stood in lanes of cleared earth beside piles of scraped-back debris: leaves and tubers, branches and broken flowers. Someone had started to salvage the training fences, dragging the fallen posts up from the spent earth and pulling out the dead foliage.

The thump of her heart was painful as Luisa took this in, but it was nothing compared to the tremor that passed through her chest as she turned to look at one specific corner of the tarmac. She felt she had to look, she had to accept the physical mark that must remain from that night as surely as the emotional scars that it had left behind. But there was nothing there. Luisa walked closer, searching for any remnant, but there was nothing. She couldn't even see the place where Cas had fallen, where she had knelt over him holding his torn chest together.

'We've done our best to clean up,' said a familiar voice behind her.

Luisa turned. 'Kath,' she said.

Her friend reached for her, pulling her into a hug. 'Luisa. It's so good to see you. I wasn't sure whether you'd ever come back.'

'I wasn't sure that I would, either,' Luisa admitted, as they separated. 'But I had to see it, at least.'

Kath gave her a steady look and then nodded. 'Well. Let's show you the start we've made.'

They took a slow tour of the garden, Kath relating an inventory of what was left, which wasn't a lot, and what needed doing, which was everything.

'They've dumped petrol or something into the memorial pond,' Kath said. 'It's lucky we hadn't put the fish in it yet. Small mercies, eh?'

Luisa stood at the edge of the little garden of contemplation that had meant so much to her friend. The rock garden had collapsed into the small pool, which glinted with an oily sheen. The bench that Arthur had so lovingly created to fit beside it was charred almost beyond recognition.

'I'm so sorry, Kath,' Luisa said. 'All this work, destroyed. How is Arthur doing?'

'Arthur's tamping mad, is what he is,' Kath told her. 'He says he'll be back at it to replace what he'd made just as soon as there's a place he can work. *We're not going to let these bastards have the last word*, that's what he said. He's already got ideas for better benches.'

Luisa smiled faintly. 'That's good of him.'

'Harper's taken on treating the pond,' her friend went on.

Luisa looked up. 'Harper?'

'No need to sound so surprised,' said a familiar voice behind them. 'I've got a load of blue oyster mushroom spores coming. I found hessian sacks on eBay and I've talked the hardware store in town into giving us some sawdust.'

Luisa turned to see Harper standing a few feet away, her arms crossed.

'That's brilliant,' Luisa said, smiling slightly. 'Will you let me know how it goes?'

Harper's eyes narrowed. 'Why? You going somewhere? You've only just shown your face and you're planning to ditch us again already? You're not even going to help?'

'The community will help,' Luisa pointed out. 'Kath and Arthur and everyone else.'

'Yeah, and you're part of that community,' Harper said, clearly angry. 'You made yourself part of it when you came here, when you started this. And now, when things have got a bit tough, you're just going to walk out and abandon us?'

'Harper—' Kath tried to step in, but the girl wasn't having it.

'Mr P wanted me to go easy on you,' she said. 'Even though you haven't even bothered to go and see him all the time he's been in hospital. Well, I don't care. I didn't want to be here either, but he asked me, so here I am. Just like when he was here when you needed him. We're *all* here because of you. The least you can do is help, too.'

Luisa shook her head. 'Harper, I can't—'

'You can't what?' the girl demanded. She grabbed at the nearest fork and thrust it towards Luisa. 'You can't even spare us an *hour*?'

They stared at each other for a moment. Then Luisa took the fork. With that Harper turned on her heel and stalked away, her boots churning up the dry earth.

'I'm sorry,' Kath said. 'She's still struggling with what happened. I can't fault how hard she works, though. She grafts like a demon every time she turns up.'

Kath reached out to take the fork, but Luisa held onto it.

'She's right,' Luisa said. 'I don't have anywhere to be right now. I should help for a while.'

There was no quick way to fix the garden. Every square foot had to be cleared, every piece of debris picked up. Luisa rolled up her sleeves and went to work. As the hours passed more and more people arrived. It seemed that every time Luisa looked up from whatever she was doing, there was yet another new arrival looking for some way to help. Most of them were people she didn't know. Had they ever even visited the garden before? Luisa wasn't sure they had. Arthur turned up with a tray of muffins from a bakery in Workington for the volunteers.

'I asked Mo to put the word out,' he explained, after he'd hugged Luisa tightly and she'd remarked on the turnout. 'He and Siddig shot a little video to put online, asking for volunteers. I guess it's working.'

'It is,' Mo confirmed with a grin. 'We've legit gone viral! We've got nearly ten thousand views already and it only went up yesterday!'

He showed Luisa his phone, from which he'd posted a short video of the garden, complete with a before-and-after montage that featured his little sister first planting a potato at the Easter open day and then crying at the destruction of the vegetable patch. The video finished with a triumphant shot of the volunteers starting work to put the mess to rights. It was all set to P!nk's 'What About Us' and accompanied by the hashtags #defeatdestruction, #communitycanconquer-crime, #righteousrebuild and #MrPMatters.

Alliteration for the win, Luisa thought. Mo's editing skills were impressive, and if it brought in more support for the garden rebuild, so much the better.

The volunteers worked on until the late summer light gave out. Luisa, who had only intended to stay for an hour, remained until the last light waned. She leaned against the fork she'd been wielding for hours and looked at the muck on her hands. She was tired and dirty, but somehow felt better than she had for days.

'Thank you so much for coming,' Kath said, pulling her into a hug as they locked the gate for the night.

'I'll be back tomorrow,' Luisa said. 'We should go over the finances together. See what's left in the pot.'

Kath gripped both of her hands and squeezed them, smiling. 'All right, lass. We'll do that.'

Chapter Fifty

Two mornings later Harper arrived at the garden site early, as had become her custom. School was still out for summer and her days were so much emptier now: there was nowhere else she had to be. She'd thought about trying to explain herself to Carl, maybe even asking if he would take her back at the garage, but what if he wasn't as understanding as Mr P? She couldn't risk it.

Anyway, Harper thought, as she pushed through the unlocked gate and into the garden, she'd found that this was where she wanted to be, amid the ruined dirt of a place she'd never thought would be anything to do with her. When this had started she'd been here because she had to come, because she owed Mr P. Sure, she still owed him, probably more than ever before, but now Harper found she wanted to be here. It was the only place she felt her anxieties over the world and her place in it lift. Well, here and in Max's garden bus, but that was still his secret. Besides, Kath needed her. The club kids needed her, too. She and Mo were the eldest of the group, and in the absence of Mr P, they'd found that the littles looked to them. They couldn't run the club without him. Instead, they'd all gravitated to the garden, where Kath and Arthur had welcomed them with metaphorically open arms, a literally open biscuit tin, and a whole rack of scavenged garden implements.

'Morning,' called Kath's cheerful voice from behind her. Harper turned to see the older woman coming from the direction of the gym carrying two full mugs of steaming coffee. One of these she held out to Harper when she got close enough. 'There you go.'

'Thanks,' Harper said, taking the mug. It still seemed strange that the two of them now knew each other well enough to do this, the simple act of making each other hot drinks without asking about milk, about sugar.

'Big day today, eh?' Kath said, as they stood side-by-side for a moment, contemplating the patch of land before them.

Harper shrugged. 'I guess.'

Kath squeezed her arm briefly. 'It'll be grand. And listen, Luisa just called, wanted me to let you know something. Apparently there's a team from BBC News coming. There's nothing to worry about,' she went on, as Harper reacted. 'It's about the publicity, lass. We've got to raise some money sharpish. We're running out fast.'

Privately, Harper wondered why the cash they needed couldn't come from Owen Lawrence. He obviously had plenty to spare. She'd had two phone calls with him since the gala, or more specifically since that first day she'd cleared the air with Mr P. Lawrence's company wanted to pay for her college expenses so that she could study Mechanical Engineering as long as she would agree to work for them for two years after she graduated. It was because of the water unit, apparently – something about wanting to incorporate it into an actual house.

Harper had listened because she couldn't afford not to, not if it was a chance for her to get to college despite everything that had happened. But things had changed for her now. She'd spent her entire life wanting to get out of Collaton, but weirdly, in the wake of the attack on the garden, as she and the neighbours she'd never really known before had worked to bring it back to life, she'd begun to think differently. She'd had the idea here, hadn't she? If it was going to work, it should work here.

'Anyway,' Kath went on, 'Luisa's on her way and so is the reporter and his team. They want to be here to see you get to work.'

'Right.' Harper swallowed her nerves and nodded at the small shed they'd erected the week before as a stop-gap. It was where the mycelium filters were waiting to be lowered into the contaminated pond. She'd checked them yesterday and consulted with the mycologist who'd been advising her via Zoom. Together they'd decided they were ready to be deployed. 'I'd better go and make sure they haven't sprouted mushrooms overnight then, hadn't I?'

Later, the garden was full of spectators as she slid the lumpy hessian sacks into the contaminated water. Kids and parents alike stood alongside the BBC journalist and his camera team, watching as Luisa helped her cover both them and the pond with heavy black timber boards constructed by Arthur. They would help cut out the light so that the mycelium could do its work in peace and also make sure the sacks remained submerged in the water.

'And just like that,' Harper heard the journalist say to camera as she and Luisa stepped back, 'a simple organic solution hopes to solve at least part of the terrible destruction inflicted on this community garden.'

The journalist wanted to talk to Harper directly, too. She tried her best to ignore the great, shiny black eye of the camera as she answered questions about why she thought the garden was important and how she'd come up with the idea of using mycoremediation to solve the issue of the pond.

Later, once the journalist finally had everything he wanted to capture, Harper overheard him talking to Luisa as his gaze wandered across the tidier, but still-bare site.

'I have to admit, I admire the drive here,' he said. 'But it's extremely late in the year, isn't it? Even once the site's finally clear, you're not going to be able to get the place back to where it was before the end of the season, are you?'

'Maybe not,' Luisa admitted. 'But we can try.'

'Do you think you'll be able to maintain local interest if there's nothing to show for so much hard work?' the reporter pressed.

'It might be difficult,' Luisa agreed, 'but we will do our best.'

The conversation left a niggling worry at the back of Harper's mind that lingered as the day wound to a close.

She went home to a quiet house. Max appeared for dinner, their evening routine slowly beginning to reassert itself. They hadn't talked much about what had happened the night of the fire, but Max was smart, he must know what was going on. Harper hadn't raised it with him, though. One thing at a time, she'd thought. But now, she realized that Max might, in fact, hold the key to solving several problems at once.

'How's the garden bus?' she asked, once her brother had settled himself at the table and started eating. 'How are your plants doing?'

He made a face. 'Okay.'

'Only okay?'

'They're all too big,' he said.

Harper nodded and let the companionable silence drift for a little while. This was going to be delicate.

'You know what happened to the garden round the corner?' she asked. 'We've been trying to make it better, but today someone said it's too late in the season to replant the garden now.'

'It is,' Max agreed. 'The plants won't grow fast enough before it gets cold.'

Harper nodded. 'It's a pity really, isn't it?' she said. 'All that work that everyone put in, and boom – it's all over, just like that.'

Max shrugged. 'They can put in bulbs,' he said. 'For next year. Like those tulip ones you got me.'

'That's true,' she agreed, still cautious. 'But – the thing is, Max, I wondered whether you might like to give some of the plants in your bus to the garden? Like . . . as a kind of present?'

Her brother stopped chewing and stared at his plate, his fork frozen in mid-air.

'It would only be ones you didn't have room for,' Harper said, quickly. 'Ones that are going to die because they haven't got enough light or room and are too big or whatever. And if you decide that you don't even want to do that, it's fine – I'll never mention it again. I just thought . . . it might be good for everyone? You get to save the plants you've grown and the garden gets to have some actual plants in it – this year. What do you think?'

Max remained absolutely still for at least a minute, as if he'd been turned to stone. Harper wasn't sure if he was thinking or if this was some kind of new withdrawal that she hadn't encountered before. How long was he going to sit like this? She kicked herself for saying anything. What did it matter if the garden didn't work this year? There was always—

'Okay,' Max said.

Harper smiled, relieved beyond belief. 'That's brilliant, Max. Does that mean I can ask Luisa to come with us to visit the bus?'

Max frowned, still staring at his dinner. 'Why?'

'I think it would be easier than me trying to explain,' Harper pointed out. 'And we'll need help to move the plants.

I don't think we can do it just the two of us, do you? She's a good person, Max. If anyone has to know about the bus, she's the right choice. I don't think I can ask Kath to crawl into a scrapyard.'

Max was silent for another minute. 'All right,' he said, eventually. 'But it's still mine.'

Harper nodded. 'I'll tell her. I'll ask her to come tomorrow morning, yeah? First thing.'

Chapter Fifty-one

Luisa had no idea what to expect from Harper's text asking her to come to her home. When she pulled into their street she could see the girl leaning against the low garden wall of one of the houses. To her surprise Luisa saw that there was a small boy with her. *This must be Max*, Luisa thought, as she pulled to a stop. She'd never met Harper's brother before, but the family resemblance was striking.

'Hi,' she said, climbing out of the car. 'Is everything okay?'

'Fine,' Harper said, looking down at her brother. 'Still sure?'

The boy gave a silent nod.

'This is my brother, Max,' Harper said to Luisa. 'He's got something he wants to show you. Go on, Max – after you.'

To Luisa's surprise, they didn't go inside the house. Instead, the boy took off along the road at a run. She and Harper followed behind, reaching the end of the row of houses and then turning a corner. Max had already disappeared.

'It's this way,' Harper said, indicating a narrow alley that led directly behind the backs of the houses. 'I probably should have told you to wear a hard hat, actually.'

'What?'

'You'll see.'

She plunged into the alleyway. Luisa followed, pushing brambles out of her face and trying not to get tangled in the junk lurking at her feet. Up ahead she saw Harper draw to a stop, waiting for her to catch up. Of Max there was no sign.

As Luisa reached her Harper shifted aside a rusted piece of corrugated iron sheeting that had been resting against the scrapyard's old wooden fence.

'Through there?' Luisa asked, eyeing the hole behind.

Harper shrugged, the glint of a challenge in her eyes. 'If you want to see what Max has got to show you. It's worth it, I promise.'

Harper dropped to her hands and knees, crawling head first through the hole. Luisa glanced up and down the alley and then followed suit, glad that she was wearing her battered old garden gear. She breathed a sigh of relief when she was clear of the metal mountain – only to see Harper vanish beneath an even bigger pile of debris a few feet ahead of her.

'Harper,' she called, crouching down to peer at a gleam of light somewhere ahead. 'I don't like this.'

There was no answer. The scrapyard had grown ominously quiet. Luisa followed, trying not to think about the collective weight of the junk teetering above her. When she emerged at the other end of the tunnel, she remained kneeling, for a moment completely speechless.

'What—?'

Harper was standing over her, holding one hand out to help Luisa up. 'Welcome to Max Dixon's Collaton Jungle,' she said, with a wicked grin.

It was a *bus*, Luisa realized. Bright morning light filtered down from the stairwell above, but the lower deck was still in gloom. The scent of loam was heavy in the air. Luisa slowly got to her feet, careful not to disturb any of the containers that had been pushed into the doorway. She recognized a frantic tangle of climbing beans in an old Belfast sink, sinewy stems reaching for any available sun they could find as they clambered over a frame made of rusted car parts. There was a courgette scrambling over the edge of the old step; neat heads of frizzy lettuce leaves tucked into a collection of old ice cream tubs. The greenery grew denser further into the lower deck. Everywhere Luisa looked, something was growing. Everything was stretching itself towards the windows, each plant desperate to press its leaves to any light they could find.

From upstairs there came the sudden gush of water. It resolved into a sound a bit like concentrated rain.

'Come on,' Harper said, with a little laugh at Luisa's stunned silence. 'You haven't seen the half of it yet.'

Harper disappeared up the stairs. Luisa paused at the bottom, staring at the huge plant that had been secreted into what had once been the luggage compartment. 'Is that a *pumpkin*?'

'Yes,' said a small voice from the top of the stairs. It was Max, peering down at her with a serious face. 'But it hasn't got enough light.'

'Max?' Luisa asked. 'Did *you* do all of this?'

He disappeared again. Harper stood aside with a little tip of her head and Luisa went up ahead of her to the top deck. It was flooded with a light filtered through the chlorophyll green of a thousand leaves. Everything here was a frenzy of colour and fragrance. The air thrummed with life – the industrious buzz of bees, the graceful flutter of butterflies. A forest of sweet peas had wound themselves around the bus's chrome piping, throwing out masses of paintbox blooms to tumble between the bright green of their leaves, reaching overhead into natural living arches that some Instagram influencer would pay hundreds to replicate. The pretty blue dots of forget-me-nots were scattered between overflowing pots of nasturtiums and the daisy-like faces of multicoloured osteospermum. Hollyhocks brushed the ceiling, their tissue-paper flowers in shades of pastel pink and vibrant yellow. Cornflowers nodded their heads between drifts of orange poppies.

There were vegetables up here too: tomatoes already fruiting in vivid reds and yellows; more courgettes; peas and broad beans; big buckets of potatoes; more salad. There were strawberries spilling from makeshift hanging baskets formed from plastic punnets and baling twine, tied up to dangle between the sweet peas.

There was so much growing that there was barely room

for Max to pick his way between the pots, which had spilled from the benches to fill almost every inch of the floor. Space was so limited that in some places pots were stacked on pots.

'Oh my God,' Luisa said, when she finally found her voice, because what else was there to say? 'Oh my *God*. This is unbelievable.'

Harper was still standing on the stairs, leaning against the only space that seemed to be free of anything growing. She gave the first real smile Luisa had seen from her since the night of the gala.

'Isn't it?' she said. 'I couldn't believe it the first time I saw what Max had done, and that was before anything was even really growing. Now it's the most beautiful place I've ever been in my life.'

'Yes,' Luisa said, still stunned. How many people had it taken to get the garden site going the first time around? And this little boy had managed this alone, in the middle of a scrap heap he had to crawl on hands and knees to get into. 'For me, too.'

'Max is worried that it's going to waste, though,' Harper said as they both watched the boy carefully make his way back towards them. 'He thinks everything's going to die because he planted too much.'

Luisa looked around and saw that he was right. The riotous scramble for life was too frantic. Some of the tomato leaves were beginning to yellow. A few of the sweet peas were dying back at the root.

'Harper won't let me move stuff away from the windows on the outside,' Max said, matter-of-factly.

'It's too dangerous,' Harper pointed out. 'Move one thing too many and *splat* – it'd be Flat Max, wouldn't it?'

Max shrugged, as if this was incidental.

'Anyway,' Harper went on, 'that's why Max wants us to move some of his plants to the community garden.'

'No,' Max said, emphatically, staring at his feet.

'I—' Harper looked stunned for a moment. She glanced at Luisa with a frown and then back at her brother. 'Max – have you changed your mind? But I thought – last night you said that's what you wanted? And we showed Luisa how to get here this morning.'

Luisa looked around again, at the wonderful space, the too-crowded plants. 'I can understand you not wanting to give up any of your amazing garden, Max,' she said, gently. 'But what if I promised they were looked after? Believe me, once we've taken some out, the rest will be much healthier.'

'I know,' Max said.

Luisa looked at Harper, both perplexed. Neither of them were quite sure what to say.

'Then,' Harper said, cautiously, 'we *can* take some out?'

'No,' Max said again. 'Things will still die. The pumpkin will still die.'

He was right, of course. Even if there was more room up here, even if they took out enough plants to admit more light to the ones upstairs, it wouldn't help any plants on the lower level.

'Well,' Luisa said, trying to find a way to be encouraging, 'maybe that's true. But that just means that you'll have learned that for next year, you need to plant a pumpkin up here, doesn't it?' she said. 'Or . . . maybe you'd like to plant one outside, with Harper, in the garden?'

Max shook his head vigorously.

'Okay,' Harper said. 'That's fine, Max. Don't worry. It's your—'

'You can't just save some,' he said. 'You have to save the whole garden.'

'The whole—' Luisa looked around. 'Do you mean the whole bus?'

The boy nodded. 'You have to move it.'

'You want us to move the *whole bus* into the garden?' Harper asked.

'The pumpkin won't die then,' Max said. He gave Luisa a piercing look. 'Will it? Everything will live.'

'Well, I can't guarantee that,' Luisa said, honestly. 'But your plants would have a really good chance. Especially if you continue to look after everything as well as you have been while it's been here in the scrapyard, Max.'

The boy nodded and then turned away, immediately busy with tending his extraordinary crop of sweet peas. Harper leaned in to Luisa.

'How would you do that?' she asked, quietly. 'I mean, someone must actually own this junk, right? And even without that . . . how the hell do you move a double-decker bus full of plants?'

Luisa contemplated Max's remarkable garden again. 'I think we'd probably need to buy the scrapyard. Then we'd need to hire a crane. A very big one. And a flat-bed truck.'

Harper huffed. 'I thought we were running out of money?'

'We are,' Luisa said. 'But I think I know someone who'll be willing to give it to us.'

Harper looked at her. 'Who?'

Luisa sighed, not sure how this was going to go down. 'At the gala, someone offered me a job. A place to move on to, after I was finished at the Collaton project. If I tell her this is what I need to say yes to working with her, I bet she'll pay for it.'

Harper stared at her. 'You'd leave? Just like that?'

Luisa smiled. 'If it means making this work? Yes. Harper, I wasn't going to stay forever anyway, was I? And look at everything you've managed to do without me around. You don't need me. *This* is how I can help now. By leaving.'

'But—' Harper began, stopping when Max reappeared in front of them.

'How will people know that it's mine?' he asked. 'The bus? When it's in the garden?'

'We could make a plaque that we can put on the outside,' Luisa suggested. 'It can say "Max's Garden Bus". How about that?'

Max was quiet for another moment. 'People will have

to have tickets,' he said, after more careful thought. 'They won't be allowed in otherwise.'

Luisa smiled. 'I think we can make that work.' She looked at Harper, then reached out to briefly squeeze the girl's arm.

Chapter Fifty-two

Cas watched the replay of the bus being moved out of the scrapyard on the ward's single television as he packed the last of his belongings into his bag. The transportation of the bus had been a staple on the national news cycle ever since the event itself. For Cas, it was a slightly surreal experience to see his hometown occupying the 'feel good' story slot, the one all the news producers wanted to sign off with to end their broadcasts on a positive note. Since the revelation about the bus had broken, the event had taken on a party feel. Drone footage showed the streets between the scrapyard and the garden square lined with people wanting to watch as Max's remarkable garden was transported from its old home to its new one.

There was Luisa too, of course, her smile beaming at him from the screen as the journalist asked her about the second regeneration of the garden, her voice as she spoke. *Max's amazing bus has given everyone here new hope.*

Cas zipped up the bag, listening to the murmuring chat

about the garden from the other residents of the ward. He was glad to be leaving, even if he was going back to Chris and Becky's spare room. It was only for now, he told himself. He'd find his own place soon enough. In truth, what Cas needed now was to feel in control of his own life again.

'I think your ride is here, Mr Pattanyús,' the ward sister told him with a smile, indicating the door to the ward as she passed.

Cas looked around, expecting to see Harper, who had insisted that she wanted to pick him up, but instead he saw a face that made him falter, just for a moment.

'Luisa MacGregor,' he said.

She smiled. 'Hi.'

He wasn't sure how to react. The last time they had seen each other he'd been in a daze of medication and she had been trying to get away. 'I didn't expect to see you.'

'Harper told me you needed a lift home, but the Mini's playing up,' she said, coming closer. She was dressed in blue jeans and a fitted teal-coloured shirt. It wasn't until that moment that Cas realized how rooted that last, drug-muddled glimpse of her from the night of the gala had become in his memory. 'She asked me to come instead. But if you'd rather I call someone else for you—'

'No,' he said. 'No, of course not. Thank you for coming.'

Luisa smiled again and then looked away, glancing around the ward. She seemed awkward, hesitant. Cas understood. She had been uppermost in his thoughts every day for weeks, but now she was here he wasn't sure quite how to talk to her.

'I'm sorry I haven't been to see you before,' she said. 'I really should have—'

'No.' Cas stopped her. 'Luisa, you don't need to apologize or explain. Let's agree on that right now. I completely understand.'

She smiled again. 'Okay.'

'Okay then,' he said, softly. 'Let's get out of here.'

They were both quiet as they walked out of the hospital into sunlight. Cas followed Luisa across the car park and felt an odd frisson to see her old Land Rover. They got in and Cas looked out of the window to steer his gaze away from her, remembering the last time they had driven into Collaton together. How incandescently beautiful she had been, even in the intermittent light of the street lamps they had passed beneath on that fateful journey. He'd thought he'd be beyond this by now, the fierce tug towards her. At least it meant his body must be healing, Cas reflected, rather ruefully.

'Do you mind if we make a slight detour before I take you home?' Luisa asked, oblivious to his thoughts. 'Unless you're too tired?'

'I'm fine,' he said. 'What did you have in mind?'

She glanced at him, a slightly apprehensive look on her face. 'I wanted you to see the garden. But perhaps it's too soon?'

'No,' Cas told her. 'It's a good idea, actually.' He had no

intention of dropping the club even if it would be months before he'd be up to full speed again, so he'd have to go back to the square eventually. Best to do it in her company, she who had been there the night it all happened.

Cas expected the garden to be busy, but when they pulled up he saw that the gate was shut.

'I told everyone I needed the place to myself for a few hours this afternoon,' Luisa said, quietly, as if she had read his mind. 'I thought it'd be for the best.'

Cas looked back towards the gym as she unlocked the gate. He wondered if he should have suggested going in there first. He wasn't sure how to explain to her that, actually, his most potent memories of that night hadn't happened in the garden, but between them, in that doorway, in the moonlight.

He'd known about the triumphant arrival of Max's garden bus, but when they stepped through the gate Cas stopped dead, taken utterly by surprise. He'd expected the rest of the space to still feel barren, a work in progress, but it wasn't.

'I know,' Luisa said, beside him. 'It's amazing, isn't it?'

Beyond the tarmac entrance there was colour everywhere, vibrant yet out of focus, as if they had stepped into a Monet painting. Shades of green swirled in knots and whorls – from emerald and olive to pale peridot frosted by silver, there was an entire virescent backdrop painted with the garden's leaves alone. Bursting between them came star-bright spatters constellating in every hue as a thousand eager plants threw open their blooms to the late summer afternoon: yellow, cerise, lilac, scarlet, indigo, azure, vermillion. Their collective scent rose as thick as morning mist, laced through with the drone of insects hard at work.

The double-decker bus had been placed where the first greenhouse had once stood. The vehicle looked, not like something that should be consigned to a compressor, but an art exhibit in progress. There were ladders leaned against it and someone was obviously in the process of painting a huge mural across its flanks – the undoubted talents of a graffiti artist being put to use. The opulent display of flowers and leaves being painted on the outside matched what Cas could see pressing through the bus's open windows – were they sweet peas he could see, cascading from the top deck?

The path that they had built from the old factory wall was still there and had been swept clean. As Luisa led him slowly along it they passed between the vegetable patches on one side and the flower beds on the other. Far from being empty ground, Cas could see rows and rows of plants. They weren't all at their peak, but neither were they crushed beyond recognition, either. Here and there were tools stuck in the ground next to small piles of weeds, evidence of the committed labour that had gone into this second transformation.

'Some of these came out of Max's bus and they were all already well on their way,' Luisa explained. 'Then, after the news footage of the bus went out, people started turning up from all over with more – vegetables as well as flowers. One of the DIY places got a "plant collection" together and people donated to that – that's where the cauliflowers and cabbages came from. A little organic nursery all the way down in Cornwall donated plug plants, too.'

They reached the memorial pond, which been rebuilt and repopulated with fresh soil and plants. The pond itself was covered with a heavy wooden board. There was an information board nailed to a post beside it, with an explanation of how the garden was experimenting with mycoregeneration to decontaminate the petrol-polluted water beneath.

'The water won't be checked for another few weeks,' Luisa explained. 'But Harper's confident it's going to work. She's invited classes from the school to be here for when we take up the grille.'

'That's a wonderful idea,' Cas said.

Luisa smiled. 'It was Harper's. She's been a powerhouse since everything happened, Cas, and I know it's thanks to you. She told me you'd asked her to help Kath the first time she came to visit you. And now,' she added, 'you really need to come and experience the garden bus. It's something else.'

They made their way back up the path, Cas quietly taking everything in. When they reached the tarmac again Luisa went ahead but he paused, looking for the small space where he'd fallen that night. There was no visible marker, but still he knew just where it had happened, somehow. He felt Luisa reappear beside him. She surprised him by lacing her fingers through his. Cas looked down at her.

'Okay?' she asked.

He ran his thumb across her knuckle. 'Yes,' he said.

She looked past him to the patch of tarmac he had been contemplating. 'Kath's got plans to put up a shed over that spot,' she said, softly. 'It's going to be a mini-café that sells cake and coffee.'

Cas smiled slightly. 'That sounds like another good idea.'

He expected her to slip her hand out of his, but she didn't. Instead they walked to the bus with their fingers still tangled together. She only let go of his hand when she opened the door of the bus and stepped up into it. Inside was a ticket dispenser of the sort more usually seen at deli counters in supermarkets. Luisa pulled two yellow slips of paper from the machine and handed one to him.

'It's the rules,' she said. 'Max won't let anyone in without a ticket.'

'Okay,' he laughed.

'Trust me,' she said, with a smile as bright as any she'd ever sent his way. 'You've never seen anything like this.'

Chapter Fifty-three

Luisa went ahead of him up the stairs, her nerves building. It had been easier than she'd thought it would be to walk with him into the scene of his almost-demise, but now they had reached the part of the meeting of which she was still less sure. Given everything that had happened, Luisa had imagined that she might feel differently once she saw him again, but she didn't. She had also thought that he might have changed, that he might look at her differently now – in a cooler way, perhaps, without the warmth in his eyes that she so associated with him. But no. He was the same Cas who had stunned her by appearing out of the shadows that first night she had visited Collaton, the same solid presence that had thrown her settled mind off-balance every time they had met since.

Luisa climbed the curving stairs, leading Cas into another world. If he'd thought the garden outside was verdant, the upper deck of Max's garden bus surpassed it in every way possible. The central aisle was still there, but to make her way along it Luisa had to edge her way through hanging flowers, ducking beneath boughs laden with blooms and foliage. The air was humid, the whole place holding the atmosphere of a hothouse at a botanical garden. She could feel Cas following behind, hesitating every time he had to manoeuvre his bulk carefully around another delicate plant. She looked back over her shoulder and saw him edging his way past the little fig tree that was overgrowing the third bench. The sight of his cautious movements made her smile.

She pushed aside one last curtain of tumbling sweet peas and reached the rear of the bus. The last, long bench had been left clear of pots. Arthur Larkspur's expert handiwork had replaced the original seat with beautifully polished antique oak that a salvage yard in Penrith had donated for him to use. Large cushions upholstered in rich green and gold velvet added a touch of decadence to the unusual bower. Luisa took a seat among them and Cas slid into the space beside her.

'Wow,' he said, looking back down the tunnel they had made their way through.

'I know,' she laughed. 'Isn't it amazing?'

Cas shook his head. 'I can't believe what that boy managed to do. Genius clearly runs in that family.'

'It's incredible,' Luisa agreed. 'You know, at first I didn't want to come back here, to Collaton. I didn't think I could. But I'm glad I did. If the past few weeks have taught me anything, it's how resilient a community can be, especially together. What they've managed to do here is astonishing.'

'What *you* managed to do,' Cas told her, quietly. 'None of this would have happened without you.'

'That's not true. Nothing here has anything to do with me. Everything you can see has been done since—' Luisa broke off, shook her head, tried again. 'Since that night.'

Cas surprised her by reaching out a hand to cover one of hers. 'It *is* down to you,' he said. 'You reminded people what it is to build a garden.'

She watched his thumb trace over her skin. Here he was, offering her support, when he was the one who'd almost ended up dead. A shiver passed through her and Cas must have felt it because he squeezed her hand. Luisa let herself look at him – *really* look at him. He was dressed in faded blue jeans and a soft white shirt open at the neck, and he looked good. *Really* good. Luisa could not equate this with the way she had last seen him in that blank white hospital room, or before that, when he had been lying out there on the tarmac of this garden, dying beneath her hands.

'I'm so glad you're okay,' she told him, the words inadequate to the depths of her feelings at that moment.

'Also thanks to you,' he pointed out, softly. 'I would have bled out before the ambulance arrived if you hadn't been there. And I'm so sorry, Luisa, that you had to go through that. I can imagine how difficult that has been for you, given your history.'

She looked away, watching a bee hum busily in and out of the funnel of a mimulus flower. 'I won't lie,' she told him. 'It *has* been difficult. But that's why I wanted to come here with you today. One of the reasons, anyway,' she amended, looking at him again. 'It was a little selfish, I'm afraid. I needed to see you as you are now, rather than—' Luisa broke off, unable to say it aloud.

'I'm fine,' he said, his voice still soft. 'It's remarkable how quickly the body can heal. Far faster than the mind, I think.'

Luisa smiled. 'That's true enough.'

They sat there like that for a while, thinking their own thoughts, surrounded by a quiet garden.

'Can I tell you something?' Luisa asked, eventually. 'It might take me a while to get it out.'

Cas nodded, eyes warm but face serious. 'Take as long as you like.'

She took a breath and looked away. She'd thought endlessly about how she would explain this to him, but now that it came to her actually speaking it aloud she'd forgotten every practised line.

'After Reuben,' Luisa began, eventually, 'I shut everything down. Emotionally, I mean. That was the only way I could get myself to function again physically. I sunk myself into work, into a job that meant I could pretend I hadn't given up on my own career, just delayed it for a while. But "a while" became indefinitely. Life carried on and it carried me with it. I thought I was fine. I thought I had moved on. But it turned out I was still just ticking over, going through the motions. Surviving. I might have gone on like that forever. But then—' She took a breath, but she had to get this out. She had to be honest, with herself as well as him. 'Then I came here, to Collaton. I met you, and without even realizing it I began to remember what it was to let myself really feel.'

She stopped for a moment. Cas said nothing, just waited quietly for her to continue.

'I remembered what it was to want to build a garden, to take an idea and make it real, to watch things I had planted flourish and grow. And then you were attacked, and—' Luisa took a breath. 'After that, I finally realized that I never had moved on, not properly. I'd just been in a holding pattern. I'd been hiding, staying safe. But life is more than that, isn't it? More than just finding a way to survive. More than choosing the safe option.'

Luisa turned a little towards him and found Cas watching her intently.

'The thing is,' Luisa said, her voice husky. She cleared her throat. 'I was never supposed to be a permanent feature here. The garden was always supposed to be turned over to the community once established. And I'm not needed here any longer. Kath's already taken over most of the management and there are so many volunteers ready to help, with more signing up every day. Which means it's time for me to move on.'

A frown flickered across Cas's face. 'Move on?' he repeated. 'Where to? Another community garden?'

'Not exactly,' she said and explained the opportunity that had arisen at Feldspar Hall, how the home she needed would come with it for the duration of the long-term project and perhaps even beyond. 'The best thing is that my taking the position means the chance to extend the garden charity as a whole,' she added. 'Caroline is committed to helping with the expansion of the scheme beyond this one site.'

Cas smiled, although it was a reserved expression. 'You'll still be involved in some ways, then?'

'Of course,' Luisa said. 'Owen and I are working to set up a board of directors for the charity, which will need to be officially registered. Actually, I'd love it if you'd agree to be a trustee.'

He looked up at her, surprised. 'Me?'

'Yes,' she said. 'We need all the good people we can get, and I can't think of anyone better than you, Cas.'

He smiled again. 'I'd be honoured. And besides—' He broke off.

'What?' Luisa asked.

Cas said nothing for a moment, then sighed. 'Luisa.' He sat very still for a moment. Then he turned towards her, his knee brushing hers. 'Luisa, you have to know that if circumstances had been different ... I would have liked the chance to know you in a different way. Not just as the friends I hope we'll always be.'

Luisa felt sudden tears in her eyes and blinked them away. It would be so easy to let the warmth she could see in his eyes wrap her up entirely.

'Cas,' she said. 'I have to completely commit to this opportunity at Feldspar Hall. It's a chance to restart a career I thought I'd left behind years ago – a career I thought had died with Reuben. And however much I—' She caught herself. 'I have to put my all into it. I have to.'

'Of course you do,' he said. 'I don't want to influence that, believe me. But for my own sake, I had to at least be clear about how I feel. And—' Cas stopped, looked away.

Luisa took a breath. 'And?'

Cas reached for her hand, lifted it to rest in his lap between both of his. 'Here's something I want you to think about. Look at me. I'm alive. I survived. I survived the worst thing I've ever experienced and that was because of you. We're both here. We're both still *here*, and so is the garden. If you're going to take anything with you from your time in Collaton, take that. The worst thing that could have happened did happen – and this time we both walked away from it. Remember this place, as it is now, and us, as we are now. We both got through it. We did. *You* did.'

She smiled through tears. 'You're right.'

He studied her face, as if wanting to set it into his memory. Then he looked into her eyes again with a slightly mischievous smile. 'Here's a thought. Maybe we should make a better memory for you to take away with you.'

She raised an eyebrow, playful, heart ticking an extra beat as she caught his mood. 'Yeah?'

'Yeah.'

He reached out and cupped her face with one hand, stroking her cheek with his thumb. He leaned in, stopping when their lips were a hair's breadth apart, when her heart was pounding so hard in her chest that Luisa thought it might actually crack a rib. Cas paused, the warmth of him so close that she could feel it. He held himself there for a beat, for two, giving her a chance to push him away or protest. But she didn't. She couldn't.

Cas closed the last fraction of space between them, kissing her softly. Luisa could feel a hunger beneath the surface, simmering. Cas drew back and then kissed her again, then again, briefly drawing her bottom lip between his. It was slow and careful and heated and it turned the deepest part of her into something molten, something with a burning fire all its own. Cas pulled her closer, wrapping one arm around her to hold her firmly against him. They kissed one last time and then he drew back to look at her through eyes that were darker than usual, but also full of laughter.

'What?' she asked, a little breathless.

Cas cast a glance around them. 'Just considering the cosmic irony of a teacher snogging on the back seat of a bus . . .'

Luisa laughed and Cas wrapped his other arm around her, drawing her in.

'Well,' she said quietly, into his ear. 'That's a pretty good memory to take away with me.'

Cas pulled back, kissing her temple and giving her a briefly serious look. 'Don't be a stranger, okay?' he said. 'Because I'm not going anywhere. I'll be right here, same as I've always been.'

Epilogue

Two Summers Later

Cas could hear the level of activity in the garden even before he walked into the square. It was after six, but the July day was still warm.

'Evening, Cas,' called Mala Reed, from where she stood on a ladder, watering the baskets that were hanging beside the pub's doors. It had been reopened for a year now and against all odds seemed to be doing well. 'Big day today, eh?'

'Evening, Mala,' he called back. 'Certainly is. Will we see you later?'

'Oh aye, I'll be there,' she said. 'I'd not miss it for the world.'

Cas waved and walked on, passing the little row of shops. Two of the three had been reborn, one as a grocer's and florist's that sometimes took surplus produce from the garden, the other as a bicycle store that did a roaring trade in hire at the weekends. The third premises was no longer a shop, but had been turned into office space for the garden, taken on when Luisa's original lease on the gym building had expired.

Looking across the square, Cas could see that the gym doors themselves were open – Mo must have gone there straight after school, as he'd said he would. Though Cas's office was once more his office and a recent grant had allowed him to invest more in the gym, improving it by far, the club still had close ties to the garden. Mo in particular, though now half way through his A-levels and heading for a career in coaching, insisted that each was an intrinsic part of the other.

'It's what you could call a symbiotic relationship, Mr P,' Mo had explained to him recently. 'They work together as one entity and each would be lesser without the other.'

Cas had no idea when this philosophical turn in Mo's personality had come about, but he wasn't going to curb it. Mo, like Harper, was one of the club's success stories and Cas was glad that, unlike some of the other kids who had ditched school the moment their GCSEs had been completed, Mo had stuck around. He was a great example to the younger ones.

Cas rounded the final corner of the garden and saw the gates standing open, voices drifting from inside, accompanying the sound of industry. When he reached the entrance he saw that the transformation he had helped to start earlier in the day had continued – seats had been arranged in neat rows across the cleared tarmac and a large projector screen was being unfurled against the garden bus, above the stage

Cas had himself helped to erect the day before. Harper was directing operations, checking the level of the screen. Cas could see Max beside the bus, using the watering system that Harper had put in place, which utilized rainwater tanks on the roof connected to a series of solar panels and hydraulic cables. It meant that the whole system could be operated from the ground by anyone, although Max was still fastidious about looking after the bus's internal ecosystem himself. Since its move into the garden, the bottom of the bus had been mostly emptied out. It was now where Max cultivated plants and cuttings that were sold so that visitors could take something from the Collaton garden home with them.

'That's it,' he heard Harper call, as he got closer. 'That's straight!'

'Evening,' he said, climbing the wooden steps to join her on the stage. 'How's things?'

Harper blew out a breath and turned to him and he was reminded, sharply, of how she had been before all this started, a stark contrast to the young woman she was now. She was still recognizably the same Harper who could stand her ground in a hurricane, she still dressed primarily in black and she still, at times, had a temper that could scorch steel. But there was a different kind of confidence to her attitude now, borne of a belief in her own abilities and the promise of a future, the path to which she had already taken the first steps. She was a year into her Mechanical Engineering course, taking to it like a duck to water, and the extracurricular work she did for Owen Lawrence's company was already helping her to make a name for herself in wider circles. In the past year she'd also moved out of the house that she and Max had shared with their father, and when she had reached eighteen, she had successfully assumed legal guardianship of her little brother. The change had been remarkable for both of them. Max was now at Collaton High School and doing well.

'I keep telling myself it's going to be fine,' Harper said, turning to look at the large, boxy item standing on a plinth at the other end of the stage. It was half the size of the Mini she had rebuilt two years before and was covered by a green tarp that hid it from view.

'That's good. Because you know it will be.'

She grinned at him. 'Always the same old Mr P. Relentlessly optimistic, come what may.'

'Hey,' he said. 'We'll have less of the old, thank you.'

'Cas!'

The shout came from behind him. Cas turned to see Kath waving at him from the small cabin that had become the garden's café. It had been erected over the spot of his near-demise and was usually surrounded by a series of colourfully painted tables and chairs, though today they had been cleared to make room for the additional seating needed for the event.

'Your usual!' Kath shouted, holding up a paper coffee cup.

Cas made his way towards her, careful not to disrupt the layout. As he went he waved to Siddig, who was mowing the small grassed area. Elsewhere he could see more volunteers making sure the garden looked pristine for the arrival of the great, the good, and the press.

'Thanks,' Cas said, as he reached Kath. 'I didn't think you were going to open this evening?'

'It's just for us, I'll be closing down before the event starts,' she said, turning away to pick something up. 'Have you seen this yet?'

She held up a copy of *The English Garden*. It showed a photograph of two women against the backdrop of the flourishing grounds of a large stately home. One of the women was Lady Caroline Percivant. The other was Luisa MacGregor. Cas reached out and took the magazine. Luisa's smile radiated from the cover and he found himself smiling too, just to see it.

It had been some time since they had met in person. Luisa's move and new role had been all-consuming right off the bat and she'd barely paused since. They'd kept in touch, not least because of his role as one of the charity's trustees, but the last two years had been busy for Cas, too. The events that had surrounded the Collaton garden on that dark night had given him an odd sort of status that he'd managed to parlay into more funding for the gym, which had in turn allowed for expansion. He was no longer the only coach, nor was boxing the only sport the club now offered and besides that they were working out how to offer training towards coaching qualifications, too. Somehow he managed it all, still alongside his day job. At one point, when there had been another twisting of the national curriculum accompanied by a swingeing slash of budget, he'd considered finishing with the teaching entirely. He could probably use his current notoriety to go into coaching commercially. That would also have given him a reason to move out of Collaton, to go south, somewhere nearer to Luisa and the future with her he sometimes still thought would be possible. But she'd given him no indication that this would be welcome and he had no intention of distracting her from what she loved. After all, as the magazine he held in his hand attested, her decision to pursue her original dream of garden design had clearly been the right one. Besides, he couldn't leave Collaton – or rather, he couldn't leave the kids.

'Doesn't she look bonny?' Kath asked, into his silent contemplation of their mutual friend. 'She was hoping to come tonight, you know, but it turns out she can't.'

Cas looked up. 'Oh?'

'Yeah,' Harper said, appearing at his side. 'She's sent a little video instead. I couldn't not have her be a part of it somehow.'

'You can keep that,' Kath said, as Cas looked at the magazine cover again. 'I've got another.'

'Thanks.' He rolled up the issue and stuck it in his back pocket. He'd read it later, when there were fewer pairs of eyes to watch him.

The evening to celebrate the unveiling of the first Collaton Water Reclamation Unit started exactly on time. It had been built less than a quarter of a mile away, in the fledgling new factory that had been established on the site of what had once been the old scrapyard. That had been at Harper's insistence: she had decided that the first units must be built in Collaton, where the idea had been planted and had grown and where it could provide new jobs for and investment into the local area.

'I know,' Harper had told him, 'that I've spent most of my life wanting to get away from here. But I don't want to do that anymore. Or at least, not yet. I still want to be able to travel, I still want to see other places and maybe I'll live somewhere else one day. But right now, I want to make sure I do something for this place.'

He couldn't help smiling at that. 'I'm glad,' he told her. 'There are good people here, Harper.'

She'd given him a grin. 'Yeah,' she'd said. 'And you're the best of them, Mr P.'

It had been at least a year since she'd needed to call Cas that, her graduation from high school also moving her from student to friend, but still, he suspected that he would always be 'Mr P' to Harper Dixon. He was fine with that.

He recalled this as Harper stood in front of a full garden of observers ranging from local supporters to company executives and national press.

'As you can see,' Harper said from the podium, 'the garden is thriving and so is the community around it. None of this would have happened without the efforts of one woman, Luisa MacGregor. Sadly she couldn't join us today, but she's sent a brief video message for everyone here.'

Harper stepped aside and Luisa's face flashed up onto the projector screen behind her. There were cheers from the club kids who remembered her, applause from everyone else, including Cas.

'Hello, everyone,' Luisa said, from the screen. 'I'm so sorry I couldn't be there to join you in celebrating Harper's fantastic achievement today, but I just wanted to thank you for supporting her amazing innovations – and, in turn, the garden. I think it shows . . .'

She spoke for a minute or two and Cas let himself feel the pang of her absence as he listened. He wondered how it was possible to miss someone he had never really known. He had dated here and there in the past two years, but none of those partnerships had gone beyond the casual. This was a situation that his friend Chris found exasperating but Cas had no intention of launching into another relationship like the one he'd had with Annika, where it had never been right and they'd both known it. He was too old to settle. Besides, he had plenty to keep him busy.

The presentation continued, culminating with the reveal of the Collaton Water Reclamation Unit and an announcement of the next phase of its development.

'The aim of this unit has always been to make it as standard a household appliance as a sink, an oven, or a refrigerator,' Harper said. 'As a result, I'm extremely proud to announce an ongoing partnership with Lawrence Homes. This month will begin renovation work on the row of five empty houses in this very square.' She pointed out of the garden, to the houses that edged the opposite side of the street to the gym. 'This will involve the incorporation of the Mark II Collaton Water Reclamation Unit directly into the kitchen of each home. This project will also be part of a construction apprenticeship scheme we have established between the colleges at Barrow-in-Furness and Carlisle and Lawrence Homes, creating learning and career opportunities for future generations of workers. Most importantly, we are also actively working to involve high schools along the whole of the coast to encourage youngsters who may already have an interest in learning such skills but no outlet to pursue their talents.'

Another storm of clapping filled the garden as Harper prepared to conclude her presentation.

'Two years ago,' she said, once her audience had quieted again, 'this place and everything that has come out of it since was nothing but a tiny seed of an idea. It seemed impossible that it could ever be anything more than that. Now look at how it has taken root and flourished. I hope that we can continue to plant and nurture more seeds exactly like that one, because each one has the potential to change the future for all of us. As part of that, we will also be establishing the Reuben MacGregor Innovation Fund, a research bursary available to young people under the age of twenty-five to develop ideas and philosophies for technologies that may help us navigate the difficult future towards which we are heading.'

After Harper's presentation, the garden gathering took

on a festive feel. The sun had finally begun to set, and music filtered from a sound system set up in the bottom of the garden bus. The solar fairy lights that Cas himself had helped to string between the trees blinked on one by one. Kath had organized a group of volunteers to make canapes from the garden's produce, served on wooden platters made by Arthur's students in his woodworking classes. There were glasses of champagne, too.

Cas drifted through the gathering, talking with the many friends he had made as a result of his involvement in both the gym and the garden. There was still the odd journalist, too, who wanted a soundbite from him about his experiences since the night he'd almost lost his life, right here on this piece of tarmac.

'I have always believed that people are inherently good,' he said, as he always did. 'Collaton proves what a community can achieve when it comes together.'

The evening was a fitting celebration of everything they had all achieved, especially Harper. Cas told himself that there was nothing missing, nothing, but still there was a hollow feeling in his heart.

Eventually the crowd began to thin out as people started to leave: Collaton was a long way from a lot of places, and some people had travelled far to be a part of the evening. At length it was only the regulars left, still filling the place with laughter and chatter: Harper and Mo, Kath and Arthur, all the others who had helped to make the garden a reality.

It was then that Cas saw her. She was leaning against the fence beside the entrance gate, a smile on her face, watching her friends enjoy each other's company. For a moment Cas thought he had conjured her out of his imagination, out of a wish he'd been harbouring all night, all year. But no, he realized, when she saw that he had noticed her and smiled at him, it was her.

'Hi,' she said with a wider smile still as they walked towards each other. She was wearing a white silk dress that floated about her legs as she moved. For a moment he had the strangest thought that she'd stepped straight out of the cover of the magazine rolled up in his back pocket.

'Luisa MacGregor,' he said. 'I didn't think you could make it.'

She glanced at the rest of their friends, who hadn't yet spotted her. 'I wasn't sure I would, and then I didn't want to cause a distraction by arriving half way through. Mala let me watch from her upstairs window.'

Her hair reflected the glint of the fairy lights overhead as she looked up at him. There were a million things he probably should have said just then, but what came out of his mouth was what he'd been thinking throughout the evening.

'I've missed you.'

She smiled again, bright enough to knock him off his feet. 'I've missed you, too.'

There was an exclamation from behind them as Kath realized just who it was Cas was talking to. In the next moment they were surrounded. He stood aside as Luisa was enveloped in hugs and well-wishes, as she was peppered by a million questions.

'Actually,' she said, 'I wonder if we could save the proper catch-up until tomorrow? I've got something else I need to do tonight.'

Cas felt everyone look at him. 'What?' he said.

'I was hoping I could take you to dinner, Mr P,' Luisa explained. 'I think we've got a lot of catching up to do. If no one here minds me whisking you away?'

The darkening garden was enveloped in a silence, in which it seemed to Cas as if their friends were holding their breath. He looked at Luisa for a moment.

'If you're otherwise engaged, it's fine,' she said. 'We could get coffee from Kath's tomorrow, or—'

'No,' he said. 'No, dinner would be great.'

There was a collective release of breath. Cas suddenly wondered just how much a source of speculation his non-relationship with Luisa had been.

They said their goodbyes and headed out of the garden, making for her old Defender. As he reached the passenger door he glanced at his watch.

'I'm not sure there's going to be anywhere open, you know, not in Collaton,' he said, as they climbed in. 'It's after nine already.'

'Oh,' Luisa said, lightly. 'In that case we'll have to find something else to do instead.'

'Right,' he said, raising his eyebrows. 'Any suggestions?'

'Well,' she said, flashing him a smile so bright Cas found himself catching his breath, 'I've heard about this salsa club in Carlisle that I've been wanting to go to for years. And right now, I really feel like dancing.'

Acknowledgements

The idea that became *The Forgotten Garden* has been in my head for a long time in various different guises. Getting it onto the page in this form involved a large team of dedicated, talented people.

At Simon & Schuster, huge thanks to my editors Louise Davies and Clare Hey both for liking the idea in the first place and then for their brilliant guidance and advice. Thank you to Pip Watkins for another beautiful and evocative cover; to Sara-Jade Virtue for her genius at brand direction; Sabah Khan and Laurie McShea for marketing; to Tamsin Shelton for the copyedit; Maddie Allan and Kat Scott in sales for getting it out there and production controller Francesca Sironi for keeping it on schedule. As ever, I owe such a lot to my agent, Ella Kahn at DKW, for her faith in me and for always being able to get me over my inevitable mid-manuscript worries.

Thank you to Polly MacGregor, who knew this story in its very earliest form, for not minding that I borrowed her name for Luisa!

A book is nothing without readers, and readers find books through booksellers, librarians and bloggers. Thank you to all the wonderful bookshops and libraries out there that have championed and stocked my books, including my local bookshops Sam Read Bookseller in Grasmere and The Hedgehog Bookshop in Penrith. Meanwhile, I have found the online book-blogging community to be a delightful group, and I am so grateful to you all for choosing to read and talk about my books online!

The coast of West Cumbria is a beautiful place, but although I live in the same county, it's a long way from our home. Thank you to my wonderful and patient husband Adam Newell for the research trips that helped me decide where to set this. If you've seen the talk about the new coal mine planned for the United Kingdom – well, it would be pretty much exactly where I decided to set the fictional town of Collaton.